THE BIRDS OF THE LONDON AREA

A NEW NATURALIST SPECIAL VOLUME

The aim of THE NEW NATURALIST series is to interest the general reader in the wild life of Britain by recapturing the inquiring spirit of the old naturalists. The Editors believe that the natural pride of the British public in their native fauna and flora, to which must be added concern for their conservation, is best fostered by maintaining a high standard of accuracy combined with clarity of exposition in presenting the results of modern scientific research. The volumes in the main series deal with large groups of animals and plants, with the natural history of particular areas or habitats in Britain, and with certain special subjects. THE NEW NATURALIST SPECIAL VOLUMES, on the other hand, cover, in greater detail, a single species or group of species. In both the main and special volumes the animals and plants are described in relation to their habitats.

EDITORS:

JAMES FISHER, M.A.
JOHN GILMOUR, M.A.
JULIAN HUXLEY, M.A., D.Sc., F.R.S.
L. DUDLEY STAMP, C.B.E., B.A., D.Sc.

PHOTOGRAPHIC EDITOR:
ERIC HOSKING, F.R.P.S.

THE NEW NATURALIST

THE BIRDS OF
THE LONDON AREA

SINCE 1900

By a Committee of
The London Natural History Society

R. C. Homes (chairman)

Miss C. M. Acland   C. B. Ashby
C. L. Collenette   R. S. R. Fitter
E. R. Parrinder   B. A. Richards

*Illustrated with 40 photographs
and 6 maps and diagrams*

COLLINS
ST. JAMES'S PLACE, LONDON
1957

Printed in Great Britain
by Willmer Brothers & Haram Ltd., Birkenhead
for Collins Clear-Type Press: London and Glasgow

CONTENTS

ILLUSTRATIONS

ILLUSTRATIONS

EDITORS' PREFACE

WE PRESENT this remarkable book as a Special Volume in the New Naturalist series; and, indeed, it is special in many ways. It is, first of all, a local avifauna. Such books now cover the British Isles in a mosaic that extends from Shetland to Cornwall, from Ireland to Kent. Most of them are primarily of interest to the ever-growing band of local bird-watchers, or to geographical ornithologists working on comparative distribution and habits. But a precise and scholarly avifauna of some special areas deserves special publication, and special attention in scientific circles. Such an area lies within a twenty miles' radius of St. Paul's Cathedral — for many years the special province of the London Natural History Society. With the possible exception of the parish of Selborne in Hampshire, immortalised by Gilbert White, London has the longest continuous history of ornithological observation in the British Isles.

Since ornithology became popular, London, with its vast population, has probably had more bird-watchers than any other part of Britain; and its unique environment has provided them with much to see. The list of London birds is an extraordinarily large one. It contains many rarities, and many birds of great scientific interest, like the black redstart and the little ringed plover, which have colonised the London area within the memory of most of the present generation of bird-watchers. The great London reservoirs are the best places in Britain on which to see some of our rarer winter wildfowl visitors. Within London are all sorts of fascinating ornithological problems — for instance, the roosting of the starlings in central London, and the problem of the origin of this starling population.

Bird-watching in London in the twentieth century has been no desultory affair of scattered observations and casually gathered notes. On the contrary, it has been a highly organised business, managed by the recorders of the London Natural History Society, carried out with great expenditure of energy and time, chronicled with scientific accuracy and meticulous care. The final result is a picture in detail of wild bird distribution and habits which those who are interested in changes in animal life, distribution and habits will quarry for years ahead. This book's information will still interest and gratify enquiring scientists, we predict, another half-century from now; and will unquestionably stagger the present-day reader with its demonstration that London not only has

viii

a fascinating (and extremely complex) natural history, but a cadre of enthusiastic naturalists worthy of it.

The group of distinguished workers who have contributed to this book, have managed a most gratifying evenness of approach and treatment. Readers will scarcely believe that it has been the product of so many eyes and hands.

Particularly notable in their evenness of treatment are the introductory and ecological chapters, which are in many ways the most important feature of the book — at least to the general naturalist rather than the ornithological specialist. No book on an avifauna has ever been blessed with such a profound analysis of its physical setting, its different habitats, its communities, its seasonal changes. It was these introductory chapters that commended *The Birds of the London Area Since 1900* as particularly suited to the New Naturalist Series. Our contributing authors are evidently many things besides accurate field-men, historians, zoologists, botanists and students of the literature. Unquestionably this book will inspire bird watchers far beyond the London area; it is a natural history in which the word history has a real meaning.

In praising the introductory ecological third of this book, we would not wish to suggest that the brilliant systematic section is of secondary importance; for here are its bones and muscle. Each species treated with the utmost lucidity and economy; so that every important record has been condensed without being maimed. We know of no better example of the disposition of a quart in a pint pot.

Although throughout the preparation of this book Richard Homes — the London Natural History Society's President at the time of completing this book — has been at pains to advise us that it has been a co-operative work of which he has been spokesman and amanuensis, we feel that his able colleagues will be certain to echo our sentiments when we say that his guiding and co-ordinating hand has been responsible for much of the evenness and crispness in the presentation of all sections of this book.

The Birds of the London Area Since 1900 is a living proof of the standing of British amateur natural history. Only in a remote sense can any of its contributors be said to be of professional status in the world of natural history. Most of them, including their Chairman, are purely amateurs who earn their living in all walks of life — mostly in business.

Apart from its introductory third, which will be read with appreciation and delight, this book is not designed to be consumed at a sitting. Its systematic two thirds constitutes a well-arranged storehouse of information to which all London naturalists will be compelled to go in the future. We predict that when they do go — to check the status of a species or a group of species — they will inevitably linger by the way, and read around, and ponder to themselves — spending some hours that they never intended to spend. They will find that nature has few more devoted and scientific chroniclers than the members of the London Natural History Society, who have made something far more than a hobby out of their spare time.

THE EDITORS

Part One

INTRODUCTION

THIS BOOK has been prepared by a committee of the London Natural History Society with the object of tracing the changes since 1900 in the very varied population of birds in and around London, the largest urban agglomeration in the world. As long ago as 1908 an Ornithological Research Committee was formed by one of the two bodies that combined in 1914 to form the present Society, which adopted as its *Area* a circle of 20 miles' radius from St. Paul's Cathedral. It is this Area which we have used for our purpose, as a study of the effects of building and the many other forms of development associated with big cities requires the inclusion not only of the whole of the built-up districts but also of a stretch of the surrounding country for comparison.

Departure from the usual convention in local natural histories of adhering to administrative or geographical boundaries is essential in order to study the impact of London on bird life, and our circle, which embraces over 1200 square miles, covers all of Middlesex and parts of Buckinghamshire, Essex, Hertfordshire, Kent and Surrey. Assuming that close building stretches more or less uninterruptedly for an average of ten miles from the centre, this inner part of the circle still only covers about a quarter of our province and the rest, though more built over than most other parts of the country, retains a considerable extent of typical rural scenery. The relative size of the inner and outer zones can be appreciated by reference to the diagrams on pages 110 and 111.

Our reasons for choosing 1900 as a starting point are threefold. The Society's own records go back as we have seen to about that time; books on the birds of Surrey and Kent appeared in 1900 and 1909 respectively and summaries appeared for several counties in the Victoria County Histories published about that time. We have carried the story to the end of 1954 wherever possible.

With the theme of the effects, direct and indirect, of London on bird life, we have given not only the usual systematic list with accounts of distribution throughout the Area, but have also devoted a much higher proportion of the total space than is usual in works of this nature to chapters on the principal habitats, on migration and on roosts and flylines where these are of special significance. A general description of the physical features is given in the opening chapter, which serves as an introduction to the more detailed accounts of the various habitats, of which Inner London has pride of place since it is the part most affected by man. Within the forty square miles, defined by A. Holte Macpherson as Inner London, 160 different species have been recorded during this century and 37 have bred, 20 of them regularly. The tufted duck, pochard, kestrel, coot, jay, black redstart, pied wagtail and goldfinch have been gained as breeding species, and only the rook, of those which once bred regularly, has been lost. The number of rare visitors which have been seen at one time or another is quite remarkable in view of the depth of the built-up zone on all sides.

In the suburbs any quantitative survey of bird population is extremely difficult owing to the presence of innumerable small plots of private property to which there is no access; we have tried, however, to show what species have succeeded in adapting themselves to the highly artificial conditions, and we include a summary of one valuable study of a district before and after housing development, showing in particular the great increase of starlings.

Foremost among the various water and marsh habitats are the reservoirs, and it was about the turn of the century when the great expansion of these was taking place with far-reaching results that were little appreciated at the time. From just over 500 acres in 1900 they now occupy over 3000: at peak periods in winter they harbour most of the 10,000 or so ducks then in the Area, and nearly 100,000 gulls spend the winter nights on the larger waters. Although before 1922 only scattered observations at the reservoirs were published, chiefly for the Lea valley, they were watched more and more regularly as time went on and changes in the status of many of the ducks and grebes can be traced. At one reservoir there were once over 400 great crested grebes, and during migration periods over a hundred black terns have been seen at one water in spring and 300–500 common or arctic terns in autumn.

The reservoirs, with their wealth of birds, are a direct consequence of London's expansion, and so are the gravel pits which have increased in number tremendously with the greater use of concrete for building. A survey of selected pits undertaken by the Society has provided valuable material for our purpose. The pits have been an important factor in the spread of a new breeding species, the little ringed plover, and provide nesting sites for over half the Area's great crested grebes. One of the chief habitats for reed warblers, yellow wagtails and other marsh species, they do much to compensate for the lack of natural marshes.

The surroundings of the Thames below London have long been well-drained, but the grazing fields with their accompanying dykes and the mixture of saltings, clay pits, refuse dumps and other rough ground still harbour a number of the commoner marshland species; there is actually a colony of over a hundred pairs of reed warblers only about ten miles from St. Paul's.

Like the reservoirs the sewage farms are yet another result of London's growth whose ornithological importance was until comparatively recently appreciated by very few observers. From a large number of small units —another series of artificial marshes—these farms are being gradually closed down and amalgamated into a few modern works which in their final state are much less attractive to birds. At one farm, Perry Oaks, old-fashioned and modern conditions exist side by side, and since the last war 33 kinds of waders have been seen there including no fewer than four American species. To watch the autumn passage and rarities such as these only a few hundred yards from the constant passage of arriving and departing air-liners at the adjoining London Airport seems incongruous in the extreme.

The birds of the woodlands and agricultural land differ little from those of similar country elsewhere. Although the woods nearer in to London have suffered from the reduction of undergrowth where public access has not been restricted, the decline of gamekeeping has been a compensating advantage to the birds of prey and some of the Corvidae. Apart from the disappearance of the corncrake as in other parts of the country, the most striking changes on farmland have been the decline of the lapwing and the enormous increase of wintering gulls.

The last group of habitats discussed consists of the undeveloped land not used for agriculture or building—the heaths, commons, parks and downs. Here the chief change has been the great reduction in numbers of the ground-nesting species that has accompanied the increase of human population. The ploughing-up of much uncultivated ground during the Second World War accelerated the decline of some species, but a notable exception to the general trend has been the woodlark.

The two final chapters deal with migration and with roosts and fly-lines. The first brings together many scattered references elsewhere in the book, and puts the seasonal movements through the Area into perspective. It also discusses the results of several years of planned migration watches at vantage points in London during the late autumn immigration. That much can be seen of diurnal migration, even over the heart of London, will perhaps be surprising to those who have not taken part in these watches, and the results open up a field that would well repay further attention. The discussion of roosts and flylines also contains the results of much original research, especially the summary of an intensive study of the starling roosts in central London, in the course of which over 3000 birds were ringed at the roost in Trafalgar Square. The results from nearly 300 recoveries have shown that the vast majority of the starlings that fly in to London are resident birds from the suburbs. This conclusion is strengthened by the discovery that the greatest numbers—close on a hundred thousand—are in mid-summer, just after the breeding season when no Continental birds could be present. The little known roosts of house sparrows and crows are also discussed.

Throughout this book we have concentrated on those aspects of the subject which have special significance in relation to London, and within our allotment of space it has been impossible to discuss features of behaviour or distribution which are of more general application. If much valuable detail has been omitted it has been done of necessity, and we have been obliged to give terse treatment to the rarer vagrants in order to devote more space to the species that really belong to the Area, and to keep our material within one volume at a reasonable price. We have to thank our publishers, and particularly the editors of the New Naturalist, for their co-operation in helping to reconcile our needs for space with the bounds of practicability.

The systematic list includes 245 full species, excluding crane and pratincole, of which the exact species could not be determined with certainty, and the feral pigeon which we have discussed in some detail as it as much a feature of London (and other cities) as any species admitted to the British list. The 245 do not include various species in square brackets which have been mentioned for the sake of completeness. Some other species where the identification was in doubt are deliberately omitted. During this century 110 species are known to have nested in the Area, and about 100 still do so, or are believed to do so, annually.

In the systematic list we have been faced again and again with the difficulty of assessing changes in status owing to the enormous differences in the volume of observation at different periods. For the first quarter of the century our knowledge of status and distribution depends very largely on a relatively small number of experienced observers recording for the most part from restricted localities. For much of the Area, including the reservoirs, there is very little on record at this time, except for Hertfordshire which had from the outset an annual report on birds in the *Transactions* of the county Society, and excepting also a large number of arrival and departure dates of migrants. From about 1925 there was a slow improvement which gathered momentum during the thirties, when there was a very great increase both in observers and in the interest shown in recording. Although there was no falling-off in the number of observers during the Second World War there was a marked drop in the volume of records. After the war bird-watching became very much more popular than ever before, and there are now almost three times as many contributors to the *London Bird Report* as there were in the thirties.

It follows from the greatly varying intensity of observations over the years that the chances of rare visitors escaping detection early in our period and during the two wars were much more than they are to-day, and where the number of records for any particular species is given it is obviously a minimum with a biased distribution in time. Such totals of occurrences are based, however, on a very considerable quantity of data and they do provide some measure of the relative frequency of visits by related species. Where an opening summary of status is given; "very rare" implies less than 10 records, "rare" covers 10–24, "scarce" 25–49 and "occasional" 50–100 occurrences.

Full use has been made of the Society's own extensive records, and abstracts have been taken from all the books known to us which have dealt with London birds however sketchily. All the major periodicals concerned have been abstracted also, but by the very extent of the Area and its enormous population there must be casual references scattered in the local literature that have not come to our notice. We trust, however, that the many thousands of items indexed will have given a true picture of all the resident species and regular visitors, and if a few records of the rarer ones have not come to light this is of less importance.

The illustrations have almost all been taken in the Area, and have been chosen to illustrate characteristic features of the environment rather than to provide a wealth of portrait studies. A few of these have been included, however, mainly of birds that are of special interest in the London Area.

Of the previous writing on the subject we have already mentioned the histories of Kent and Surrey birds, but since 1900 there have also been W. E. Glegg's Histories of the Birds of Essex (1929) and Middlesex (1935). There has been no full county history of Hertfordshire birds, but an annotated list by H. H. S. Hayward appeared in the *Transactions* for 1947 of the Hertfordshire N.H.S. and Field Club. Sections on birds are included in most of the Victoria County Histories early in the century. The birds of central London have had a fairly extensive literature, which is referred to in the chapter on Inner London. Among the other more important works of which we have made use are Beadell's *Nature Notes of Warlingham and Chelsham* (1932), Walpole-Bond's *The Birds of Bromley (Kent) and its Neighbourhood* (1901), Collenette's *A History of Richmond Park* (1937), Dixon's *The Bird Life of London* (1909), Fitter's *London's Natural History* (1945) and *London's Birds* (1949), Harrison's *The Birds of Kent* (1953), Power's *Ornithological Notes from a South London Suburb* (1910) and a chapter by H. J. Turner in Grinling's *A Survey of Woolwich and West Kent* (1909). Much important information has come from the journals of the Essex Field Club, Essex Bird-Watching and Preservation Society, Hertfordshire N.H.S. and Field Club and the Selborne Society, and from the periodicals *British Birds, Country-Side, The Field, Middle Thames Naturalist, South-Eastern Bird Report* and *Zoologist*. Finally, a long series of papers and notes have appeared in the *London Naturalist* and the *London Bird Report,* of which an index for the years 1916–1948 was published in the *L.B.R.* for 1948.

The authorship of the various chapters has been given, but the systematic list is the responsibility of the editorial committee. Its preparation has been largely the work of C. B. Ashby, R. S. R. Fitter, R. C. Homes, E. R. Parrinder and B. A. Richards, with contributions from Miss C. M. Acland, L. Baker, C. L. Collenette, S. Cramp, D. Goodwin, P. A. D. Hollom and W. G. Teagle. It is particularly gratifying that the committee should include C. L. Collenette, the secretary of the Society's first ornithological committee in 1908.

Assistance has been received in various ways from many members of the Society. E. M. Nicholson has made valuable comments on the chapter on Inner London, and P. W. E. Currie has done the same for several chapters. F. H. Jones and H. P. Medhurst have often interrupted their work on the current records to assist us with the last few years. L. Baker, W. D. Melluish, P. R. Griffiths, and Mrs. R. E. Teagle have devoted considerable time to drawing the maps. For special reports or manuscript notes covering a great many years we are particularly indebted to C. H. Andrewes, H. G. Attlee, T. L. Bartlett, C. H. Bentham, J. F. Burton, the late J. E. S. Dallas, R. W. Hayman, G. E. Manser, G. K. McCulloch, H. Murray, H. E. Pounds, R. Spencer, G. Taylor, Professor E. H. Warmington, R. B. Warren and C. A. White. Mrs. Sylvia Lloyd generously placed at our disposal the valuable notes of her late husband, Bertram Lloyd, and we have derived much useful information from the detailed notes compiled by the late W. A. Wright in his long and valuable study of the Lea valley reservoirs. For statistical information about the London reservoirs we have to thank the Metropolitan Water Board to whose officials the Society owes a great deal for their co-operation. We are grateful to the Hampstead Scientific Society for permission to use their records and to the Wimbledon N.H.S. who presented to us their complete records. To the many others who helped us with original information, we apologise for the lack of space for full acknowledgment. For the same reason we have often been obliged to omit observers' names, especially when the records have already appeared in the *London Bird Report* to which reference is only made in exceptional cases. For assisting with the typing of the manuscript our thanks are due to Miss A. M. Davis,

Miss R. Davis, A. V. Pettit, T. G. Nordal and particularly to F. J. L. Mitchell. Again this list is not complete and we thank also those other members of the Society who helped from time to time.

The nomenclature used is that of the *Check-List of the Birds of Great Britain and Ireland* (1952) for Latin names. The English names are those given in the Check-List as amended in *British Birds*, 46: 1–3. In particular we have deliberately omitted, following the practice of that periodical, the hyphens separating birds' names after a noun used as an adjective.

In describing the normal periods of migration individual contributors have used the method which they have considered most appropriate to the data. To obtain the median date given in some accounts the annual first (or last) dates are arranged in chronological sequence, the median being the middle date of the series.

References in frequent use have been abbreviated as follows:—

B.B.	..	*British Birds*
L.N.	..	*London Naturalist*
L.B.R.	..	*London Bird Report*
N.H.S.	..	*Natural History Society*
Zool.	..	*Zoologist*

THE PHYSICAL SETTING
by R. S. R. Fitter

THANKS to their freedom of the air, birds are less closely tied than other animals to their immediate physical background. Nevertheless the geography, geology, physiography and climate of a region have an important bearing on the composition of its avifauna. In the London Area this direct relationship is perhaps less significant than the effect of subsequent changes due to human influence, but even so the ecology and distribution of the birds cannot be fully understood unless it is taken into account.

Virtually the whole of the London Area falls within what is known to geologists as the London Basin. The central feature of the Area is the valley of the Lower Thames, which enters it between Wraysbury (Bucks) and Egham (Surrey), and is tidal from Teddington Lock (Middlesex) to the point where it leaves the Area again at Tilbury (Essex) and a point midway between Northfleet and Gravesend in Kent. On either side of the Thames the land slopes down from the chalk hills in the shape of a somewhat elongated saucer that is open at one end. The southern rim of the chalk saucer runs more or less east and west along the crest of the North Downs, but the northern rim runs in a north-easterly direction some miles outside the Area, so that the north-eastern quadrant of the London Area, as defined here, is devoid of chalk, except for some small inlying patches between Purfleet and Grays in riverside Essex. Even in the north-western quadrant the chalk only occurs round the boundary of the Area, and for the most part lies beyond the River Colne. The greater part of the basin or saucer north of the Thames is filled with London clay, the rest of the area being covered with various sands and gravels. Broadly speaking, the Thames with its estuary and tributaries provides the natural water habitats, while the chalk underlies the open grassland and beech-woods, the clay the dense oak-woods and damp grassland, and the sands and gravels the lightly wooded heathlands and birch-woods. However, the hand of man, ever more heavily exerted over the past two thousand years, has reduced to artificial, or at best semi-natural, status virtually all the habitats that survive within twenty miles of the centre of the greatest concentration of human population in the world. All the grasslands and heathlands are grazed by cattle or mown or trodden by humans, all the woodlands are either planted or managed, and all the waters are either polluted or artificially purified, while a vast area has been completely transformed by the spade and plough, or covered with buildings, roads, docks, reservoirs, gardens, orchards, parks and playing fields.

The physical basis of the London Area, as has been said, is in the shape of a shallow, elongated saucer. This is bounded on the south by a range of chalk hills, the North Downs, and between Buckland (Surrey) and Riverhead (Kent) the Area actually overlaps into the quite distinct region of the Weald. In broad outline the Weald consists of a series of horseshoe-shaped ridges, the remains of a huge dome pushed up by a primeval earth-movement, but only one of these ridges, of the Lower Greensand formation and running from Redhill (Surrey) to Brasted Chart (Kent), affects the London Area. At Tilburstow Hill in Surrey it reaches a height of 590 ft. The crest of the North Downs, with its steep south-facing escarpment, runs through the Area from a point about a mile east of Box Hill (Surrey) to Kemsing on the east side of the Darent valley in Kent. It lies over the 700-ft. contour-line at a good many points, and above Oxted and Limpsfield in the extreme east of Surrey reaches an altitude of 877 ft. North of the Thames the several ranges of low hills nowhere attain a height of much over 500 ft. Indeed the country is best regarded as un-dulating rather than as crossed by specific ranges of hills. Only the lowest slopes of the Chilterns come into the Area, in the neighbourhood of Rickmansworth (Herts).

In the London Area the valleys are more significant than the hills from a faunistic point of view. The principal valley is, of course, that of the Thames, which in its lower reaches within the Area has muddy banks, but not the extensive tidal flats characteristic of most east-coast estuaries. All other rivers in the Area flow into the Thames; the ones whose valleys are still important features of the landscape are the Lea, Colne, Roding, Darent, Mole and Ingrebourne. Only very small portions of the valleys of the Wey, Misbourne, Chess, Gade, Ver, Mimram and Stort lie within the Area.

Although much of the North Downs is cultivated, many areas, especially on the scarp, but also on the dip-slope in places like Banstead Downs, still show fairly extensive stretches of semi-natural chalk grassland, a habitat much favoured by the skylark. Several of the birds typical of the great expanses of chalk downland elsewhere in the south of England, notably the wheatear and the stone curlew, are, however, missing. North of the Thames, the bird life of the grassland on the chalk hardly differs from that of any other grassland. A few beech-woods survive on the southern chalk, holding such characteristic species as the wood warbler. Wherever the chalk outcrops it is liable to be quarried, and these quarries often harbour hole-nesting birds, such as the jackdaw and the stockdove.

The great bulk of the clay-lands of the London Area are composed of the London Clay, lying in a broad band on either side of the Thames and separating it from the chalk. In parts of Essex, Middlesex and Hertfordshire there are also deposits of boulder-clay, representing the southernmost extremity of the ground moraine of an ice-sheet that once covered almost all England north of the Thames. In the extreme south a third type of clay, the Wealden, laps into the Area south of Oxted (Surrey). On the summits of the North Downs considerable tracts are covered with a deposit of Clay-with-Flints. The only remaining habitats on all these clay-lands that can be considered even semi-natural are certain woodlands, such as Epping Forest (Essex), and those lying south of Hertford, north of Ruislip (Middlesex), and scattered over the North Downs. The predominant tree in all these woods is the oak, accompanied in parts of Essex and Hertfordshire by the hornbeam. Such woods are a typical habitat for the nightingale, blackcap and garden warbler.

The sands and gravels of the London Area are scattered in many places. There is a large mass of Bagshot Sands in western Surrey, which overlaps into the Area on its south-western boundary, and these sands are also responsible for the heathy nature of the summits of the Hampstead and Highgate hills. Patches of heathland underlain by other sandy formations and by upland gravels are scattered throughout the Area; they include Wimbledon Common, on Plateau Gravel, and the higher parts of Epping Forest, on Pebble Gravel. On some of these heaths there are stretches of birch-wood, where redpolls and other finches often feed. All the main river valleys have terraces of gravel, representing former beds of the river at a time when its valley was much broader than it is now. Few of these valley gravels have anything approaching a natural vegetation, and most of them have been either built over or dug out for various industrial purposes. The resultant pits, however, provide an important habitat for the sand martin and little ringed plover. When flooded, they become the equivalent of small meres and lead to significant increases in such species as the yellow wagtail, sedge warbler, great crested grebe and coot.

The water habitats of the London Area are naturally mainly confined to the river valleys, the most important of which have already been mentioned. From Hammersmith to Woolwich the Thames banks are so built-up and industrialised that the river holds few birds except swans and gulls, which are scavengers depending on human refuse. Above Hammersmith, and particularly above Sunbury (Middlesex), the Thames banks become increasingly lined with the sedges, alders and willows that are characteristic of other large south-country rivers. Below Woolwich the river becomes more like the upper reaches of muddy east-coast estuaries such as the Essex Blackwater, and has a winter population of gulls and a few waders. The rivers falling into the Thames below London Bridge, such as the Lea, Roding and Darent, are rather heavily industrialised towards their mouths. Those joining the Thames further upstream are normal south-country streams throughout their length, except where bordered by suburban development or light industry. Apart from Dagenham Breach, which was formed by an incursion of the sea, there are no natural sheets of water in the London Area, but so many gravel pits have become flooded, and so many ornamental waters and reservoirs have been created or constructed, that parts of the valleys of the Thames, Lea and Colne are almost as rich in freshwater bird communities as, say, the mere district of Cheshire and Shropshire. The reservoirs are especially noted for their concourses of ducks, and at night also of gulls. Since most of the reservoirs have been constructed in or close to areas that barely a thousand years ago must have been marsh, fen or swamp, the duck, in coming to Staines or Littleton or Chingford may well be returning to haunts known to their ancestors when Caesar was fording the Thames. Natural swamps, bogs and marshes are now virtually extinct in the Area, but they have been replaced by artificial marshes in the shape of sewage farms, where many waders rest and feed on migration.

The slow transformations of nature over millions of years are as nothing to the far-reaching changes wrought by man in a mere couple of thousand. On the Land Utilisation map of England a huge splash of red obliterates the area between the warm brown of East Anglia's arable acres and the dark and light green patch-work of Wealden woods and pastures. Red stands for the urban areas, and indeed man's dwellings stretch almost uninterrupted from Cheshunt in the north to Leatherhead in the south, and from Gravesend in the east to Maidenhead in the west. A small part of this vast area is completely devoid of vegetation, but not of birds, for pigeons and sparrows can live and feed, and starlings can roost, in places where not a speck of soil exists. As one goes outwards from St. Paul's and away from the Thames, the density of vegetation gradually increases. Bombed sites are overgrown with weeds; trees are planted in squares and churchyards; parks and gardens appear. Lawns, flower-beds, allotments, waste ground, railway banks, all contribute to the increased amount of animal and vegetable food available for birds. At the time of writing (1955) there is still an extensive open space in the heart of the City, with even larger tracts in the East End, where bombs and incendiaries fell in 1940–41. Presumably this ground will shortly be completely built up again, but while it remains open its weed-grown ruins provide an ideal habitat for the black redstart.

As a broad generalisation the London Area can be said to consist of three concentric zones. In the middle is a nucleus of buildings in an area where the vegetation is sparse, and through this run the murky waters of the Thames. These wholly built-up districts are surrounded by a region of houses with gardens, interspersed with parks and other larger open spaces. To the bird population, for which the central area is equivalent to a close-set range of cliffs and caverns, the houses-with-gardens belt is an acceptable substitute for open woodland. However, only the rather more hardy of the woodland birds can adapt themselves to it. In fact the birds that can thrive in the wooded scrubland of Hampstead and Purley are almost exactly the same species as those of the birch-woods of north-west Sutherland, the bleakest part of the whole British Isles: chaffinch, great and blue tits, spotted flycatcher, song thrush, blackbird, robin, hedge sparrow and wren. By the same token the starlings and pigeons of the City have their counterparts in the starlings and rock doves of the cliff-bound coast of northern Scotland.

The outermost zone consists of what most people term loosely "the country", and is predominantly devoted to agriculture and its allied pursuits, forestry, horticulture and fruit-growing. The farmland can be broadly divided into arable and grassland; market-gardening land is largely equivalent to arable as a habitat for birds. Orchards have their own specialised avifauna, including especially the goldfinch and formerly also the wryneck. Most of the woodland in the Area is preserved for its amenity value rather than cultivated as a crop, and there are few coniferous plantations. There is also comparatively little rough pasture or heath grazing in the London Area. Most of what remains has been preserved for amenity, and much of this is consequently too frequented by human beings to have a very rich bird life. In parts of Surrey, however, the commons, such as that at Bookham, are particularly rich in woodland and heathland birds. Even so near London as Mitcham Common such a scarce breeding species as the stonechat survived long after it had become virtually extinct inland in many other parts of southern England. Another interesting specialised agricultural habitat is formed by the fresh marshes of the Thames estuary below Woolwich, which, although they are less rich in species than those described in Gillham and Homes's *Birds of the North Kent Marshes*, yet still support an interesting relic of a bird community associated with less populous grazing marshes.

The climate of the London Area is characterised by the dryness typical of eastern and the warmth typical of southern England. Rainfall nowhere much exceeds 30 inches in a year, nor falls much short of 20 inches. The highest rainfall occurs, as one would expect, on the more elevated parts of the North Downs, and more surprisingly on the Epping Forest ridge, which does not reach a height of 400 ft. The lowest rainfall occurs in the Thames valley, particularly down in the Essex sector. It is only twenty miles from Tilbury to the Shoeburyness district, which is the driest in the British Isles. Variation in the distribution of rainfall within the Area is not sufficient to have any direct effects on the distribution of the birds. Temperatures and amount of sunshine in the London Area vary little from those prevailing in the rest of southern England, and here again it is unlikely that the small differences between one part of the Area and another can affect the bird population, except in so far as the frequency of frost influences farming and market-gardening operations.

There is one important exception to the foregoing statements. The central built-up part of London has its special climatic peculiarities, which amount almost to a distinct local climate. Its temperature, for instance, in both summer and winter, is significantly higher than elsewhere, and it is the only part of the British Isles with a July isotherm of 64° F. This is evidently due to the warming of the atmosphere by the great mass of buildings. On the other hand Central London has much less sunshine than the outer areas. Bunhill Row in the borough of Finsbury, for example, can show an annual average of only 1,226 hours compared with as much as 1,613 hours at Biggin Hill on the North Downs in Kent. Put in another way, Bunhill Row gets only 3 hours 20 minutes of sunshine a day, compared with 4 hours at either Kew or Greenwich; and it will be remembered that the Royal Observatory has just been removed from Greenwich to Sussex because of the increasing pollution of the atmosphere. It is this pollution which is the cause of Central London's lack of sunshine. In 1936–37 solid matter was deposited in Lambeth at the rate of 322 tons per square mile, and in the same winter there were 69 milligrams of sooty suspended matter in 100 cubic metres of air in Victoria Street as against only 15 at Kew. It is possible that this atmospheric pollution, both directly by causing disease and indirectly by reducing the supply of plant and insect food, has a much greater effect than the resultant diminution of sunshine in reducing the variety of bird life in Inner London.

INNER LONDON

by S. Cramp and W. G. Teagle

THE CENTRE of a great modern city may seem at first a bleak and unrewarding home for birds, yet the variety of species found in the heart of London is greater than might be expected and the density compares well with that of many other habitats. Too precise an interpretation of the census work so far completed would not be justified but it is probable that the number of breeding birds in Inner London as a whole lies between 40 and 50 birds per ten acres.* Inner London itself contains a variety of habitats, but this generalisation is given to show that the density is considerably greater than the average density of land birds at this season in Great Britain as a whole, which according to an estimate by Fisher (*Watching Birds*, 1941) is slightly over 20 birds per ten acres. From his figures it appears that the congested centre of London, although supporting a smaller population of breeding birds than such favoured habitats as orchards, allotments and parkland, carries a larger number than moorland, coniferous forest and most types of farm-land.

The term "Inner London" was first used by A. Holte Macpherson to describe a rectangular area with its boundaries set four miles east and west and two and a half miles north and south of Charing Cross. These boundaries, although artificial, enclose an area of ecological significance, including most of the densely populated core of the capital. The closely packed buildings which cover much of the forty square miles are relieved by a number of large parks and in some districts by squares and private gardens (*see map on p. 30*). Through the area flows the tidal Thames, its tributaries now all banished below ground, though artificial waters are found in the parks and in the docks adjoining the lower reaches of the river. Some of this land has been built on for centuries and nearly all of it for more than a hundred years. It forms the core of the greatest urban agglomeration in the world, which has continued to spread throughout the years, so that there is little open country within ten miles of the centre.

---

* This approximation is based on counts of nests in two areas in Bloomsbury and Lambeth, on regular counts throughout the year in many central squares and on estimates of the breeding population in four of the Royal Parks.

Yet some birds have held on despite the lack of vegetation and the noise and bustle of man, while others have learned to exploit the opportunities offered by one of the most recent of habitats.

In the pages which follow we discuss the successful species and their ways of life in each of the main habitats of Inner London—the closely built zone, the bombed areas, the public and private squares, the gardens of houses, the parks and the docks and waterways. There follows a short account of some of the species which occur as migrants or erratic wanderers. * Then, after a discussion of the main ecological factors affecting the species living in the area, the chapter ends with a summary of the changes in the last fifty years or so.

East of Westminster and south of the Thames there are thousands of acres with rarely a lawn or flower-bed. Elsewhere squares and gardens are more frequent, though even here most of the land is tightly packed with buildings. The dominant breeding birds of these closely-built areas are the house sparrow and the feral pigeon. The sparrow is more numerous and more evenly spread, though its numbers are greatest where food is abundant, near markets, grain docks and squares where bread is provided. The loose colonies of pigeons are distributed more erratically, for the birds range more widely in search of food and nesting sites are the chief determining factor. They prefer recesses or sheltered ledges for breeding. Church towers, railway bridges, bomb-shattered buildings, Classical porticos and Gothic ornaments may provide acceptable sites. The sparrow is less restricted, for any small hole or cranny will serve its purpose, in holes made by bomb splinters, behind the ventilation grids of modern office blocks, in cavities where the ends of floor joists once rested, and in or behind statuary. If holes in buildings are lacking it will build in creepers on the walls of houses, wedge a bulky nest behind a drain-pipe, or take to the trees, building an untidy structure amongst the twigs or using a natural hole.

Both sparrows and feral pigeons are largely scavengers, feeding on the scraps provided by man. Bread is now their staple diet, though the sparrow is readier to supplement this with seed or, especially when it is feeding young, with insect food. The feral pigeon feeds more often in the roadway, though infrequently in busy ones, its ability to make a rapid and almost vertical take-off usually saving it from destruction. In the sixties of the last century Shirley Hibberd wrote of robins feeding in the open roadway of the Strand and Ludgate Hill, and Aleph noted rooks feeding like the sparrows among the cab-wheels in the City (Fitter, 1949). Early in this

* Full details of the distribution of the commoner birds in Inner London, arranged under species headings, together with an account of all migrants and rarer visitors between 1900 and 1950, will be found in *B.B.*, 43 : 433–456.

century London's busy horse-traffic still ensured a ready food-supply for sparrows, and its decline has probably played a part in reducing their numbers. Modern traffic provides little food, and less opportunity to eat what food there is. Except in the early mornings or on Sundays it is now rare to see any bird feeding in the main streets, and in the quieter ones the feral pigeon is the most common, followed by the sparrow, and, less often, the woodpigeon, the starling and, in winter, the black-headed gull.

Sparrows and feral pigeons share these barren areas with smaller numbers of other breeding species. The kestrel, only a visitor at the beginning of the century, was first proved to breed in 1931, and there have been nesting birds present in all recent years, with as many as five pairs in 1950. They favour chimneys, steeples and towers, and have reared young on a number of high buildings, including the Houses of Parliament. Sparrows appear to form their chief prey, but the bombed sites no doubt also provide insects and occasional mice, and the creation of these waste areas has almost certainly helped the increase of the species in recent years.

Starlings and woodpigeons are more common in the parks and squares, but they do breed in the closely built districts. Starlings nest readily in holes in buildings, but prefer those within easy reach of lawns where food is plentiful, and though woodpigeons will nest on buildings they are far more likely to breed in trees. In recent years plane-trees in busy streets have been chosen for nesting, some more than a hundred yards from any open space. The mallard, a wanderer from the parks, has several times nested on the flat roofs of tall buildings, and lately even jays have attempted to nest on buildings and in trees in busy Kensington streets.

From October until March numbers of black-headed gulls drift over the streets, dropping down to scramble with pigeons for scraps on window-sills or to catch bread thrown from office windows. Although they were seen feeding in the roadway of a London street as early as 1917, the habit is still an uncommon one, though more often noticed in recent years. In these months and to a lesser extent in spring and summer, when the main roost is in St. James's Park, the bird population of the built-up areas is increased each night by thousands of roosting starlings whose habits are discussed fully in a later chapter.

There are smaller areas within the densely built zone which have an ecological importance of their own—the railway stations and sidings and the markets. Sparrows and feral pigeons are the common birds of the stations, but the woodpigeon has been seen feeding on the tracks outside Waterloo and inside Charing Cross, while a pair nested for several years on a girder under the roof of the old St. James's Park Station. On railway sidings the black-headed gull is also found in winter, and it has been recorded perching on tenders outside Victoria, taking bread thrown by drivers and firemen. In most of the markets sparrows and feral pigeons are again the common scavengers. At Covent Garden they feed regularly in the roadway and sparrows search the straw in carts and lorries and examine loads of vegetables for insects. In winter greater black-backed, herring and black-headed gulls scavenge amongst the fish refuse at Billingsgate Market.

The air attacks of 1940 and 1941 caused extensive devastation in the closely built zone. After the raiders came the demolition workers, and parts of central London were completely transformed, especially around St. Paul's, where hundreds of ragged walls and yawning basements replaced the warehouses that formerly flanked the narrow streets. Before long plants colonised the rubble, followed by insects; together they provided new food for birds.*

In the bombed areas, both large and small, the sparrow is dominant. The ruined buildings offer nesting sites and the weed-grown basements provide seed and insect food. Feral pigeons have appropriated ledges and the larger holes, though they feed mainly in the streets. Starlings and woodpigeons feed occasionally on the smaller sites. The more extensive ones, however, have attracted new birds, notably the black redstart. It first bred in Inner London in the precincts of Westminster Abbey in 1940, before the bombing began, but the nesting sites and abundant insect life of the blitzed areas have greatly aided its spread. The first young were seen in the City in 1942, since when this has been one of the main strongholds of the species, not only in London, but in all Britain.

The pied wagtail, which formerly nested occasionally in some of the parks, has bred regularly in small numbers in the Cripplegate ruins since 1946 at least, and, as already noted, the kestrel has been helped in its increase in the last ten years by the bombed sites, with their sparrows, mice and insects. The first nest to be found in the City during this century was in 1946, when a pair reared young in a building near Dean's Lane. Although kestrels frequently hunt over Cripplegate and other City bombed sites they have usually nested elsewhere. Blackbirds were seen at Cripplegate as early as 1944, but when Currie (*L.N.* for 1949, pp. 81–84) made his survey of the area they were still scarce. A pair nested in 1949, but the birds were elusive and shy, frequenting the deepest basements. They have increased since and their nests have been found in holes in buildings. Currie found that feral pigeons were present in surprisingly small numbers, and though woodpigeons foraged in the roads and basements they usually nested in trees outside the area. A few starlings breed each year. Mallards have not nested yet at Cripplegate, but since 1941 they have raised broods

---

* For a description of the vegetation of a typical bombed area and the ecological factors concerned, see F. E. Wrighton (*London Naturalist*, 1947–50. 1952).

at other sites, often small ones, where the basements had been converted into emergency water tanks. These tanks also attract the grey wagtail, usually as a passage visitor and winter resident, though a pair reared two broods at Cripplegate in 1952. Goldfinches, blue tits, robins and wrens have also been seen frequently in recent winters.

The areas in the City that suffered the worst damage during the raids were those where modern building followed the haphazard street pattern of mediaeval London. Thus conservatism in town planning aided the black redstart and pied wagtail. New ideas in town development gave rise else-where, particularly in the centre and west, to another bird habitat—the residential square. Few other cities have so many islands of vegetation to break the monotony of the built-up areas and enrich the bird life of the urban zone. These squares, despite their name, are of various shapes, oblong, circular and oval, and range in area from less than one acre to five or six. Their lay-out also varies, but nearly all contain trees of up to eighty or ninety feet in height (chiefly plane, tree of heaven, lime and black poplar), with smaller flowering trees, shrubberies, flower-beds and lawns. There is little undergrowth, and the shrubberies, which provide the main cover for species which do not nest in holes or at a safe height, are usually limited in extent, especially in the squares open to the public, which have greatly increased in number since 1939.

There are significant differences between the birds of the public and private squares. The bread liberally provided by visitors in the public squares attracts numbers of house sparrows and pigeons, but the presence of people, especially small boys, makes nesting difficult for all birds. A few sparrows use the trees, but most prefer to nest on nearby buildings, and all the feral pigeons nest outside the squares. In the private squares, where crumbs are less frequently scattered, there are noticeably fewer sparrows, while the feral pigeons are rare or absent. The woodpigeon nests in nearly all squares, however small, and it is the third most numerous species in the public ones. Its nests are usually inaccessible, often from forty to fifty feet high in the trees, though sometimes as low as fifteen feet. Starlings are al-most as common, though more irregularly distributed. Lack of tree-holes may account for their absence in some places; even in the thriving Russell Square colony only a minority of the nests are in trees, most being built some eighty feet up beneath the tiles of an adjacent hotel. In some open places, however, such as the Embankment Gardens, they are not found at all, despite the fact that there are lawns for feeding and no apparent lack of suitable nesting holes.

The blackbird is another species which now nests in or near most of the squares, private and public, though it appears to be a relatively recent addition to the urban areas. In Montagu's *Ornithological Dictionary* (1831) it is said that "in winter it approaches houses and towns and during severe storms it haunts the garden, coming close to houses and even to windows, picking up crumbs of bread." It has long been common in the parks, but its invasion of some central districts is quite recent, for Bertram Lloyd, resident for many years in Bloomsbury, did not hear his first blackbird there until the winter of 1935. By 1937 the species was nesting in Lincoln's Inn Fields, and it now breeds regularly in many parts of this central area. Even so, its numbers are probably restricted by the lack of suitable nesting-sites, for the shrubberies in many of the squares are not dense enough to be safe, so that birds are forced to resort to adjacent gardens or to build high in trees, sometimes in typical mistle thrush situations in the forks.

Song thrushes are now uncommon, confined to a few of the private squares, though they were resident in Lincoln's Inn Fields as recently as 1940. They may have been affected by the increase in blackbirds, for Col. R. Meinertzhagen tells us that the last pair of song thrushes in one Kensington square disappeared in 1940, after being persistently harried by the blackbirds. The mistle thrush, on the other hand, has increased in recent years. In 1929 it was rare outside the grounds of Holland House and Kensington Gardens, but it now nests in a number of both public and private squares with large lawns, often building in remarkably exposed sites, including trees close to busy pavements.

Great tits have been known to nest only in the private squares, and have never been common. Blue tits are a little more numerous, and do occasionally nest also in the public squares. The provision of nesting boxes in Lincoln's Inn Fields did not lead to any increase in the numbers of breeding blue tits, which suggests that they may be limited by the shortage of suitable food rather than lack of nesting holes. They have been known to attack milk bottles there for some years. The jay may in time become an established bird of the squares. It is a frequent visitor to several private ones, and has bred in Ladbroke Square for several years, and in Thurloe Square in 1951, while in 1950 a pair reared young in a small Bayswater square open to the public.

There are other species for which the public squares have more risks than attractions. They are usually avoided by the carrion crow which, though nesting too high for interference, is wary of man. The spotted fly-catcher, with a more vulnerable nest, prefers the quieter squares and gardens. Robins are winter visitors to a few with good cover, and they have bred in Ladbroke Square. This large garden, restricted to residents, has a rich bird population. Mallard, song thrush and great tit are known to have bred there, and chaffinches and hedge sparrows have been seen in the breeding season, as well as in winter. Chaffinches were said to have been common in Bloomsbury in the last century, when the squares were private, but they are now seen only on passage. They have been reported from private squares elsewhere in the breeding season.

Tawny owls range widely and have been seen and heard in many squares, and may nest occasionally, although most of the occurrences are in autumn, winter and early spring. Black-headed gulls sometimes visit the squares in winter to share the bread with sparrows, pigeons and others, but so far they have taken little advantage of this potential food supply. At the height of their autumn passage lesser black-backed gulls have rested on the games pitches of Vincent Square in recent years.

The lack of variety in the bird life of the closely built areas has been discussed earlier. Where the houses possess gardens, however, the picture is more diversified. Such gardens are found mainly in Kensington, St. John's Wood and Brondesbury in the west and north-west, but also, though less numerous and usually smaller, in Bayswater, Westminster and Bloomsbury. They range from small plots with little more than grass, planes and privets to what are almost private parks, like the garden of Lambeth Palace or the grounds of the mansions on Campden Hill.

In the small gardens of the central area the sparrow, starling, blackbird and woodpigeon, with more rarely, the blue tit, spotted flycatcher and mistle thrush may nest. All these species, with the addition of the robin, were found breeding in 1950 in the large garden of Lambeth Palace, which provides another example of a quiet extension to an open space where birds are much disturbed. Thus, also, the gardens of Queen's Walk offer sanctuary to the birds of the Green Park, and in one (the garden of Lancaster House) blackbird, woodpigeon, robin, hedge sparrow and jay have nested. On the other hand, some gardens in Kensington have benefited by their proximity to the wooded reserve of Holland House grounds, as witness the jays which bred in Holland Park Road in 1947 and the greater spotted woodpeckers which were suspected of nesting in Campden Hill in 1946.

Some of the numerous gardens of St. John's Wood owe their variety of species not only to their size but also to bomb damage and neglect, which have resulted in extensive belts of unkempt lawns and tangled shrubbery. Here, besides the sparrow, starling, blackbird, and woodpigeon are great and blue tits, chaffinches, greenfinches, song thrushes, hedge sparrows, wrens and tawny owls, with goldfinches probably breeding. In 1953 at least two pairs of blackcaps reared young in these neglected areas, and the hawfinches which were seen feeding young in nearby Regent's Park in 1951 and 1952 may have nested in some secluded garden in the district. Here, and at nearby Kilburn and Primrose Hill, there are small numbers of swifts, now probably the only colonies in Inner London, though definite nesting records are few. In 1928 three pairs were seen by Stuart Smith feeding young under the eaves of the General Post Office in the City, but it is unlikely that swifts have bred in any numbers in central London for some years, probably because of a shortage of suitable food rather than any lack of nesting sites. In most of the areas where houses with gardens predominate the feral pigeon is relatively uncommon, with its colonies small and infrequent.

The main parks of Inner London are situated in or near areas already well provided with squares and gardens. A continuous belt of green, formed by St. James's Park, the Green Park, Hyde Park and Kensington Gardens, extends from Whitehall to Kensington Palace, and beyond the gardens of Campden Hill lie the woodlands of Holland House. Regent's Park and Primrose Hill are adjacent to St. John's Wood, while Battersea Park, although flanked on the south by solidly built-up land, faces across the river to the grounds of the Royal Hospital, which lie close to the squares and gardens of Chelsea and South Kensington. Dockland's South-wark Park and Victoria Park, Hackney, are the only large open areas in the congested monotony of the eastern half of Inner London.

The Royal Parks have received much attention from ornithologists, particularly in the last twenty years. For Battersea Park also, the picture is fairly complete, but many of the other open spaces, especially Victoria and Southwark Parks, have been sadly neglected.

Four of the five largest parks (Regent's Park, 472 acres; Hyde Park, 361 acres; Kensington Gardens, 275 acres, and Battersea Park, 200 acres) are in the western half of the area. They all possess large tracts of trodden grass-land with tall trees of many species (but little undergrowth), shrubberies, flowering trees, lawns and flower-beds and miles of asphalt paths. Yet each has an individual character, determined mainly by the differing propor-tions of these main features. They are visited by thousands of people daily, especially in the spring and summer, and the areas closed to the public (mainly shrubberies and flower-beds, though there are a few special sanctuaries) form a relatively small part of the total, so that birds nesting on the ground or in low cover are at a disadvantage. All four parks have ornamental waters (Kensington Gardens and Hyde Park 48 acres, Regent's Park 22 acres and Battersea Park about 15 acres), with islands that provide additional sanctuaries when boaters are not allowed to land on them. They have many breeding species in common—mallard, mute swan, moorhen, woodpigeon, tawny owl, carrion crow, great tit, blue tit, mistle thrush, song thrush, blackbird, robin, spotted flycatcher, starling, chaffinch and house sparrow. The jay, spreading apparently from the grounds of Holland House, has nested regularly in Kensington Gardens in recent years and occasionally in Hyde Park. Jays first appeared in Regent's Park in 1934, having perhaps infiltrated from Hampstead, and they nested close by on

Primrose Hill in 1938. There were no further records for some years, but they have bred regularly since 1951 and also more recently in or near St. James's Park and the Green Park. In Battersea Park they nested in 1947 and in other years since. Greenfinches have bred in all except Hyde Park, where the hedge sparrow also appears to be uncommon as a nesting species. The greater spotted woodpecker is another bird which has spread from the grounds of Holland House, first to Kensington Gardens, where it has bred in most years from 1940 onwards. Nesting attempts have been made in Hyde Park, while it has been seen frequently in recent years in Regent's Park, breeding successfully in 1952, and in Battersea Park, where birds probably nested in 1949 and 1950. The wren's position in the parks is rather insecure and though the species often tries to breed in Kensington Gardens and Battersea Park it is probable that it is most often successful at the present time in Regent's Park.

In a detailed study made in 1947 (*L.B.R.*, 13: 37–45) it was shown that 25 species then nested in Kensington Gardens compared with only 19 in Regent's Park. The six additional breeding species were the jay and greater spotted woodpecker, which have already been mentioned, and the stock dove, jackdaw, coal tit and treecreeper. The small colony of stock doves which has been present in Kensington Gardens for some years appears to have increased recently, and the species has begun to spread to other parks. Nesting occurred in both Battersea Park and Regent's Park in 1952 and 1953, and birds have been seen in St. James's Park and the Green Park. The coal tit is present in small numbers and its breeding is erratic. It has nested in Kensington Gardens only in 1947, but small young were seen in Regent's Park in 1951 and 1953. The jackdaw and treecreeper are still restricted to Kensington Gardens for nesting. Although tree-felling drove the rooks from Kensington Gardens before 1900, the small jackdaw colony has managed to survive so far, with not more than six pairs present in recent years and often less. Treecreepers, which were first known to nest there in 1945 and are now resident, are even less numerous. Though the disparity in the number of land species nesting in the two parks has almost disappeared in recent years, the woodland birds are still numerically stronger in Kensington Gardens, because the trees are more numerous and more closely planted, whereas the grassy spaces which are a feature of Regent's Park are too subject to human interference to allow ground-nesting birds to flourish. During the last war, when the games pitches were closed to the public, yellow wagtails bred there and skylarks were more frequent, though they are not known to have nested.

Battersea was the first London park to provide definite breeding records of the goldfinch, which nested there in 1949 and 1950. In Regent's Park a pair had been seen with young in 1945, and nesting has been proved each year since 1952, while in 1950 an adult was seen with two juveniles on the adjoining Primrose Hill. The kestrel, which frequently hunts over the parks, but prefers to nest outside them, on buildings, made an unsuccessful attempt to use the old nest of a crow in Battersea Park in 1950.

There are several other species which, like the yellow wagtail, have bred occasionally in the parks since 1900. Pied wagtails, which have nested in the past in Kensington Gardens, Hyde Park and the Zoological Gardens, now breed less frequently in the parks, but young were seen being fed in Regent's Park in 1946 and in Battersea Park in 1949, while adults were noted collecting food in St. James's Park in 1950. Willow warblers bred twice in Hyde Park in the twenties and at least once in Regent's Park in the thirties. More recently, Regent's Park provided a new breeding species for Inner London when in 1953 a pair of whitethroats nested in some enclosed and overgrown land in the north of the park, while in 1954 two pairs of willow warblers bred on the same site. The lesser whitethroat is rarely recorded even on passage, but a pair bred in Hyde Park in 1921, and a single male stayed in Kensington Gardens throughout the summer of 1942. Linnets, usually spring and autumn visitors, have also occasionally stayed during the breeding season and a pair was suspected of nesting in Hyde Park in 1918. The early years of the century provided two unusual records—swallows nesting in a deer-shed at the Zoo in 1907 and 1908, and a young cuckoo reared by robins in Regent's Park in 1905.

The mute swan, mallard and moorhen nest on most park waters, but the lake in St. James's Park is the main breeding haunt of other species, for though small (about 5 acres) it is free from the disturbance of boating and the pinioned birds are an attraction to wild duck. The nesting of pochard there was perhaps entirely dependent on the presence of pinioned birds and their park-bred offspring, but in recent years the species has spread to other parks, nesting in Regent's Park in 1953 and 1954 and in Battersea Park in 1954. It has been the chief nesting locality of the tufted duck for many years, for although this species nested in Hyde Park and Kensington Gardens from 1924 until at least 1938 there was a long gap before, in 1954, young were again seen on the Serpentine. In Regent's Park they nest only occasionally. The coot has been a resident in St. James's Park since 1926, helped perhaps by the introduction of pinioned birds and by the placing of coots' eggs in moorhens' nests; more than twenty pairs have competed fiercely for nest sites in recent years. the coot has bred very occasionally in Hyde Park and Kensington Gardens, and more recently appears to have established itself in small numbers in Regent's Park. The little grebe has been less successful. It colonised a number of park lakes in the last two decades of the nineteenth century, and in 1898 Hudson considered it to be as well established as those two other recent colonists, the moorhen and woodpigeon. It left St. James's Park after the summer of 1914, when the lake was drained, and has since nested there only on three occasions. Regent's Park was also a breeding locality between 1927 and 1929 and more recently the grounds of Buckingham Palace were favoured, but there has been no evidence of nesting in London since 1949. Herons have never nested in the inner parks, but they are regular visitors to the more extensive lakes, usually in the morning or evening.

As already mentioned, the bird life of Victoria Park (217 acres) and Southwark Park (63 acres) has been little studied. Victoria Park would certainly repay more attention from ornithologists. Much of it is open and well-frequented, with little shelter for birds, and the lakes are small and disturbed, but about 1912 one of the first broods of tufted ducks in Inner London was seen there. They are known to have nested again in 1937 and 1950 and probably have done so in other years. Greenfinches nest there and in 1950 a goldfinch was seen feeding young. The variety of birds in Southwark Park is much poorer, but young tufted duck were noted in 1939.

In winter large numbers of gulls visit the park lakes and more water-fowl appear. The gulls are mostly black-headed, with smaller numbers of common gulls, but herring gulls and both black-backs also occur. The visiting duck are mainly mallard, pochard and tufted duck. Scaup have been seen in many recent winters, especially on the Round Pond, and in some years have remained for several weeks. Kingfishers are fairly frequent visitors, both in autumn and winter. Coot and moorhen increase, especially on the lake in St. James's Park. Tits are more numerous, but some species, such as greenfinch, chaffinch and song thrush appear to be scarcer in winter in some parks. Some may wander to private gardens in search of food; thus, E. M. Nicholson reports greenfinches in his Chelsea garden every autumn, while robins and wrens only appear there in winter.

A census of the birds of Kensington Gardens based on a series of counts in the winter of 1925–26 by E. M. and B. D. Nicholson (*Discovery*, August, 1926), when repeated in 1948–49 by the present writers (*L.B.R.* for 1949, pp. 41–48) showed that considerable changes had occurred. Tufted duck, common gull, black-headed gull, jay, mistle thrush and blackbird were more numerous, while mallard, moorhen, woodpigeon, wren, starling and house sparrow had decreased. In the case of the resident land-birds and the gulls these probably represent real changes in the population over the twenty-four years, but the numbers of duck fluctuate in different winters and more extended counts would be necessary to establish a clear trend. Counts made on the Round Pond (7 acres in extent, with no cover of any kind) in the winters of 1946–49 showed that the peak figures for mallard ranged from 60–120, for tufted duck from 60–180, and for pochard from 20–30. The maxima for black-headed gulls varied between 500 and 650, and for common gulls between 30 and 35. The numbers of other gulls were usually much smaller, but in 1948, unusually large parties of herring gulls were present on occasion, as many as 60 being counted by C. H. F. Parsons on February 5th. Details of counts of the winter birds in St. James's Park and the Green Park in 1949–50 have also been published (*L.B.R.* for 1950, pp. 48–52). The wooded islands in some of the parks are used by roosting woodpigeons in winter, and by starlings in the summer and autumn.

Space is too limited to mention in detail all the smaller parks and open spaces, but reference should be made to Ranelagh Gardens, part of Chelsea Hospital grounds. Here mallard bred in 1949 and greenfinch in 1951 and 1952, while greater spotted woodpeckers made an attempt in 1950. A more unlikely place for bird-watching is Brompton Cemetery, which in recent years has been found to harbour a richer bird breeding population than some of the smaller parks. Black redstarts nested in 1950, besides great tit, hedge sparrow, song thrush, robin and spotted flycatcher, and young jays and goldfinches were seen. In 1937 two broods of mallard ducklings were hatched in the long grass amongst the tombstones.

Until 1952 one of the most important open spaces in Inner London, the grounds of Holland House, remained in private hands. Visits by ornithologists were infrequent, so that a clear historical picture of the breeding birds is lacking, but it is known that from the seclusion of these Kensington woods several species colonised the public parks, while others found in its undergrowth the cover they needed for nesting—cover which elsewhere is rarely spared by the tidy gardeners. The jay and the greater spotted woodpecker bred first there, before spreading further afield, and the stock dove may have done so. Lesser whitethroats nested in 1915 and possibly again in 1921, and in 1929 A. Holte Macpherson wrote that willow warblers and blackcaps usually bred in small numbers. In 1937 Eric Simms obtained two unique nesting records for Inner London when he found a chiffchaff's nest with eggs and saw fledgling marsh tits. Since its acquisition by the London County Council the woods in the northern half have been preserved as a sanctuary. The warblers have not yet regained their former strength (though a willow warbler was seen with food in 1953) but two new breeding species have been added—the green woodpecker, which bred in 1952 and 1953, and the sparrow hawk, which deserted after laying a single egg in 1953.

Finally in our study of the main habitats, we turn to the docks and waterways. The Thames, tidal and polluted, winds through the area from Battersea to Limehouse. Its former marshes have given way to wharves and embankments, but at low tide considerable stretches of gravel and mud are exposed, attracting the dominant birds of the river, the gulls. At high tide many of them move no further than to the anchored barges and river-side buildings to rest and preen. Only within the last seventy years have the gulls become the prime scavengers of London's river. The black-headed gull came first, and it is still the most numerous. A passage migrant in the middle of the last century, it may now be seen on the river from mid-July until March and infrequently at other times. The common gull increased during the first quarter of this century and is now resident between October and March. The herring gull is mainly a winter visitor but the lesser black-back is most numerous as a passage migrant, especially in autumn. Since the early 1930's a few have wintered and immature birds are present throughout the summer. Greater black-backed gulls, formerly rare, have become much more common, especially in the last ten years, over 50 having been seen at times between Waterloo and Black-friars. They also occur from time to time in the summer months. All the gulls are scavengers, picking up refuse floating in the stream or left by the receding tide, and fighting for scraps in the rubbish barges. Greater black-backs have been seen eating eels at Waterloo Bridge, and common and black-headed gulls feed on organisms taken from the mud itself, paddling with their feet to bring them to the surface.

The mute swans which occur on the river throughout the year also seem to be mainly scavengers and the largest herds are found near rubbish dumps and barges. Other common birds of the tide-line are the feral pigeons (many of which nest beneath the Thames bridges) and, in smaller numbers, carrion crows. Large flocks of sparrows join the pigeons at places where the grain barges are unloaded, but they spend little time along the mud.

The pollution of the Thames in Inner London has undoubtedly lessened in the last fifty years, and fish have been found as far down river as Battersea. Despite this improvement duck are not reported frequently in any numbers. A few mallard may be seen at all seasons, though below Battersea they occur mainly from February to June. They have nested occasionally along the river, sites including a decayed raft, a disused barge and the timbers used when the present Waterloo Bridge was under con-struction. Hard weather may bring large flocks of mallard, which are then often joined by tufted duck and pochard. Coot and moorhen are rather rare, and waders are infrequent (see *L.B.R.* for 1953, pp. 42–57, for an account of the habits and seasonal variations in numbers of species frequenting the Thames in Inner London).

The docks, some 200 acres of standing water, have been little studied. Probably too disturbed to support a rich bird life, they are, like the river, frequented by all five species of gull, especially in winter. The mallard is the most common duck, breeding not infrequently at Surrey Docks, where the largest and quietest waters are found and some basins have rafts of timber which provide nesting sites. Tufted duck occur in hard weather. Unlike the river some of the docks are well provided with fish, as are the canals along certain stretches. At the pool where the Regent's Canal and the Grand Union Canal converge tufted ducks, swans and gulls are seen, while mallard and moorhen have nested. Further east, where the long-boats glide between the tree-lined banks of Regent's Park, kingfishers and herons have been recorded.

Although only the hardy and adaptable can thrive in the urban area, it must not be thought that other species avoid entirely the centre of London. There are many migrant species which appear with great regularity and other birds of more casual occurrence which are often rare enough to excite the attention of gatherings of ornithologists.

More intensive field work by many observers in the last few years has revealed that a number of migratory species, at one time infrequently recorded, do in fact occur annually. The regular migrants are common sandpiper, cuckoo, swift, skylark, swallow, house martin, sand martin, fieldfare, redwing, wheatear, whinchat, redstart, blackcap, garden warbler, whitethroat, lesser whitethroat, willow warbler, chiffchaff, wood warbler, spotted flycatcher, pied flycatcher, tree pipit and yellow wagtail. A few of these species, of course, can also be classed as regular or occasional summer residents. Among the less usual migrants which have been seen are corncrake, black-tailed godwit, green sandpiper, greenshank, dunlin, stone curlew, little gull, black tern, nightjar, wryneck, ring ouzel, reed warbler and marsh warbler. This list is by no means exhaustive and within the last few years there have been such oddities as a black-eared wheatear in Regent's Park, a great grey shrike in a back-yard in Camden Town and a turnstone in the basement of a bombed site in Chelsea.

Birds on the move through the area often choose the urban equivalent of their normal environment. Thus wheatears are found amongst the broken boulders of building stone which lie tumbled in bomb-damaged City basements, while whinchats seek their food among the coarse vegetation of the bombed sites. For a few hours a whitethroat may haunt the dusty brambles of the Hyde Park sanctuary or a sedge warbler be found skulking in the bamboos beside the Long Water in Kensington Gardens.

The hawthorns of Green Park, the shrubberies and games pitches of Regent's Park and the sheepfold in Kensington Gardens seem to be especially attractive to migrants. The sheepfold, flanking the small copse behind Peter Pan, appears to be rich in food for insectivorous birds. Leaf and other warblers visit it, at least one redstart is usually recorded each year and spotted flycatchers, often in fair numbers, haunt its chestnut paling. The lakes and large ponds in the parks attract parties of swifts, swallows and martins, while the common sandpiper feeds along the concrete banks of these ornamental waters as well as on the foul and muddy margins of the Thames.

Hard weather brings in the fieldfares and redwings, some of the former often remaining after conditions have become kinder. A prolonged frost usually results in a small invasion of skylarks and meadow pipits, and unusual duck can sometimes be seen amongst the tufted and mallard in the parks. In 1947 a long-tailed duck was seen on the Thames between Southwark and Hungerford bridges just after a severe spell, and another, or the same, was present in St. James's Park, apart from occasional absences, for four months up till early August, during which time it became tame enough to take bread offered by the public.

Red-throated divers, black-necked, red-necked and Slavonian grebes, Leach's petrel, cormorants, great and arctic skuas, shags, guillemots, razorbills and puffins have all appeared in Inner London, and there is one record of a little auk. Many of the sea-birds are picked up sick or oiled, sometimes in unexpected places. In 1935 a puffin landed in the middle of the Strand and held up the traffic.

For a species to establish itself in Inner London it must find sufficient food and a safe nesting site, while being able to tolerate the close presence of man. There is plenty of food available though it is restricted in variety. Those species which can feed on bread are fortunate, and for grain-eaters the transition is easy. The feral pigeons feed almost entirely on bread, and woodpigeons rely largely on it, though feeding also on weeds, buds and green shoots, and, in the autumn, on seeds, acorns and berries, the majority leaving late in the season for the richer acorn harvests to be found outside the area. The omnivorous sparrow feeds on refuse, seeds, buds and both flying and crawling insects, but bread forms the staple part of its diet. In winter the black-headed gulls, though preferring the fattier scraps of kitchen waste, have found a number of ways, as already described, of obtaining their share of crusts, while the common gull tries to rob them by skua tactics. Coots, moorhens, swans and the three resident ducks gather eagerly when bread is scattered on the lakes. Other species which have been seen to feed on bread in Inner London are the herring gull, lesser black-backed gull, carrion crow, jackdaw, jay, great, blue and coal tits, mistle thrush, blackbird, robin, hedge sparrow, starling, goldfinch and such occasional visitors as the scaup, wigeon and long-tailed duck. Some species even feed bread to their young.

Plate 1*a*. A bombed site in Cripplegate, Inner London. (*C. B. Ashby*)
b. A London square. (*Topical Press Agency Ltd.*)

Plate 2a. Site of jackdaw colony in Kensington Gardens

b. Feral pigeons in Trafalgar Square

Insectivorous birds find conditions more difficult, for the variety and numbers of insects and other arthropods are limited. Few outdoor insects can flourish on the buildings which cover most of the area, and on the open spaces and bombed sites atmospheric pollution and lack of variety in food-plants restricts their numbers. As a result, birds relying almost entirely on insect food are few. Of these the robin and the spotted fly-catcher are the most successful. The black redstart and pied wagtail have taken advantage of the insect life supported by the new areas of vegetation on the large bombed sites. The wren is present only in small numbers and the treecreeper is restricted as a breeding bird to Kensington Gardens. The more successful hedge sparrow feeds on many kinds of animal matter in the summer, but in winter turns mainly to seeds. Among the tits, the coal tit, with its mainly insect diet, and its preference for conifers, has failed to establish itself as a regular breeding species, unlike the great and blue tits, which will also feed on buds, fruit and seeds. Inner London is well supplied with lawns in the parks and squares, whose earthworms and insect larvae help to support good numbers of blackbirds and starlings and smaller populations of song and mistle thrushes; all four species take other food, especially fruit and berries in season. The warblers, however, have had little success in breeding, though here the absence of suitable cover may be the main reason. Nesting problems, in particular the diffi-culty of finding suitable mud for building nests, may have helped also in the loss of the swallow and house martin as breeding species, but there is no lack of holes for nesting swifts, yet this species is now confined to the edge of the area. In their case a shortage of flying insects seems to be the limiting factor.

For scavenging birds there is no food shortage, and the gulls, swans, sparrows and feral pigeons can make a good living. In the parks a number of species have discovered the possibilities of litter-baskets, and not only sparrows, starlings and blackbirds but carrion crows, jays, jackdaws, chaffinches, great tits, blue tits and robins have been seen rummaging in them. Modern Londoners cannot admire the soaring kites, which were last seen in the eighteenth century, for public health reforms have helped to banish both them and their fellow garbage-eaters, the ravens, from the city streets; instead they have many gulls, modern refuse-feeders, spiralling high over the Thames. This increase of the gulls as urban scavengers has been paralleled in North America, where the herring gull, in particular, has spread and become common in winter in several large cities.

Food is only one factor. Lack of secure nesting-sites may prevent some species from becoming successful colonists. Only holes, tall trees and the inaccessible parts of buildings offer nesting sites safe from cats and children, and the majority of successful nesting species normally use such situations.

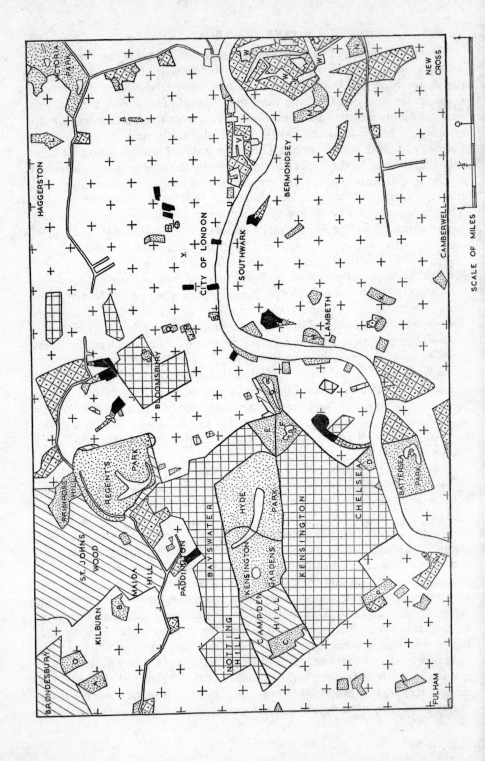

SCALE OF MILES

Fig. 1

INNER LONDON

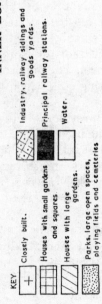

KEY

☐ Closely built.	▨ Industry, railway sidings and goods yards.
⊞ Houses with small gardens and squares.	■ Principal railway stations.
⧄ Houses with large gardens.	☐ Water.
⠿ Parks, large open spaces, playing fields and cemeteries	

A   Queen's Park

B   Paddington Recreation Ground

C   Holland Park

D   Chelsea Hospital Grounds and Ranelagh Gardens

E   The Green Park

F   Buckingham Palace Gardens

G   St. James's Park

H   Archbishop's Park and garden of Lambeth Palace

J   Lincoln's Inn Fields

K   Kennington Park

L   London Fields

M   Southwark Park

N   Deptford Park

O   Paddington Cemetery

P   Brompton Cemetery

R   Gray's Inn

S   Temple

U   Billingsgate Fishmarket

V   London Dock

W   Surrey Commercial Docks

Y   Cripplegate bombed sites

Nests in bushes are vulnerable, though enclosed shrubberies give more security. Even so, some species, like the blackbird, tend to build higher in Inner London than elsewhere. The birds of the park lakes usually nest on islands, sometimes, as in the case of the coot, building nests away from the banks upon some submerged foundation. The mallard makes more use of trees than elsewhere, often choosing holes many feet from the ground. Those species which build open nests at or near ground-level are rare. Warblers have been largely confined to the private grounds of Holland House and the wren survives in small gardens there and in some parks and private gardens. Yellow wagtails were able to nest in Regent's Park only when its grassy expanses were closed to the public. The fact that the spotted flycatcher uses elevated sites has given it a better chance than most insect-eaters in finding a niche in Inner London. Buildings offer safe sites to those able to take advantage of them, and besides those species which commonly nest on or in buildings, like the feral pigeon, swift, black redstart, starling and sparrow, a small number of mallard and woodpigeons do so in most years. All the successful nests of the kestrel in Inner London have been on buildings. The carrion crow has twice used the Houses of Parliament for nesting, but curiously enough the jackdaw, so often associated with ruined buildings and cathedral towers, is now represented only by the small tree-nesting colony in Kensington Gardens. Recently the jay has attempted unsuccessfully to nest on buildings, and mistle thrushes have built on steel scaffolding in the Temple, on the stands erected for the Coronation and in the iron canopy of a statue at St. Paul's School. The opportunities exist for other adaptable species—perhaps the herring gull, which has already nested on buildings in some coastal towns.

Lastly, in an urban environment a bird must be able to accept the presence of man, to tolerate him without placing itself or its nest in danger. This character is perhaps best shown by the house sparrow, which has been aptly described as "bold and impudent, yet wary and suspicious". This attitude has been acquired by apparently unlikely species, and earlier naturalists were as surprised by the tameness of the moorhen and wood-pigeon in Inner London as many have been recently by the growing boldness of the jays that live there. This quality may be found amongst only some members of a species; in the country jays and woodpigeons, and in most places, moorhens, are still very wary. It may be lost and regained: the slaughter of the woodpigeons in Inner London in the war years made the survivors far less approachable, but their confidence slowly increased when the attacks ceased and the numbers began to grow again (see *Ibis*, 91: 108–110 and 356–358, for a fuller discussion).

There has been a noticeable improvement in man's attitude to birds since the latter part of the nineteenth century, when larks and starlings

Plate 3a. St. James's Park with Duck Island

b. A rare visitor: a long-tailed duck with tufted ducks in St. James's Park.
(*R. C. Homes*)

C. B. Ash

Plate 4a. The Round Pond, Kensington Gardens

b. Mute swans flock on the Thames at all seasons

Sport & General Press Agency L

were shot on Hackney Marshes and gulls were massacred from the bridges of the Thames. Save for mallard, crows and pigeons, the numbers of which are controlled to some extent, the birds themselves are now rarely harmed. Indeed the plentiful supplies of food now made available, from bread in parks and squares to fat and nuts on bird-tables, must have helped some to survive.

Nests in parks, often those of the less common species, still suffer too frequent robbery or destruction by small boys, but apart from this the birds of Inner London now face only two mammalian enemies, the brown rat and the domestic cat, both introduced and both common. Cats, estimated to be kept by 44 per cent of London families and reinforced by strays (Fitter, 1949), not only act as an important check on the numbers of young sparrows, but kill blackbirds, robins and other song-birds in the parks. Adult sparrows and pigeons are usually too wary for them. The rats are most dangerous to the ducks, moorhens and coots in the parks. They were responsible for the disappearance of the tufted duck as a breeding species on the Serpentine for many years, and in 1950 they prevented any of the tufted ducklings in St. James's Park from being reared. The grey squirrel, first introduced in Regent's Park in 1905, was eliminated from the area as a result of a campaign begun about 1930. It fed on the eggs and young of various species, including mistle thrush and woodpigeon. The numbers of predatory birds are probably too limited to have any appreciable effect on the population of small birds. The kestrel is the most important, feeding mainly on sparrows. The carrion crow takes pigeon's eggs, raiding many of the early nests of the woodpigeon, which are most exposed until the leaves are out. Crows are also known to take young mallard and moorhens. Jays take eggs, young birds and adult sparrows, and jackdaws have been seen searching for pigeons' eggs on the ledges of the British Museum. Sparrow hawks, which are not common and have only once been known to attempt to breed, have attacked flocks of small birds, usually sparrows, and the peregrines which visit the area from time to time prey on the feral pigeons. Here is an abundant food supply awaiting exploitation, and in some North American and European cities peregrines have seized the opportunity, nesting on the ledges of tall buildings.

In the previous chapter an account has been given of the special climatic conditions of Inner London, and the way in which atmospheric pollution has affected the bird life; directly by causing disease and indirectly by reducing the amount of plant and insect food. Some observers have also suggested that the higher temperatures may cause blackbirds in the area to begin singing earlier than in the country. It is possible, too, that the higher night temperatures, together with the reduced wind speeds found in the built-up areas, may have played a part in inducing starlings to start roosting in the centre.

Since 1900 Inner London has seen fewer changes than almost any other part of the London Area. By 1900 there was little land to be over-whelmed by the builder. The estate of Brondesbury Park in the north-west and parts of the grounds of Holland House were taken comparatively late in the period, but most of the new buildings have merely replaced old ones occupying the same sites. In some cases the building of flats where old houses once stood has meant a loss of gardens. The two wars caused some changes, mostly temporary. The lake in St. James's Park was drained during the first war, there was the campaign against woodpigeons in the second, and during both some portions of the parks were closed, others converted into allotments. The second war, however, saw a major change —the extensive devastation caused by bombing, the far-reaching effects of which have already been described. Increased traffic in the streets, coupled with a sharp decline in the number of horses, has reduced the food for birds which scavenge in the roads and made feeding there less safe. The ageing of the trees, many of which were planted in the last century, has helped to provide more nesting sites and food for some species of birds. The influence of the grey squirrel may have been exaggerated, but its elimination has probably played a part in the increase of the blackbird and mistle thrush. Man's attitude to wild life, which had begun to change for the better before the turn of the century, has become still more en-lightened during the last fifty years. Duck-shoots are no longer organised on the Serpentine and egg-collecting has declined—the black redstart would probably have faced much persecution had it begun nesting in Inner London thirty years earlier. Finally, there is the inexorable growth of London itself, halted only temporarily by the two wars. With an ever-widening ring of buildings separating the inner area from the countryside, it might have been expected that the bird life of the centre would become steadily poorer. Instead, the reverse has taken place. The number of breeding species has increased within the last fifty years, and so also, to a lesser extent, has the list of winter visitors.

The historical record for Inner London is probably more complete than for any other comparable area in the world. From 1891 until 1940 A. Holte Macpherson contributed an invaluable series of annual reports on London birds, first to the *Selborne Magazine* (and its precursor *Nature Notes*), then to the *London Naturalist* and finally to *British Birds*, and the series was continued up to 1950 by Dr. G. Carmichael Low, Miss M. S. van Oostveen, C. B. Ashby and W. G. Teagle. For the earliest years additional material is available in the books of W. H. Hudson (especially *Birds in London*, 1898) and in Charles Dixon's *The Bird Life of London* (1909), while J. Rudge Harding furnished many useful records in his nature notes from 1912–21 in the *Selborne Magazine*. In more recent years the number of observers has greatly increased, and it would be impossible here to name all those who have supplied the material for the reports which have appeared, mainly in the *London Naturalist,* the *London Bird Report* and the Reports of the Committee on Bird Sanctuaries in the Royal Parks. Yet some parts of Inner London are still comparatively neglected, and for the early years of the period, when attention was mainly concentrated on some of the western parks, information for much of the area is often scanty. On the evidence available, it seems that there are twenty species which have probably bred or attempted to breed throughout the period. They are mallard, mute swan, moorhen, pigeon, woodpigeon, tawny owl, swift, carrion crow, great tit, blue tit, mistle thrush, song thrush, blackbird, robin, spotted flycatcher, hedge sparrow, starling, greenfinch, chaffinch and house sparrow. In addition, there are the wren and jackdaw, both continuously resident, but in such small numbers that breeding may not have been regular, and the greater spotted woodpecker, whose status early in the century is uncertain but which may have been resident and breeding throughout. The little grebe has not nested in recent years, but may return if conditions at its former breeding haunts again become suitable. There has been one certain loss in the period, the rook, while the willow warbler and blackcap, which once were said to breed regularly in the grounds of Holland House, now nest only sporadically. There are eight additions to the list of regular breeding species—tufted duck, pochard, kestrel, coot, jay, black redstart, pied wagtail and goldfinch. To these should probably be added the stock dove, which may have been resident at the beginning of the century (though definite evidence is lacking), whereas it now breeds every year, and the treecreeper, which up to 1954 bred regularly in Kensington Gardens. The great majority of these gains—pochard, kestrel, coot, jay, treecreeper, black redstart, pied wagtail and goldfinch—have been made within the last quarter of a century.

It is more difficult to assess changes in numbers, but it seems clear that, amongst the breeding species present throughout, the mistle thrush, blackbird and greater spotted woodpecker have increased and extended their range, whilst there is some evidence that the house sparrow has declined in numbers. Among the non-breeding birds the gulls show the most remarkable changes, as described earlier.

The bird life of Inner London has altered considerably even within the short span of fifty odd years covered by this brief summary. Many species have shown a remarkable ability to adapt themselves to the rigours of an urban existence. And there is no sign that the changes are at an end.

THE SUBURBS

by R. S. R. Fitter

THE PARTS of the London Area now to be discussed, comprising the whole built-up area outside Inner London, including both industrial sites and the vast wilderness of housing estates in their early stages, are second in artificiality only to Inner London itself. Over areas of many square miles there is little approximating even to semi-natural vegetation. Yet for abundance of bird life these areas have few equals. The food supply provided, both directly by kind-hearted bird-lovers, unintentionally by the operators of refuse destruction plants and grain-wharves, and indirectly by the activities of hundreds of thousands of amateur gardeners, is so great that the suburban districts have a high bird population both in summer and winter. It is unfortunately not possible to prove this statement statistically, but it is a matter of common observation that there are more birds per acre in a district where the land is wholly given over to houses and mature gardens than there are in the open country in farmland, in woodland or on heaths and commons. This does not mean, however, that there are more species of birds; merely that the actual number is larger. The figures given later on from the study by E. C. Rowberry show that the bird population of an agricultural area is undoubtedly impoverished by housing development in its first stages. By the time the gardens have matured, however, the picture must be very different. Here again we have no statistical evidence of just how different it is.

The natural equivalents of the bird habitats provided by suburban development are open woodland and inland cliffs and crags. It is not surprising therefore to find that the birds which have succeeded in adapting themselves to suburban life in the London Area are mostly of species which elsewhere in the British Isles frequent those habitats. The one element in the suburban scene for which there is no close parallel in the wild is the large amount of cultivated ground which is kept artificially bare of vegetation, in the shape of garden beds. Thus birds which feed on small animal life on the ground such as robins, blackbirds and thrushes, are able to find a much more abundant food supply than they would in woods, where they have to rely on deep shade preventing plant growth and so allowing them access to bare soil. Moreover they find the week-end gardener an excellent substitute for the mole, which is normally the only animal which will turn over the soil for them and allow them to filch worms and so forth as they come defenceless to the surface. The large expanse of lawns, which while individually often small must collectively be very extensive, also provides an artificial element, enabling probing birds such as the starling to probe much more easily than they would do in the wild. Even rabbits rarely nibble extensive patches as closely as they are cut by lawn-mowers all over the suburbs.

Excluding the inner commons and open spaces, which are mentioned in a later chapter, the more natural elements of the suburban scene consist of the larger number and variety of trees and bushes. These provide an abundance of nesting sites, as well as of food. Inland crags and cliffs are represented by houses and other buildings, which provide nesting sites but little food. Industrial sites normally represent just this crag-element, and the community which often frequents them, such as the black redstart, kestrel and pied wagtail, is rather different from the ordinary woodland-garden community.

A great many species of birds may of course occur in suburban areas from time to time. It is for instance on record that a Pallas's sand grouse was seen flying over Hendon on September 23rd, 1907. But in the present discussion it is impossible to mention more than the most frequent birds associated with London's suburbs, defined as districts where the great bulk of the land is covered with houses and gardens. Taking the breeding species first, of the 31 birds that may reasonably be regarded as typical of suburban districts, 20 are normally characteristic of open woodland, hedgerows, or scrub with plenty of trees and bushes, four are equally at home nesting in either trees or cliffs, five are primarily cliff or crag-nesters and two, the house sparrow and feral pigeon, are purely commensals of man.

The twenty species of the first group are the rook, jay, greenfinch, goldfinch, lesser redpoll, linnet, chaffinch, great tit, blue tit, coal tit, spotted flycatcher, mistle thrush, song thrush, blackbird, robin, hedge sparrow, wren, greater spotted woodpecker, tawny owl and woodpigeon.

The rook is a very typical breeding bird of clumps of trees in villages, especially near churches or manor-houses, and tends to remain in such places after they have become surrounded by housing development. For instance, at Lee, a small rookery (Plate 12 of *London's Natural History*) survived until about 1946, when the distance the rooks had to fly to the nearest open grassland or arable fields evidently became too great and they abandoned it. That rooks can nest right in the middle of urban aggregations provided that a food supply is at hand is shown by the fact that a rookery survived in Inner London till 1915, and rookeries still exist in the middle of cities as large as Bristol and Oxford.

The jay is a purely woodland bird that once it has overcome its shyness of man is able to advance into suburban areas and colonise parks and large gardens with shrubberies, and even in the last resort parks with trees devoid of any shrub layer, such as the Green Park. It is curious that in London it is the jay and not the magpie that has done this. In North Norway magpies are common town birds, but in the London Area, although they have come in nearer to the centre in recent years, they have still not succeeded in breeding in those suburbs which are cut off from open country.

Originally the five finches were probably birds of the wood edge or rough bushy country with trees for song-posts. The greenfinch in Britain has become so attached to man-made habitats that it usually nests in garden shrubs or a thick overgrown hedgerow. The goldfinch is especially fond of building in orchard trees, though presumably nothing equivalent to a Kentish plum orchard has ever existed in the wild. The linnet is really a heathland bird rather than a denizen of open woodland, but in suburban gardens it quite often nests in small fruit-trees or the low overhanging branches of conifers. The lesser redpoll may seem an odd choice as a typical suburban bird, but in parts of the Surrey suburbs its wheezy song-flight is regularly seen or heard. The chaffinch being probably the commonest British bird, it is not surprising to find it common also in the larger and older gardens of the zone.

Of the three tits the coal is the least common, but owing to the scattered conifers that have been planted in various parts of the suburbs it is more frequent than might have been expected. It seems probable that the total tit population of the suburbs is substantially increased both by the welcome habit of putting food out for them in the winter and by the frequent provision of nest-boxes in areas that might otherwise be devoid of holes in either trees or walls.

The spotted flycatcher is well known to nest in close proximity to man in town and country, and in many suburban districts it is much the commonest summer migrant that stays to breed, and is the only one to do so regularly in central London.

The three thrushes and the robin are all woodland birds that have taken whole-heartedly to suburban life, finding an abundance of nest-sites, in trees and bushes for the thrushes and in all kinds of odd crannies for the robin. In parts of Scandinavia the song thrush is still a comparatively scarce bird of the remoter pine forests, and in many parts of the Continent the robin is also a retiring bird of woodlands distant from devotees of "la chasse". It is interesting to note that in Germany and Switzerland at least the place of the robin as a garden bird is taken by the redstart, called the *Gartenrotschwanz* to distinguish it from the *Hausrotschwanz*, which is the black redstart. The hedge sparrow and the wren are both birds of all kinds of bushy places.

The greater spotted woodpecker is much the commonest of the three woodpeckers in suburban gardens. It has been suggested elsewhere that at a certain stage in the maturing of suburban gardens the trees become rotten enough to provide both food and nest-sites for woodpeckers and that it is to this factor, arising from the great Victorian movement to embellish suburban gardens, that we owe the recent spread of woodpeckers in the built-up parts of the London Area.

The tawny owl is the most typically woodland of our five breeding owls, and it is of interest to find that it is the tawny, and not the traditionally building-loving barn owl, which has become the commonest owl in the suburbs. The story of the woodpigeon's spread in London has been told elsewhere; it is one of the few birds that are probably less common per acre in parts of the suburbs than in the centre of London. This is possibly due to the fact that the suburban woodpigeons have not yet become so tolerant of man as the Inner London birds which stalk majestically about within peashooter range of the milling lunch-time crowds in the parks.

Finally, it is perhaps worth briefly referring to some of the typical woodland birds that have not succeeded in adapting themselves to life in the suburbs. They include the redstart (which as we have seen may be a garden bird on the Continent), the woodcock and the pheasant. The presence of warblers depends on the presence of sufficiently large gardens or open spaces with undergrowth. Thus, at Beckenham, for example, chiff-chaff, willow warbler, whitethroat and blackcap have all been heard throughout the breeding-season, though for obvious reasons it is difficult to prove actual nesting when one territory may overlap several private gardens. Their status on Hampstead Heath and Ken Wood is discussed later, and there as elsewhere the blackcap seems to be less exacting in its requirements than the garden warbler which is definitely not a bird of the suburbs. It may perhaps also be worth mentioning here some of the typical birds of open country that have failed to find any true lodgment in the suburbs; the skylark, meadow pipit, common partridge and red-legged partridge.

The four birds that may nest both in trees or holes and on ledges of cliffs and buildings, and therefore could make the best of both worlds in the suburbs are the carrion crow, jackdaw, starling and kestrel. Of these the crow has greatly increased in recent years, but the daw is scarce, hanging on more or less as a relic in scattered colonies in the suburbs.

The starling is a general hole-nester that is especially typical as a nester in occupied buildings in the London Area. The kestrel prefers ledge sites on buildings to tree-sites for its nests in the built-up parts of the London Area, in contrast with the preferences of the carrion crow.

The five ledge-nesters that do not also nest in the branches of trees are the pied wagtail (often also in holes), black redstart, swallow, house martin and swift. The pied wagtail is especially associated with cement works and other places where there are piles of stones in which they particularly like to nest. It is also very fond of flycatching on lawns, so that it easily finds a niche in an area with many houses and gardens. The black redstart is a very recent colonist, which nests mainly in the Inner London zone, but has also done so in several industrial sites in the suburbs, and will no doubt spread in such sites in the future. It is not properly a bird of the house-and-gardens zone. The swallow, house martin and swift, particularly the two latter, are *par excellence* birds of the outer suburbs, though the swift comes quite a long way in to the centre (see Cramp, 1950), and a few house martin colonies still exist close in, notably at Barnes, Hammersmith and Highgate.

Comparatively few birds are present in suburban districts in winter or on passage which are not breeders. Willow and sometimes also other warblers may be heard even in small gardens on passage. Fieldfares and redwings feed on the ground and in hedgerows in the outer suburbs, and in extremely cold weather may visit quite small gardens. Gulls too only come down into the smaller gardens in hard weather, but black-headed gulls especially are perpetually patrolling the air over the suburbs, and if encouraged by thrown scraps will come down and scream round a window as they do in the centre of London.

To finish this brief survey of the birds of the London suburbs, it is proposed to summarise the substance of a lecture by E. C. Rowberry on "The Influence of Housing Development on Bird Life", delivered before the London Natural History Society on June 8th, 1937. Rowberry surveyed an area of ¾ sq. m. in south-west Middlesex in 1927–28 and again in 1930 and 1936, during which period intensive housing development was in progress. The area lay on either side of the Great West Road, south of Osterley Park, which was not included in the survey, and comprised a large stretch of open fields, with hedgerows and orchards, and the Great Western Railway running through. A careful census in 1927–28 showed 42 species present, of which 32 were breeding, in the following categories:

> *Common:* Starling, chaffinch, house sparrow, great tit, blue tit, whitethroat, song thrush, blackbird, robin, hedge sparrow, wren.
>
> *More than Two Breeding Pairs:* Greenfinch, linnet, skylark, willow warbler, garden warbler, lesser whitethroat, house martin, swift, woodpigeon.
>
> *Also Bred:* Carrion crow, jay, goldfinch, bullfinch, tree sparrow, pied

wagtail, spotted flycatcher, mistle thrush, greater spotted wood-pecker, cuckoo, tawny owl, turtle dove.

Winter visitors: Meadow pipit, fieldfare, redwing, black-headed gull, lapwing.

Occasional on Passage: Rook, coal tit, goldcrest, swallow, kestrel.

Notable Absentees: Jackdaw, yellowhammer, tree pipit, green wood-pecker.

In 1930, when the census was repeated, much land had been built over, and a great deal of the orchard land cleared ready for building. There proved to be eight fewer breeding species: goldfinch, tree sparrow, pied wagtail, spotted flycatcher, lesser whitethroat, house martin, turtle dove and tawny owl. Moreover the skylark, willow warbler, garden warbler, whitethroat and greater spotted woodpecker, though still breeding, had all decreased. This fall in total numbers of 25–30 breeding pairs was offset by an increase in breeding starlings, house sparrows, great and blue tits and swifts, amounting to 23 pairs for starlings and swifts alone. Of the 13 remaining common breeders only one, the swift, was a migrant, and all the other migrants were on the down-grade. The only visitor to be lost was also a migrant, the swallow, but the black-headed gull had become a really common visitor, and two other gulls, the common and lesser black-backed, had appeared.

The final census was taken in 1936 when there had been a very great increase in the built-up area and hardly any of the original open ground was left, mainly a few playing fields and some hedges. Forty-six species were recorded, but only 22 breeding, i.e. total species up by six, breeding ones down by ten. The bullfinch, willow and garden warblers, mistle thrush and greater spotted woodpecker were lost as breeding species, but the lesser whitethroat and tawny owl regained and the magpie added. The white-throat was down to three pairs, the linnet and skylark to one each. The carrion crow, jay, linnet, whitethroat, lesser whitethroat and cuckoo sur-vived only in a six-acre wild garden and orchard. To make up the biomass, however, the number of starlings had increased by nearly a hundred pairs to 160, the swifts had gone up by two pairs to 8–10 and the house-sparrow and great and blue tits had again also increased. All other breeding species had decreased and more than one-third consisted of only one pair. The willow and garden warblers, swallow and house martin appeared on passage only. As visitors gains were registered of the herring gull, which joined the three other gulls as a common visitor, and the heron and kingfisher which came to a lily-pond.

Such is the devastating effect of suburbanisation on the birds of a farming district. Whether a gain of 120 pairs of starlings is any compen-sation for the loss of a third of the breeding species and the reduction to a single pair of many of the rest is hardly a moot point, except perhaps to an ardent sturnophile. It would seem very desirable to repeat this census so that the effect of nearly twenty years' maturing of the gardens could be discovered.

THE RESERVOIRS AND OTHER LARGE WATERS

by R. C. Homes

A T A TIME when the decrease of wildfowl is a subject of international discussion, we can still regard without misgivings the position of the aquatic species occurring around London, where the construction of many large reservoirs and gravel-pits has introduced entirely new habitats during the last century.

When Harting wrote his *Birds of Middlesex* in 1866 the only really important sheets of water outside the central parks were the reservoirs at Elstree (Aldenham), Ruislip and Hendon. The two former were constructed early in the nineteenth century to feed the Regent's and Grand Junction Canals, while the third, variously known as the Welsh Harp or the Brent Reservoir, was completed in 1835. All three have natural banks, but neither Elstree nor Ruislip reservoir lies in a main river valley, and the latter has suffered ornithologically through lack of fencing and the development of the southern end as a pleasure resort; the Welsh Harp, however, situated in the valley of the river Brent, has always possessed greater attractions for waders, and despite the proximity of the North Circular Road and of many factories it still retains a sufficient margin of 'natural' surroundings to give water-birds a sense of security, except when disturbed by speed-boats and sailing craft. The frequent occurrence there in the nineteenth century of aquatic species which are rare inland has been chronicled by Harting and mentioned by Macpherson in his review of *London Reservoirs and their Influence on Bird Life*.

The days of gravel-digging on a large scale had yet to come, and the only other reservoirs constructed when Harting wrote were relatively small ones at Barnes and Walthamstow. By 1870 their total area did not exceed 200 acres, the largest single lake being 41 acres in extent. By 1900 the

Plate 5. Black redstart at nest near St. Paul's Cathedral

Eric Hos

Plate 6a. The jay is a much increased species in London

   b. Robins nesting in shed in a suburban garden

G. L. A

total acreage was just over 500, and included the well-known Barn Elms reservoirs, most of the smaller Chelsea and Lambeth waters, near East Molesey, and all the Walthamstow group except Banbury and Lockwood. Even at this time, however, the largest sheet of water was only 59 acres. Apart from such notable exceptions as the Pen Ponds in Richmond Park and Connaught Water in Epping Forest, the principal remaining waters of any extent in the Area were the various lakes in private parks, none of which rivalled the larger reservoirs in size.

Thus, at the outset of the present century a large new series of artificial lakes had been added to the landscape and provided an enormous increase in the sanctuaries available for waterfowl, at a time when there was no longer any real marshland along the lower reaches of the Thames within our Area. It is a matter for great regret that the ornithological potentialities of the reservoirs were not realised in these early days of their existence. We do know that those at Barn Elms, completed in 1897 and less than seven miles from St. Paul's, were adopted at once as a roosting-place by the gulls, which had enormously increased in numbers in the winter of 1894–95 and which had previously concentrated principally at Chiswick Eyot and Lonsdale Road reservoirs (Macpherson, *L.N.* for 1927). However, apart from some brief notes by Cornish (1902) there is little other reference to Barn Elms until 1909, when W. A. Todd published some notes in the *Zoologist* and *The Selborne Magazine,* including a report of 16–18 great crested grebes, at that time a notable sight.

An early glimpse of the birds of the much larger Staines reservoirs, completed in 1902, is provided by two papers on the Birds of the Staines District published by Graham W. Kerr in the *Zoologist* for 1906 and 1908. He writes of as many as eighty great crested grebes at a time and of their presence throughout the year except from June to August; now they are often more numerous in August than at any other time. The only ducks mentioned are sheleduck, mallard, teal, wigeon, tufted duck and gadwall, and one can only speculate whether the others were absent or were missed through the infrequency of visits or the inadequacy of the optical equipment of the time, for the writer comments on the difficulties of identification owing to the lack of cover, the large expanse of water and its roughness whenever there was a breeze.

There are no other regular observations for the reservoirs until the early twenties, but at the Walthamstow group the great crested grebe began to nest in 1904, the tufted duck in 1905 and the heron on one of the islands not later than 1914. The great crested grebe first nested at Stoke Newington reservoirs in 1912. The dearth of information at this time is all the more unfortunate when we consider the rapid increase which was taking place in the number of the reservoirs, for by 1910 the acreage had been more than doubled to just over 1,350, with the addition among other waters of Staines (424 acres), Kempton Park (62), and Banbury and Lockwood in the Lea Valley, totalling 165 acres.

In the next ten years Island Barn reservoir, near Molesey (121), and the King George V (420), near Ponders End, were completed, bringing the total area up to close on 1,900 acres. The only subsequent additions have been the Queen Mary, or Littleton, reservoir in 1925 (707 acres), the King George VI, alongside the old Staines reservoirs, in 1947 (350 acres) and the William Girling reservoir at Chingford (334 acres), which lies between the Walthamstow group and the King George V reservoir, making an almost unbroken series of lakes in the Lea valley over six miles from end to end. There are thus now over 3,000 acres of concrete-banked artificial lakes in the London Area.

In the early twenties the reservoirs, especially those at Staines, began to be more regularly watched. Not unnaturally the ducks, which form the largest group in the daytime, attracted most attention. London ornithologists were particularly indebted to a small band of regular observers who made the causeway between the two original Staines reservoirs into one of the best known places in the country for observing wildfowl. The names of Glegg, Hardiman, Carmichael Low and Holte Macpherson will be long remembered for pioneer work at a time when the potentialities of reservoir and sewage-farm watching were still to be generally recognised, while in the Lea valley, a similar study was made by Glegg, Mann, Pethen and Wright.

At Staines a flock of twenty-five goldeneye was seen in the winter of 1921–22, and in 1922 sixty goosanders were recorded. Though there was only a handful of previous records for either species, both were subsequently found to be regular, and in the same year came the first of the smew, which were soon to be one of the most striking features of London's waterfowl population. From this time onwards the number of observers began to increase, a tendency which gathered momentum in the thirties and became even more pronounced after the last war.

Details of the numerical status of the various species throughout the last thirty years are given in the specific list, and we can consider here more broadly the total numbers of ducks of all species in the Area and the changes which have taken place in their status. In December, 1937, a census was made on most of the principal sheets of water and was repeated monthly from October to March in the following winter. Though one winter's results do not form a very adequate yardstick for comparison with those achieved since the war, it is fortunate that the effort was made when it was, as no further attempt was possible during the war. The census was resumed in 1947 and has continued in every subsequent winter at approximately monthly intervals. A list of the waters included is given below for purpose of future comparison:—

Essex: King George V and Walthamstow reservoirs.

Hertfordshire: Elstree reservoir; Hamper Mill, Moor Mill and Old Parkbury gravel pits.

Kent: Danson and Kelsey Park lakes; Ruxley gravel pit.

Middlesex: Brent, Grand Junction, Kempton, King George VI, Littleton, Stain Hill, Staines and Stoke Newington reservoirs; Ashford and Feltham gravel pits; Canons Park lake; Hampstead and Highgate ponds; Long Water, Serpentine and Round Pond, Inner London.

Surrey: Barns Elms, Chelsea and Lambeth, Island Barn, Lonsdale Road and Walton reservoirs; Ham and Walton gravel pits; Gatton, Grange, Richmond and Wimbledon Park lakes; South Norwood lake; River Thames from Putney to Teddington.

The incidence of peak numbers naturally varies from year to year, but in general terms there are on the above waters from 4,000–5,000 ducks in early October, increasing gradually until by about the middle of December there may be from about 5,500–8,500 according to the severity of the winter. This number normally increases by about 1,500 to a maximum of at least 7,000 in January: twice in this month and once in February there have been over 9,500. Taking into account that many smaller lakes and streams are omitted, there is no doubt that it is quite frequent for the total number of ducks in the whole Area at this season at the above localities to be well over 10,000. These might be composed on the average of 4,000 mallard, 2,750 tufted duck, 1,200 pochard, 500 teal, 300 wigeon, 150 goosander, 100 smew and not more than 100 in all of gadwall, shoveler, goldeneye and the rarer species inland, the balance being on waters not counted and made up principally of mallard, teal and tufted duck.

Within a month of the peak the numbers are back to about the level of the middle of December, but the most pronounced drop usually comes quite early in March and by the middle of that month there are unlikely to be more than 5,000 ducks on the waters counted. These figures are, of course, generalisations and more precise information for the various species is given in the specific notes.

We have no means of assessing the status of ducks in the Area in any detail for the first quarter of the century but, even though it was not until 1937 that an overall impression of numbers could be obtained, we have a wealth of statistics for individual species and localities, providing sufficient information to describe with confidence some of the changes that have taken place. Shoveler, once known only as scarce passage migrants, mainly in autumn, first wintered at Staines in 1937–38, and subsequently their numbers tended to increase, though except on spring passage they are still confined almost entirely to the one locality. The pochard showed some signs of an increase in the twenties, especially as a winter visitor to Inner London, and definitely became more numerous in the thirties. In some winters in the forties, not always associated with severe weather here, the numbers have been even higher though there is no suggestion of any general increase in the last fifteen years. Tufted duck were only recorded for the first time in several localities in the first decade of this century, when even flocks of twenty or so were considered of interest. There is no evidence to show when the transition to their present abundance really began, but by the late twenties and early thirties flocks of a few hundred were quite normal, and the peaks on the more favoured waters were around the five hundred mark, with a maximum of about a thousand at the Walthamstow reservoirs in 1932. Goosanders are much more numerous in severe winters than ever before, a flock of about six hundred having been seen at Littleton reservoir in February, 1947, but in more normal winters there has been on the average little change in total numbers in the last twenty years. Smew only once exceeded thirty in a flock before the winter of 1933–34, when there was a modest increase, and there was no subsequent change until an exceptionally severe spell of snow and frost in late December, 1938, brought a gathering of 117 to Molesey. In another much longer period of hard conditions in the winter of 1946–47 they were more numerous than usual in several localities, the largest flock of 125 birds being again at Molesey. In general, the average population for the winter in the whole Area is from one to two hundred, which probably implies a gradual increase since 1922. One species which may have decreased is the wigeon, for which the very fragmentary evidence suggests that they may have been commoner before available feeding-grounds became so restricted.

The rarer species of ducks inland all occur in very small numbers with some frequency and provide much of the excitement which enlivens a cold winter's day on the exposed banks or causeways of the reservoirs. Details of the more unusual visitors will be found in the specific list, but no review would be complete without reference to the remarkable series of visits by long-tailed ducks to Staines reservoirs for eight successive winters in the years 1932–39, though at other times they have only been occasional vagrants.

We have discussed the numbers of ducks and their fluctuations at some length, as for most of the day they are the dominant birds, but quite early in the afternoon in winter their numbers are dwarfed at several of the reservoirs by the huge flocks of gulls, which settle on the water in companies consisting of thousands of birds. Many writers have summarised early observations on the wintering of gulls around London (cf. *inter alia*

Macpherson, 1928; Rowberry, 1934; Glegg, 1934, 1939; McCulloch, 1939; Fitter, 1949), and it is fairly generally accepted that the first really large increase occurred in the early months of 1895. Previously the black-headed gull had been a regular visitor in much smaller numbers since at least the winter of 1880–81 (Lodge, *Memoirs of an Artist Naturalist,* 1946). The earliest roosts appear to have been on the Thames at Chiswick Eyot and at the Lonsdale Road reservoirs. With the construction, however, of Barn Elms reservoirs in 1896–97 these at once became an important roosting-place.

Details of the spread and increase of the various species of gulls will be found in the specific notes, but it is appropriate to consider here the great part which the reservoirs have played in this increase. Those at Staines were completed in 1902, and we know that at that time the black-headed gulls, at first confined largely to the Thames, were regular visitors to the Colne valley. We know also in general terms how the number of gulls have increased through the fifty years and how the larger new reservoirs have been quickly adopted for roosting purposes. It is remarkable, however, what scant attention has been paid until recently to these vast assemblages and their daily ebb and flow over our Area, and beyond. In the winters of 1952–53 and 1953–54 the total numbers of gulls using the roosts in winter were of the order of 85,000–100,000, a staggering figure when we think of the old description of gulls as occasional stragglers inland in severe weather.

In the Lea valley 35,000–40,000 gulls were using the William Girling and King George V reservoirs in mid-February, 1954, about 4,000 common and 1,000 herring gulls remaining at the former while the black-headed gulls gathered at the older reservoir. The other principal roosts were at Barn Elms, where numbers fluctuate violently according to weather conditions but were of the order of 20,000 in mid-January, 1954, consisting almost entirely of black-headed gulls; at Littleton, where there were 22,000 at the end of the same month, including about 20 per cent common gulls, a similar proportion of herring gulls and the balance black-headed gulls; at the new and old reservoirs at Staines with some 7,000 gulls in January, 1953, of which nearly three-quarters were herring gulls; and at Molesey, where there are usually up to 5,000 gulls. Fuller details have been given by Homes (1955) who suggests that the total at all roosts may consist in mid-winter of some 10–15,000 common gulls, about 10,000 herring gulls and possibly as many as 500 greater black-backed gulls, the remainder being black-headed gulls.

The only previous counts at any roost were made by Hollom (*The Handbook of British Birds,* V: 50–51) who in the late thirties and early forties at Littleton reservoir never found less than 25,000 gulls between November and March inclusive, except in snowy weather. The largest numbers were about 45,000 on March 2nd, 1940, and about 42,000 on January 28th, 1936. In an August count up to half of about 4,000 birds were lesser black-backed gulls, the remainder being common and herring gulls. In late winter and early spring there is a large influx of common gulls and probably nearly half of a total of about 37,000 on March 5th, 1940, consisted of this species. A more recent development is the increase of greater black-backed gulls, several hundred of which now roost on the Molesey-Littleton-Staines group of reservoirs.

Hollom's figures suggest that well over 100,000 gulls may have been roosting in the London Area at peak periods, and since there is no reason to suppose that the more recent counts represent the maximum numbers present on occasion there would not seem to have been any substantial change. By far the largest number of all species of gulls roost on the water, but a few are always to be found on some of the causeways separating the sheets of water or the filter-beds; the long concrete baffle running into the centre of the Queen Mary reservoir at Littleton is an especially favoured site. Hollom turned this to good advantage by catching large numbers for ringing, and it is to his success that we owe much of our knowledge of the countries of origin of the gulls, as described in the specific notes.

The evening movements as the gulls follow the Thames westwards from central London towards the reservoirs at Barn Elms, Molesey, Littleton and Staines, or as they converge from the surrounding country on these roosting-places and the reservoirs in the Lea valley, provide one of the most striking sights of London bird life.

Most gulls come into Staines and Littleton from the east, but on three winter afternoons in 1940 Hollom followed up flight lines of gulls heading for this area from directions with a westerly component. The lines were traced back to (a) between Godalming and Milford, (b) between Farnham and Bentley and (c) between Maidenhead and Hurley. An early morning observation between Wargrave and Reading showed parties moving out westwards. Thus the roosts may draw birds from a radius of over 20 miles. Within our Area it is not certain how far eastwards the Staines/Littleton birds extend, but on the Thames there is an area of overlap in central London, the majority of gulls at Wapping going east in the evening while at Westminster most of them fly to the west. Away from the Thames, at Bloomsbury, some go in the direction of the Lea valley but most head in a westerly direction.

The 'catchment area' of the Lea valley roosts is not known with any precision but some of the gulls at least come from the Brent, Islington and Potters Bar directions. In the north of the Area, birds feeding in the Maplecross and Watford districts appear to belong to the Staines roost, while birds in the Hertfordshire part of the Lea valley roost at King George V reservoir (H. H. S. Hayward). Bertram Lloyd at Hampstead recorded a morning northward flight for six successive seasons during the 1930's from about mid-October to early March. At Regent's Park and Paddington some evening flight lines are to the south-west and other gulls go towards the Lea valley. J. H. Ward states that in the nightly flight to western reservoirs, the St. James's Park birds join the river at Chelsea, Kensington Gardens birds at Hammersmith, and at Barnes a detour is made across Richmond Park to avoid the loop of the river.

Gull flight-lines may be observed throughout the year, except perhaps in early summer, but much further investigation is required for a comprehensive account.

Numerically, gulls and ducks are the important constituents of the reservoir bird community in winter, but the influence of these large sheets of water is relatively just as considerable on the population of grebes. The great crested grebe was at one time near to extinction in this country, but as already mentioned the reservoirs at Barn Elms and Staines very soon attracted them in numbers that were outstanding for the period, while Walthamstow reservoirs, with their small wooded islands, became the site of an important breeding colony, which included about 24 pairs at the time of the national census of this species in 1931. In the thirties the size of the flocks reached unprecedented heights; at Staines and Littleton alone, for example, there were 411 grebes on September 29th, 1934, more than have been counted in the whole Area in some recent censuses in the breeding season. Totals of over a hundred were quite a commonplace at Littleton, Molesey and Staines and in the Lea valley, reaching their peaks any time between the middle of August and the middle of November.

In a much more modest way the black-necked grebe also has become associated with Staines reservoirs in autumn, when parties of up to ten or so are quite a normal sight. For the other grebes the reservoirs seem to have no special attractions. Although there are few recent winters in which at least one red-necked grebe has not been seen, they are erratic in their appearance and it is rare indeed for more than three to be observed in any one winter. Slavonian grebes are equally irregular in their appearance which is most often at Staines or Walthamstow but also occasionally at gravel pits and the smaller waters of the Area.

There are fewer records of great northern and black-throated divers than of the rarer grebes, and of the twenty odd reports of the great northern eleven were in the years 1927 to 1939. Even the red-throated has only been reported about fifty times, approximately as often as the Slavonian and red-necked grebes, but most of the birds are probably suffering from some disability as at least fifteen have been found dead.

These bald figures do not really convey a good impression of the chances of seeing such interesting species so near London, as many of them make quite a long stay. Some indication of what happens when weather conditions are appropriate can be gleaned from the events in early 1937 when, following very low temperatures in the Baltic and strong east and north-east winds in the North Sea, a large number of grebes, divers and other maritime species were blown inland. Slavonian grebes were seen at five localities, including a party of four on a gravel pit, and red-necked grebes at three places, both even being seen in Inner London; several black-throated divers and two or three black-necked grebes also appeared at the same time, while a great northern diver was first seen a few days earlier (cf. *L.B.R.* for 1937, pp. 1–2).

Of the other chance visitors to the reservoirs wild swans and geese are extremely rare. Cormorants were at one time very erratic in their appearances but since the last war they have become regular winter visitors, especially to the Thames at Syon Park and the reservoirs at Walton and at Staines, where they have made good use of the buoys in the new reservoir. Shags are still purely vagrants, as are the three common auks, which appear in the most unlikely places as often as on the large sheets of water. That they have little hope of survival on fresh water even if they should settle down is suggested by the discovery at Littleton reservoir in October, 1937, of a party of sixteen razorbills, all with their intestines infected with a fluke, *Cotylerus platycephalus*, which has freshwater fishes among its hosts. Gannets and the various petrels are equally uncommon visitors, as would be expected.

Waders are unquestionably attracted by the large sheets of water and, while they may find some animal life in the cracks between the slabs of concrete on the banks and the narrow belt of algae at the water's edge, there is little in the environment to tempt the majority of them to alight or to stay for long if they do so. The common sandpiper, however, seems quite at home and other wader visitors to these hard, ostensibly unattractive surfaces have included such apparently incongruous species as greenshank, green sandpiper, knot, turnstone, Temminck's stint and sanderling. When expanses of wet mud or gravel are exposed during the construction of new reservoirs or the draining of old ones, many waders quickly take advantage of the situation to drop in while on passage.

The construction of a new reservoir on the Thames gravel provides an interesting ecological sequence. When the excavation of the bed is nearing

---

Plate 7. The West Middlesex plain: Staines and King George VI reservoirs, with Staines Moor and the River Colne in the foreground, Perry Oaks sewage farm and London Airport in the distance. (*Air Survey Co. Ltd.*)

Plate 7.

Plate 8. The Thames at Hammersmith showing Barn Elms and Lonsdale Road
reservoirs

completion large expanses of gravel are interspersed with shallow, irregular pools which provide a profusion of the margins so suited to the requirements of waders. If then there is some delay before the reservoir is filled, vegetation rapidly gains a hold in the drier parts and attracts flocks of seed-eating birds. This environment of bare gravel, pools and low vegetation proves attractive to a variety of species for breeding, so long as the disturbance from bulldozers and other machinery is not too pronounced. Notable among the species to be found under such conditions are little ringed plover, of which several pairs bred for a time at both the large reservoirs most recently constructed, whinchat, skylark, yellow wagtail, redshank, lapwing and red-legged partridge. When such a reservoir is eventually filled the vegetation is killed, but at the King George VI reservoir, which was first filled at the end of 1947, the level of the water was lowered again in the late summer and autumn of 1948 until gravel edges re-appeared with many islands and pools, providing ideal conditions once more for waders, of which no fewer than 27 species were recorded in the four years, 1947–50. These included both the phalaropes, little stint and curlew sandpiper, Kentish and grey plovers and oystercatcher. The reservoir was filled a second time in the summer of 1949 and practically emptied once more in August, so that in places gulls and coots, for example, could stand in the shallows with their bellies clear of the surface. The final filling took place in April and May, 1950.

Terns also are frequently drawn to the reservoirs on migration, and to take a recent if exceptional example, as many as three to five hundred common or arctic terns were hawking over Staines reservoirs one day in August, 1950, but by the following day not more than twenty remained. Sandwich and little terns are seen occasionally, but the black tern is a more frequent visitor and may often be seen feeding over the reservoirs or other waters during its passage through south-eastern England. Unfortunately the bareness of the reservoirs offers little inducement for them to stay long, though in recent years there have been some exceptionally large flocks. In the spring of 1950, when the passage was on a remarkable scale, there were as many as 121 at Staines reservoirs in the middle of May, and large parties were seen at many other localities. The Staines flocks were the largest in the country and provide further evidence of the great drawing power of the London reservoirs in concentrating aquatic birds on migration.

Among other species which are regular visitors to the reservoirs are pied and grey wagtails, the hirundines, and especially swifts. It is particularly difficult to assess the numbers of the last species when a big passage is in progress, as at such times swifts, in particular, may seem to fill the air around and over the water. There is some evidence that swifts are more numerous in spring than in autumn, and there have been at least two occasions, at Staines and Walthamstow respectively, when it has been estimated that there were about two thousand present at one time. The peculiar summer movements of the swift, usually attributed to sudden deterioration of the weather, have also been observed, "thousands" being reported at Hampton on June 14th, 1939. In autumn, midges are sometimes so numerous at the reservoirs that they rise in clouds along the causeways and the flat grass-covered tops of the banks, and as a result of the abundant food-supply the reservoirs act as focal points to concentrate swifts and hirundines on migration, which when travelling at a height may be attracted in the first place by the large sheets of water.

Although the reservoirs have concrete or stone sides and no marginal growth of reeds or sedge to provide nesting sites, the causeways and outer slopes of the banking are usually grass-covered, even in some cases planted with bushes, and give enough cover for the nests of a few mallard, two or three pairs of gadwall (at Barn Elms), a small number of tufted ducks (especially at Barn Elms and Walthamstow) and very occasionally pochard. At many of the sites these same banks or causeways harbour small colonies of yellow wagtails and meadow pipits, while more surprisingly, in view of the absence of reeds, Walthamstow reservoirs for many years supported a colony of reed warblers, which nested in bushes such as elder and privet. In the Lea valley, also, sand martins have bred regularly in drain-pipes in aquaducts.

Although great crested grebes and coot have occasionally attempted to attach nests to booms or small stone projections at reservoirs without any natural cover, the only group of these artificial waters where they are able to breed regularly is at Walthamstow, where the wooded islands provide some shelter. In 1934 Glegg commented that the majority of the breeding tufted ducks and great crested grebes of Essex were then in the Lea valley, and when we consider also the enormous influence of the island that existed for a time at the new Abberton reservoir, near Colchester, the potentialities of the London reservoirs if there were more suitable cover for breeding provide a fertile subject for the imagination. As it is, there has been for many years a flourishing heronry on one of the Walthamstow islands, where the birds enjoy a freedom from disturbance that they probably missed at the colony in Wanstead Park which in recent years has averaged about five pairs only. Herons also visit the other reservoirs regularly for feeding.

Having reviewed the composition of the normal bird life of the reservoirs and glanced briefly at the more transient species, it remains to consider the special features of the different basins or groups of waters and how these affect the distribution of the species using them. An all-important factor is the depth of the water. A little over four-fifths of the whole expanse, namely about 2670 acres, has a normal depth of 28 feet or over, and another 112 acres (the Chelsea and Lambeth group) is over 20 feet. Only a little under 500 acres are less than this depth, including, in the Thames valley, Barn Elms, Barnes and Kempton Park and, in the Lea valley, all the Walthamstow group with the exception of Banbury and Lockwood.

If the duck population is divided into the surface-feeders, the diving ducks of the genera *Aythya* and *Bucephala,* and the saw-bills, certain habitat-preferences at once emerge. The surface-feeders are found in greatest numbers on the large, deep waters, and are much less numerous on the small, shallower basins at Barn Elms and Molesey. This is illustrated in the following table of the relative numbers of mallard on the three largest reservoirs in comparison with those on the remaining waters of the Metropolitan Water Board on two dates in late 1950:—

	Total acreage	Percentage	Total mallard		Percentage
King George V Littleton Staines	1551	53	8.10.50	1525	72
			12.11.50	2060	76
Remaining M.W.B. reservoirs	1399	47	8.10.50	585	28
			12.11.50	649	24

The normal depth of water at the three reservoirs named ranges from 29 feet to 38 feet. It is probable that the habitat preference on the part of the big flocks of winter visitors, as distinct from the local population, is for large expanses of water because of the greater freedom from disturbance. Mallard obtain their food only to a limited extent from the animal and plant life around the banks and use the reservoirs mainly as a harbour during the day, obtaining the greater part of their food from adjacent agricultural and marshy land, including sewage farms; there is thus no need for them to avoid the deeper waters in spite of the absence of shallows in which to feed. This preference for the largest sheets of water may be the reason why no large flock is found on the Walton reservoirs which have a normal depth of 42 feet but an area of only 126 acres.

The other surface-feeding ducks all show the same tendency, though as they are in much smaller numbers the majority confine themselves to an even more restricted choice of locality, possibly acquired through flocks developing a tradition of safe haunts which combine freedom from disturbance by day with a good food-supply close at hand. Thus, of the teal which spend the winter on the reservoirs the great majority are found at Staines and Island Barn reservoirs, both little disturbed, with depths ranging from 29 to 39 feet; these teal show a marked contrast with other flocks which stay in thick cover at gravel pits or in river valleys, but very few indeed spend the day on the smaller, shallower reservoirs. Although

Island Barn is one of the deep reservoirs, it has a much more gentle slope than most, with the result that there is a considerable area of shallow water round the side. Moreover, the water seldom rises high enough to reach the vertical part of the bank at the top, thus enabling a narrow band of vegetation (including even *Salix* sp.) to maintain itself. In this marginal zone teal and shoveler have often been seen feeding.

Wigeon also show a marked preference for the deeper reservoirs, notably Staines, Littleton and Walton, but in their case feeding activity by day is concentrated chiefly on the grass banks fringing the reservoirs or separating the various basins. At Walton, in particular, it is a common sight to see a small party grazing on the banks, and when undisturbed they are usually to be found resting on the grass rather than on the water. Shoveler are almost confined, except on spring migration, to Staines and the new King George VI reservoir alongside and have been seen in early September feeding very actively on the surface round the inflow pipe, where presumably the river water coming in would contain a considerable quantity of animal life.

By contrast, the pochard and the tufted duck, the most numerous ducks in the Area after the mallard, prefer the smaller and shallower reservoirs of Barn Elms and the Walthamstow group, which vary from 10 feet to 19 feet in depth. Large flocks of pochard also appear from time to time at the shallow Welsh Harp, but in this species there are occasional exceptions to the usual preference when large numbers elect to spend the winter months at Staines reservoirs or the even deeper Stain Hill basin. Unfortunately, not enough is known to explain these departures from the normal in terms of possibly abnormal food-supply, but more usually the pochard congregates in its largest numbers at the places where the depth of water conforms to its diving requirements, which appear to be for a depth of not over 15 feet and preferably much less.

Though the tufted duck is more widespread around London than the pochard, the greatest numbers still occur with remarkable regularity at Barn Elms, which has a depth of 12 feet, and in the Lea valley where they prefer the four basins in the Walthamstow group with a depth of only 10 feet. It seems reasonable to assume that they definitely choose these shallow waters because they are able to obtain their food on the bottom, so that in their case food rather than freedom from disturbance is the governing factor. Small flocks of a hundred or more spend the winter at many other localities, but the numbers on the deeper waters are seldom very great. Some few hundred habitually spend the day in winter on the Walton reservoirs, which are 42 feet in depth, but these lie alongside the much shallower Chelsea and Lambeth group which vary from 21 to 28 feet and where certainly tufted ducks are often feeding assiduously around

Plate 9. Walthamstow reservoirs showing the wooded islands

Plate 10. The heronry at Walthamstow is within close distance of factory chimneys

the inflow pipe. It must be remembered that for none of the ducks is the main part of the day the chief feeding period inland, where tidal conditions do not influence the daily rhythm as they do for some of the surface-feeders and the sawbills in our estuaries.

Of the sawbills the goosanders appear to prefer deep waters, whereas the smew concentrate on much shallower reservoirs. When the numbers of goosanders are not abnormally large the main flock is usually at Walton reservoirs (42 feet), while at other times large numbers have been seen at Littleton where the depth is only a few feet less. Goosanders can often be watched diving during the day and are not infrequently trapped accidentally in one of the suction towers at Walton, but a good proportion of their food is probably obtained from nocturnal visits to shallower lakes such as the Pen Ponds in Richmond Park. Smew are most regular at the Welsh Harp, Barn Elms and Lonsdale Road reservoirs, and are seen much less frequently on the deeper waters. The Chelsea and Lambeth reservoirs, which at one time regularly supported a fair-sized flock in winter, have now been practically deserted by this species, possibly as a result of the much greater disturbance from anglers since the last war.

It is not easy to discuss the question of food-supply at the reservoirs in the absence of quantitative biological studies or of any extensive analysis of stomach contents from the bird population. Freshwater biology of reservoirs has been discussed by Pearsall, Gardiner and Greenshields (1946) and by Macan and Worthington (1951), but they do not examine the subject from the ornithological standpoint. In general, the newer reservoirs are too deep and too steep-sided to support many rooted plants, but the older ones are often shallower with more gently sloping sides. In contrast with the lakes of the north and west of England, which drain from mountainous regions and are often relatively poor in plant and animal life, the London reservoirs derive their water from a fertile and calcareous source, which is rich in those elements that foster the growth of aquatic plants. Not only is the water from the drainage basin of the Thames highly fertile, but it is usually contaminated by organic matter, giving rise to a large growth of bacteria. It has been noted that storage reservoirs receiving river-water develop a high fertility almost as soon as they are filled, as algae are introduced with the water. Pearsall *et al.* calculate that a reservoir in the Thames valley holding about 7,000 million gallons might, at certain times, contain 110 tons dry weight of the alga *Fragilaria crotonensis,* whereas in Windermere a similar volume of water would contain only three tons dry weight of *Asterionella* at the height of the season.

Though the floating algae, constituting the phytoplankton, and those algae which grow on the mud or stones of the sloping banks are unquestionably at certain times of the year very abundant, these periods are in the spring and autumn and not when the ducks themselves are most numerous. The full development of algal growth is usually checked by the introduction of copper sulphate into the water, but it is impossible to say if this is a limiting factor on duck population as no statistics exist correlating the amount of food available with the daily requirements of the birds frequenting the reservoirs. A large part of the fauna, including many or most insect larvae, molluscs and annelid worms, spend their whole time on or in the bottom vegetation or mud, and it seems almost certain that they are present in sufficient quantity to provide at least the pochard and tufted duck with an adequate supply of food. As already mentioned, it is on the shallower waters, where they can dive easily to the bottom, that these two species are most numerous; from the bridge in St. James's Park, for example, they can be seen swimming underwater and apparently running their beaks over the surface of the mud and through the bottom-growing plants. At the Chelsea and Lambeth reservoirs coot are regularly to be seen feeding most actively in the centre of one of the basins where an underwater causeway results in a belt of shallower water, and there can be little doubt that they are feeding on plants growing on the causeway itself. Goldeneye also show a great predilection for the same part of the reservoir. At the other deeper reservoirs coot, when feeding, are usually to be seen close to the edge where the slope of the bank provides a narrow belt of shallow water.

What proportion of their food the surface-feeding ducks obtain from the reservoirs as distinct from nocturnal visits to agricultural land, sewage farms, gravel pits or the banks of rivers and streams, must remain a matter of conjecture until their feeding habits have been more closely studied, but in Essex mallard and teal have been seen regularly in the evenings flighting from the reservoirs to gravel pits further up the Lea valley; there are also reports of wigeon flying east over Yardley Hill at dusk. At Berwick Pond teal come in at night to feed, and at one sewage farm at least it is a common feature to see ducks arriving in the late evening. Very little, however, is on record of the evening movements of ducks in the Thames valley.

This brief sketch of the food problem as it affects the winter duck population may be inconclusive, but is intended to show that there is a profitable field for future research in correlating the freshwater biology of the reservoirs with the distribution of the birds using them, and in the study of the ornithological effects of the introduction of copper sulphate and chlorine.

Special references

MACAN, T. T. and WORTHINGTON, E. B. (1951). Life in Lakes and Rivers, New Naturalist No. 15. London, Collins.

PEARSALL, W. H., GARDINER, A. C., and GREENSHIELDS, F. (1946). Freshwater biology and water supply in Britain. *Freshw. Biol. Assoc. Brit. Emp. Sci. Pub. 11* : 1–90.

THE GRAVEL PITS

by E. R. Parrinder

WATER-LOVING birds are well provided for in the London Area, despite the loss of most of the natural marsh. Other chapters have described the importance of the reservoirs and sewage farms and this chapter deals with the bird-life of the excavations for sand and gravel.

The sand and gravel extraction industry expanded greatly just after the First World War, when the use of concrete became more widespread. By 1938, the output in the London Area was more than four times the pre-war figure for the whole of England and Wales. After the second war, more and more pits were opened and in 1947 (according to the Report of the Advisory Committee on Sand and Gravel, 1948) there were over 70 active pits in the Area and nearly as many which although disused had not been filled in. Most of the flooded "wet" pits are in the terrace gravels of the Thames and its tributaries, especially in south-west Middlesex, the Colne valley, the Lea valley above Chingford, south Essex west of the Roding and the valleys of the Cray and Darent. Both "wet" and "dry" pits exist in the glacial and plateau deposits between Watford and Ware, but the largest number of completely dry excavations are the sand pits in the Greensand areas of Surrey and Kent.

A few of the larger gravel pits, for example those at Hamper Mill near Watford, Sewardstone in Essex and Mitcham Junction in Surrey, were visited regularly between the wars but the others were largely ignored by ornithologists, who favoured the more obvious attractions of the reservoirs and sewage farms. In the 1930's and after, however, many previously unknown pits were visited in connection with the censuses of great crested grebes and of ducks. The discovery, in 1944, of a breeding pair of little ringed plovers at one of the south-west Middlesex pits acted as a further spur and led to the mapping, from the air and on the ground, of all pits then open in the Area. The next step was an intensive study of four selected pits, carried out by the Ornithological Section from 1948 to 1951. The Report of this Survey, published in *L.B.R.* No. 17, described the bird-life, at all times of the year, of the chosen workings and in one case comparisons were made with an adjacent control area of unexcavated land. This important survey has provided the material for much of the present chapter.

Two of the pits studied were in largely built-up areas and two in more open rural surroundings. With the exception of part of one, all were disused but ecologically they differed widely. The area of water ranged from $6\frac{1}{2}$ to $77\frac{1}{2}$ acres and of the surrounding land associated with the workings from 23 to 180 acres. The depth of the water ranged from less than 6 feet to 30 feet. Two of the pits had vertical sides and two shelving. One pit had extensive reed beds; at the others the aquatic vegetation varied from algae to small beds of reeds, willow-herb, reed-mace and scrub willow. There were differences, too, in the fish present in the water, in the character of the surrounding land and in the degree of disturbance. As might be expected, the bird population varied with the differing habitats: only three species, skylark, reed bunting and yellow wagtail, bred at all four pits while the number of breeding birds per ten acres ranged from 3.3 to 30. Divergences of this nature are characteristic of the gravel pits, which provide a less stable habitat than the reservoirs. Moreover, many of the pits suffer from excessive disturbance of nesting birds, being unfenced and often open to intrusion by gangs of boys.

The early stages of both wet and dry pits sometimes provide suitable conditions for both sand martins and little ringed plovers. A pit near Radlett where excavations began in September, 1945, had a colony of 65 pairs of sand martins in the following summer. At the "dry" glacial pits little ringed plovers may be attracted by the shallow pools in the long gullies which are formed by the power drag lines. Pits in terrace gravel are usually worked with excavators and flood quickly but sandy deltas are formed near the washing and grading machines and, despite the disturbance, little ringed plovers have nested on these deltas at a number of the London pits. Another favourite site is the stony plateau from which the excavators operate. Adjacent root fields have also been used for nesting: the essential requirement appears to be a sandy or muddy edge for feeding and they do not breed at pits where all the sides are steep.

At least in the early parts of its life, the ecological character of a gravel pit is always changing. Coarse vegetation, scrub willow, rose-bay willow herb and other plants and grasses grow up quickly when part or the whole of a pit becomes worked out and disused. Aquatic vegetation develops in the water (which at wet pits is commonly about half of the total area) and reed and sedge may appear. These changes bring about changes in the bird-life. Little ringed plovers, if they have nested, are forced to find other sites when the vegetation becomes dense. The water may attract breeding pairs of mallard, moorhen, coot and little and great crested grebes. More than half of the total breeding population of great crested grebes in the

London Area (about 119 pairs in 1953) nest at gravel pits, especially at those with small islands which provide sanctuary from predators. On one occasion, in 1948 near Poyle, a Slavonian grebe stayed for the summer and attempted to build a nest. Tufted ducks breed at several of the older pits and pochard have nested occasionally where the cover is dense, as at Feltham, Old Parkbury and Sewardstone.

The rough, often marshy ground surrounding many of the pits provides nesting sites for skylarks, reed buntings, yellow wagtails, whinchats and occasionally redshank and snipe. Reed and sedge warblers occur at some of the older pits; as many as 24 pairs of reed warblers nested at the pit at Mayesbrook Park, in Essex, before it was turned into a lido. Tree sparrows have colonised several of the pits and at Feltham both tree and house sparrows breed in the woodwork under a conveyor, with gravel constantly passing a few inches from their nests. A pair of pied wagtails once nested successfully in a very similar position on the machinery at Old Parkbury.

In the last year of the Gravel Pit Survey a comparison was made of the population of Moor Mill pit and an undeveloped area about a mile away, where the ecological conditions were similar to those which were presumed to have existed before the pit was excavated. Nine species were common to both areas while three (rook, robin and wren) nested only at the control area and seven (reed bunting, yellow wagtail, reed and sedge warblers, mallard, snipe and coot) bred only at the gravel pit. A further five species, which did not occur in the control area in 1950, had nested at Moor Mill in one or more of the other years of the Survey.

As well as providing nesting sites, the gravel pits are attractive feeding and resting places for many water and marsh loving birds. In the summer they are visited by herons, kingfishers, lapwings, hirundines, swifts and other birds breeding in the neighbourhood. In the migration seasons, they are second only to the reservoirs and sewage farms for the number and variety of the birds which pass through. Waders are attracted by the sandy or muddy edges, spits and miniature islands at many of the pits. But although more than twenty species of waders have been recorded relatively few are regular at particular pits and, no doubt because of the smaller feeding areas and greater disturbance, they do not stay for so long as at the reservoirs and sewage farms. Numbers are usually small; an exception is the flock of 20 ruffs seen at one of the Wraysbury pits on March 10th, 1949. As might be expected, the river valley pits, with marshy vegetation, are especially attractive to green and common sandpipers. At Old Parkbury, in the Colne valley, a pair of common sandpipers stayed throughout the summers of 1950–1954 and in 1955 their nesting was proved. Both this pit and the nearby one at Moor Mill have been watched regularly in recent years and the waders seen have included dunlin, ruff, wood sand-piper, greenshank and ringed and little ringed plovers.

Terns are sometimes seen on migration at the pits with large areas of water. In the spring of 1946, when there was an exceptional passage of black terns, half of the occurrences in the Area were at gravel pits.

The most evident of the passerine migrants are the hirundines and swifts which may congregate in large numbers over the water. Wheatears, whinchats, meadow pipits and wagtails all occur on the rough margins. In the late autumn, the pits with reed beds are sometimes used as roosts by pied wagtails, hirundines and starlings.

The Gravel Pit Survey showed that although the number of species in the winter at the pits studied was rather less than at other times the total number of birds was often higher, and this is probably true for other pits. Large flocks of finches find an abundance of weed seeds on the rough surface of the ground surrounding the flooded areas, and tree sparrows are often present. All the regular water birds, mallard, tufted duck, coot and moorhen, increase and at some of the larger pits there may be sizeable concentrations of duck, although, of course, the numbers do not approach those at the reservoirs. Small flocks of teal frequent many of the older pits, where there are reeds or growths of willow. Most of the other ducks which visit the London Area are occasionally seen at the gravel pits; wigeon, pintail, goldeneye, goosander and smew are not infrequent in small numbers at some of the larger waters, such as those at Feltham, West Hyde, Sewardstone and Ruxley.

The great crested grebe does not congregate at the gravel pits in the winter, as it does at the reservoirs; the little grebe, on the other hand, prefers the smaller areas of water and flocks of a score or so are not infrequent. Gulls, especially black-headed gulls, are winter residents at many of the pits. Snipe come to the marshy areas of the wet pits: at Moor Mill, in one of the survey years, they increased from one breeding family to a winter maximum of 29 birds. At the same pit, a jack snipe appears to have stayed throughout the summer in 1948 and perhaps also in 1949. At some of the pits lapwings and occasionally golden plover feed on the rough margins. Other, less common, winter visitors in recent years have included osprey, cormorant and shag and short-eared owl.

The Gravel Pit Survey concluded that "the digging of the the gravel pits with subsequent flooding and attendant growth of vegetation tends to increase the variety of the local bird-life, at all seasons of the year". This statement is perhaps over cautious: there can be no doubt that the bird-life of London has been greatly enriched by the presence of these areas of water and waste land.

THE RIVER VALLEYS AND SEWAGE FARMS
by C. B. Ashby

London had its beginning on two small hills rising above a marsh dominated by the easterly-flowing Thames and watered by a drainage system of rivers which arrived, as they do now, from the north and from the south through shallow valleys. Such of the Thames marshes as remain below London, and the standing waters of the reservoirs and gravel pits which have been formed in the main valleys, are discussed elsewhere. For the moment we consider the river courses and inland marshes, and particularly the marsh-like sewage farms which discharge their purified effluent into the rivers.

All our rivers flow into the Thames, those of main importance being the Ingrebourne, Roding and Lea in the north-east; the Darent, Wandle, Mole and Wey in the south; and the Colne which, together with many streams and cuts, winds down our north-western boundary and across the plain of west Middlesex to its confluence with the Thames near Staines. From the water meadows of Egham and Chertsey the Thames itself runs wide and deep between banks which become increasingly formalised downstream. Typical riverside vegetation is restricted and the water level is maintained by a system of weirs and locks to Teddington, below which the river is tidal and the silted gravel margins are exposed at low water. Industrialisation and development of the lower parts of the Lea and Roding are as severe as that of the London Thames, and some of the smaller rivers of the built-up areas, as for example parts of the Brent and Wandle, have been debas d by urbanisation and polluted by factory waste and road drainage. Happily the valleys of the chief rivers remain for the most part verdant and of considerable importance as habitats for birds.

These valleys support a breeding population which ranges from the homely moorhen to the grey wagtail, a bird perhaps more usually associated with fast hill streams but which has nested on some of the lowland rivers around London throughout our period. Approximately ten nesting pairs of grey wagtails are now reported annually, but probably this is less than the true number, as other pairs are thought to be nesting on various streams below the North Downs and elsewhere. They are irregular in their choice of sites but mill races and weirs are likely places, as for example the mills at Godstone where one or two pairs have nested regularly since 1912. They also nest sparsely on the Thames and most other rivers, but not yet in the London corner of Essex. The yellow wagtail, in part a nesting species of dry farmland, is around London found very largely on sewage farms and on the banks of the main reservoirs. It is also a bird of the pasture bordering some of the rivers of the Area. Reed and sedge warblers, reed buntings, kingfishers and some 200 pairs of herons are other species whose distribution is closely linked with the immediate surroundings of the rivers. Redshank and snipe breed in selected spots in the valleys but are becoming adversely affected by drainage and the war-time and post-war reclamation of marginal land. Out of the breeding season, parties of finches feed in the rough river pastures and waste lands, and siskins in flocks of up to 50 resort with redpolls to the alders at the water's edge. These alder-lined stretches sometimes support a high and varied winter population. On a date in February, to take one instance, eighteen species were seen along 150 yards of the River Mole below Leatherhead.

If the weather becomes exceptionally severe ducks are driven to find open water on the Thames. Under such conditions in early 1947 fifteen species of duck were present on the river between Chelsea and Richmond, with mallard in flocks of up to 300 and a mixed company of pochard and tufted duck 1500 strong; besides flocks of 80 wigeon, 150 teal, 15 pintail, 18 scaup, 20 goldeneye and 37 smew. Parties of goosander up to perhaps forty are a normal winter sight on the Thames about Kew and upstream to Molesey, and even such maritime birds as merganser, long-tailed duck, puffin, razorbill and gannet find their way into the river on occasion. To this list of species which, despite the presence of craft, at times frequent the Thames may be added the red-necked grebe and two species each of divers and terns. Shags are infrequent but out of the breeding season cormorants are regular, particularly about Syon Reach, where they often perch in the trees. Easily outnumbering all others are the gulls and even the greater black-backed is now a regular and by no means uncommon visitor to the London reaches of the Thames. Of all the many attractions the river holds for the gulls, the refuse barges which lie below Hammersmith bridge are second to none, and here crowds of gulls of six species—including in some years the glaucous gull—gorge themselves to repletion. The swans of the Thames breed on its islands and the private parts of its banks, and by the end of the breeding season form large flocks which may exceed a hundred.

All the other rivers of the Area are small compared with the Thames and the highest concentrations of typical waterside birds not unnaturally tend to occur in the marshy areas which remain, or have been formed, in their valleys. A hundred years ago snipe used to be shot on the outskirts of what is now central London, but by 1900 there was no appreciable amount of natural marsh in our Area. Marshy spots along the rivers have progressively declined but not altogether disappeared. The river verges may be pasture or wasteland, often with luxuriant vegetation though seldom damp enough or in sufficient depth to be termed marsh. Staines Moor, although drained, has some characteristics of a marsh, with dense herbage along the Colne, and is much favoured by yellow and variant wagtails, reed buntings and sedge warblers in summer. In winter its low-lying level grassland has been visited repeatedly of recent years by flocks and parties of grey geese, usually whitefronts, up to about 60 in number. In places the London rivers flow between high, eroded sandy banks; elsewhere there are small reed-beds, particularly at bends. For the muddy strands and secluded pools set in thick cover typical of a good bird marsh we look, however, to the sewage farms, gravel pits and, of late, reservoirs under construction.

The largest sewage farm in the Area is the old established one at Beddington, in Surrey (c. 600 acres), but the farm with the most attractive area of 'marsh' is Perry Oaks, in the lower Colne valley. In the north-east the farm near Romford is important and well placed, being only two miles from the widening Thames. In the Roding valley there is a farm at Chigwell and several others of less account. Along the course of the Lea, which to a flying bird presents an unbroken chain of lakes (man-made) for thirteen miles between Hoddesdon and Walthamstow, there are sewage farms of long standing at Edmonton and Ponders End and three others which, ornithologically speaking, have been more recently discovered. North and north-west of London a number of these farms have been closed as part of the programme of centralisation referred to in Professor Abercrombie's Greater London Plan (1944). Recently, in 1951, Watford farm—particularly notable for large numbers of green sandpipers and jack snipe —was closed down. South of the Thames the farm within the racing track at Brooklands was modernised and much reduced during the war but others at Molesey, Epsom and Elmers End continue. There are thus at present about a dozen farms of main ornithological importance, besides a very much larger number of small works, sometimes overgrown with weeds, which although of no attraction to waders on passage provide refuge for warblers, reed buntings and other species which may succeed better there than in the more open and trampled parts of the river valleys.

The habitat provided by the main sewage farms is very variable. In briefest outline, the system of purification involves the pumping of sludge in liquid state on to shallow settling beds formed by low, earthed-up banks on level ground. Rank vegetation which is allowed to grow more or less unhindered on these banks thus encloses muddy pools of some acres in extent and, as these dry off with the cessation of pumping, muddy islands and strands appear and support a growth of persicaria and other plants sufficient to form satisfactory cover. The attraction of sewage farms to waders thus varies with the stage of drying reached by the settling beds, as well as with their extent and the proportion of the farm so allocated. In wet seasons the water level may be so high that hardly any mud remains exposed, while in autumns following hot, dry summers there may be large expanses of mud of sufficient age to support adequate cover, and with enough moist edge to provide feeding for flocks of waders eighty strong. When completely dry the bed may be ploughed and sown with a crop or with rye grass, which may in turn be flooded and grow lush; or the sludge may be dug out and transported from the farm for use as manure. If not too dry, and especially if flooded by rains, partly dug sludge beds are still of much attraction to waders, which may be very inconspicuous on the weedy and now broken surface of the mud.

Unlike natural marsh, sewage farm marshes are thus in a constant state of change, with new fields being flooded and others being transformed by drying and crop rotation, though one or two settling beds on a farm are sometimes allowed to remain undisturbed, except for the addition of fresh sludge, for a number of years. This has been the practice at Perry Oaks with the result that the number and variety of waders seen there has been almost beyond belief.

Watching birds at sewage farms on the scale practised to-day is of comparatively recent development, but soon after 1900 G. E. Lodge was recording dunlin, green sandpiper and other waders at Ponders End and Edmonton. In 1901 he found there the only nesting pair of ringed plovers known in the London Area. In that year snipe nested and redshanks were present in summer, although apparently no record of their breeding on London sewage farms was obtained until one or two pairs nested there and at Beddington in 1910. Shooting at Edmonton in the early years produced dunlins in 1905 and 1912, four greenshanks in 1906 and one in 1909, a black-tailed godwit in 1911, a ruff in 1912 and two three years later. Doubtless much else was shot, but apparently these are the only wader records of that period which have been preserved.

Little more was heard of sewage farms until Dr. G. Carmichael Low found dunlin, little stint, ruff, greenshank, redshank, ringed plover and jack snipe at Langley between 1923 and 1929. By this time farms at Theydon Bois, Walthamstow, Molesey, Epsom and Harrow had been visited but seemingly only such waders as a few common and green sandpipers, greenshank and redshank were discovered. T. H. Harrisson (1931), watching at the open field type of farm at Harrow (now no more) between

1925 and 1930 found a remarkable scarcity of waders and other passage birds, although he was aware of a considerable movement of waders at the Brent, Elstree and Ruislip reservoirs and, by night, over Mill Hill.

In 1931, P. A. D. Hollom began observations at the 35-acre farm at Brooklands and by the autumn of 1936 he averaged one visit every two or three days from mid-July to mid-September. He found a well-developed passage in spring as well as in autumn. Besides the commoner waders he discovered turnstone, wood sandpiper, avocet and black-tailed godwit (*B.B.*, *28:* 342–3), and grey plover, bar-tailed godwit, little and Temminck's stints (*B.B.*, *30:* 346–7). The variety of species was thus mounting but the numbers of passage waders seen on the farms was still small. Flocks of the size seen to-day were unknown. During the thirties, when there was a steady increase in the number of qualified observers, more and more attention was paid to sewage farms.

To-day all the main sewage farms are regularly watched by a large force of observers, and during the migration seasons some at least are visited almost daily. Waders are present in all months, and in winter curlew and dunlin, and exceptionally knot and sanderling, may be brought in by hard weather. Winter flocks of snipe, particularly on the flooded fields of rye grass at Beddington, run into hundreds and although shooting is licensed at this season on this and some other farms its effect is seemingly not important. Jack snipe flush so reluctantly that until recently it was unusual to see more than ten in any one place. Lately more intensive searching has shown that twenty, or even at times forty or more, may concentrate at sewage farms such as those at Epsom and Beddington. Ruffs, which are mainly passage birds, have of late been seen on our sewage farms also in winter and very early spring, with up to six at Beddington in early 1954 and a most exceptional flock of 120 at Perry Oaks in March and April of the same year. Apart from a few isolated records this is a new tendency in the London Area, although in 1946, for example, J. Staton (*B.B.*, *40:* 222) reported the annual occurrence of flocks of up to thirty ruffs in mid-winter on the sewage farm at Nottingham. Green sandpipers winter in small numbers on the London farms which, except in the very severest weather, remain sufficiently open to provide regular feeding grounds for lapwings, gulls and starlings in their thousands, together with appreciable flocks of redwings, fieldfares and chaffinches. Bramblings appear in some years but the flock of two to three hundred at Perry Oaks in early 1953 was exceptional. Golden plover up to perhaps thirty associate at times with the lapwings, and moorhens, ducks and very occasionally grey geese resort to the irrigated fields. Carrion crows, so often thought to be solitary, are of normal occurrence at Beddington at all seasons in feeding flocks of up to eighty or more. Winter fly-catching parties of pied and grey wagtails along the concrete channels are sometimes joined by one or two black redstarts or stonechats. Prominent among the many other species which use the farms for feeding are meadow pipits, which rise calling on every side, and herons, which may appear in flocks of perhaps twenty; while the large, grassy, well-treed farm at Beddington has harboured several short-eared owls for periods of up to four and five months. In both the winters of 1953–54 and 1954–55 the survey conducted at this farm by B. S. Milne produced maximum day-time counts exceeding 10,000 birds. These figures, which take no account of many thousands of starlings which congregate at evening on the farm before flying off to the London roosts, are mainly composed of feeding and resting flocks of starlings, black-headed gulls and lapwings, together with redwings (up to 1,200), fieldfares, snipe (up to 600), finches and skylarks.

Spring migration on the sewage farms is noteworthy for the sudden April influx of yellow wagtails, and the appearance of waders on passage. Usually waders are fewer and their stay more brief than in autumn, and such parties as the thirteen black-tailed godwits seen at Elmers End in March, 1947, and seventeen sanderlings at Perry Oaks in May, 1954, are exceptional.

In autumn the waders, now including many birds of the year, spend days or weeks on the farms and as they depart their place is taken by fresh arrivals. All the main farms of the Area attract waders at this season and at Perry Oaks in particular, despite the presence of an over-large number of bird-watchers, the autumn passage compares favourably with that of an East Anglian marsh. Little stints, wood and curlew sandpipers, for example, are regular and have all been seen here in numbers of up to nearly twenty. On a single pool, to quote the *L.B.R.* for 1950, there were present on one day in September an (American) pectoral sandpiper, a Baird's sandpiper, two little stints, eleven curlew sandpipers, several ringed plovers and dunlins, and a winter plumaged sanderling; all together and visible at the same time. A pectoral sandpiper was seen there again for ten days in the following autumn, and in September, 1952, one which frequented a rubbish-tip pool at Epsom sewage farm was trapped and ringed but remained for a further five days. At Perry Oaks in 1953 a lesser yellowlegs was present at intervals from late August to December, and a second bird (distinguished by slight plumage differences) appeared in September. This remarkable farm in this remarkable autumn also sheltered a buff-breasted sandpiper from mid-October to early November. Perry Oaks, so far as London ornithology is concerned, was "discovered" by Lord Hurcomb in 1946, but had existed since the thirties when it was of very restricted size. Its subsequent development and expansion on what was formerly orchard land followed the closing in 1936 of a number of farms including those at Uxbridge, Ruislip, Roxeth (Newton) and Pinner.

From late July to the end of October passage waders are continuously present at Perry Oaks, and to a lesser but not inconsiderable extent on many other farms of the Area. Whimbrel and black-tailed godwits in ones and twos and small parties are early in their appearance, and small numbers of dunlin and ringed plover are the forerunners of flocks which may build up in August to sixty or seventy of either species. By the time the main bulk of the wader passage is in full swing in August and September most redshanks are gone, but the passage of certain other waders, notably ruffs (in flocks up to nearly thirty) and common, wood, green and curlew sandpipers, extends for the best part of three months. Greenshanks, either singly or in parties of up to eight, tend to pass through mainly in the latter half of August and the beginning of September. In most autumns sanderlings, knots, turnstones, spotted redshanks, grey and little ringed plovers are seen intermittently. Little stints appear chiefly in the later part of the passage period, usually in small numbers but occasionally in flocks of ten or even seventeen. In contrast, the Temminck's stint is almost unknown, though why this should be so when the farms are otherwise so attractive is not clear. On some days in autumn there are noticeable influxes of pied and yellow wagtails, hirundines and swifts. It is impossible here to refer to all that has been seen, but these passage movements of waders and others, and the value of the sewage farms in revealing them when otherwise they might pass on unseen, are further considered in the chapter on migration.

In summer the farms still play an important part in the ornithology of the Area. By 1952, for example, C. A. White had compiled a list of twenty-six species recorded as breeding annually at Perry Oaks. Lapwings, redshanks and snipe nest regularly on the farms but the survival of their young is often at the mercy of ploughing, grass cutting and flooding operations in the fields. Teal have been proved to breed once on Epsom sewage farm, and shoveler have nested at or near Perry Oaks in most years since 1948. Outstanding is the breeding colony of black-headed gulls at this farm, which probably started in the early forties and in recent years has varied between approximately 150 and 250 pairs. Colonies of tree sparrows of up to fifty or more pairs nest on the farms at Romford, Beddington and elsewhere, and collectively the farms provide one of the main breeding habitats of the yellow wagtail.

There remains one watery habitat to be considered: the ponds, lakes and disused pits which lie scattered round London in every county. The Black Pond on Esher Common is a heathy pool of great beauty but very little seems to be seen on it. Stockers Lake, near Rickmansworth, is more productive but it has the advantage of lying in the valley of the Colne and forming one of a chain of waters. Numbers of grebes and duck are regular in winter on the Pen Ponds of Richmond Park, which are disturbed by numerous visitors but nevertheless attract and hold rarities from time to time; for example, Bewick's swans in 1948 and a little bittern in 1954. Fetcham mill-pond is noted for its dabchicks which may be watched to perfection in the deep water above the spring; and Berwick Pond, near Rainham, is best known perhaps for its being the summer haunt of garganey. Our natural ponds may be hardly significant when compared with the many artificial waters which lie as thickly in the terrace gravels of our river valleys as tarns in Shetland; but they are nevertheless additional retreats for birds, and as such are doubly valuable in a London hinterland which for many years has been in danger of being over-run.

THE THAMES MARSHES BELOW LONDON

by J. F. Burton, R. C. Homes and R. B. Warren

TEMPTING though it may be to dwell on the distant days when harriers, bearded tits and other rarities by present-day standards haunted the marshes bordering the Thames within the boundaries of the County of London, our concern now is with the twentieth century and principally with the last ten years, since very little earlier information is available. The term "marshes", used frequently in this chapter, is to some extent a misnomer and has outlived the days when the ground was permanently wet: now most places which are termed marshes on the map consist of low-lying ground, often below high-tide level but long since drained by dykes and now used for industrial purposes, allotments, rubbish dumps, grazing or sometimes as arable land. The ensuing account shows where the typical species first appear or become numerous, but for convenience the ducks, waders and gulls are discussed separately at the end.

Among the small breeding passerines most characteristic of these marshes are the linnet, corn and reed buntings, skylark, meadow pipit, yellow wagtail and the reed and sedge warblers. On the Greenwich Marshes, some five miles from St. Paul's and the first open ground of any extent bordering the Thames east of London, linnet, skylark (about ten pairs), reed bunting (one to two pairs) and yellow wagtail have all retained a footing, but it is not until Woolwich Ferry is passed that the building zone on the south bank really gives way to open ground represented by Plumstead, Abbey Wood and Erith Marshes which stretch in a continuous belt of four miles up to the industrial works at Belvedere. The principal features of these marshes are the numerous allotments and the large, dense reed-beds, which in some of the fleets adjoining industrial sites are still undisturbed by cutting. The allotments are haunted by goldfinches and linnets and have also supported in recent years a few breeding pairs of whinchats and an occasional pair of stonechats, while even at the end of our period the reed-beds were occupied by well over a hundred pairs of reed warblers. Corn buntings, meadow pipits and sedge warblers also appear on these marshes for the first time as we follow the river downstream.

On the north bank the docks stretch further out from London, and the first appreciable area of open ground is Ripple Level, some 9–10 miles from St. Paul's and lying between Barking Creek and an industrial agglomeration that includes the Ford motor works. Skylarks and meadow pipits, however, are regular on some waste ground west of Barking Creek largely occupied by the Beckton gasworks. Ripple Level consists of flat pasture land, criss-crossed by dykes and very bare, but nevertheless its summer bird population includes many pairs of yellow wagtails (about twenty in one recent year), several pairs of skylarks, meadow pipits, redshanks, lapwings, partridges and probably a pair or two of whinchats. The industrial area is separated from the next marshes by Dagenham Breach, the site of a former incursion by the sea, which once covered over 1,200 acres but has long been much smaller and is too heavily polluted to attract many birds. Beyond, some 12 miles from St. Paul's, lie the Hornchurch Marshes, an area roughly a mile square bordered on the east by the Ingrebourne River. Their chief feature is an enormous rubbish dump with "cuttings" formed by overgrown drainage ditches. Here the linnet becomes numerous; corn buntings, sedge warblers and whinchats appear, while reed buntings are common but yellow wagtails are less numerous than on Ripple Level. Reed warblers are found for the first time along the north bank of the Thames at the mouth of the Ingrebourne, which has extensive reed-beds along both banks. Further on again lie the Rainham, Wennington and Aveley Marshes, which cover a larger area but even so are nowhere over a mile in depth. Corn buntings become much commoner and over twenty singing males have been counted on the Rainham Marshes, which incidentally were a traditional haunt of the bird trappers from the East End; meadow pipits also become more conspicuous at this stage. The town of Purfleet and a series of railway sidings separate the last stretch from the West Thurrock Marshes, which before their development after the First World War were of much greater ornithological interest than they are to-day (Horn, 1921).

On the south side of the river, opposite the Rainham and Aveley Marshes and beyond Erith, lies Crayford Ness and the mouth of the river Darent with the first tract of saltings. Separated from the Darent only by a group of hospitals on the Dartford Marshes is an area of very mixed habitats known generally as the Stone Marshes, which include two small tida fleets, many overgrown dykes and ditches, a series of flooded clay pits and dense thickets of thorn as well as arable and pasture land. A large quantity of slurry is pumped by Littlebrook Power Station into settling tanks on the adjacent levels and attracts large flocks of gulls and parties of waders. From Stone eastwards both the flooded clay pits and the chalk quarries that occupy the fringe of the low-lying land become a prominent feature of the landscape, one quarry extending over a mile from north to south.

A number of the local breeding birds of the marshes, such as meadow pipits and reed and corn buntings, largely disappear in early August, but as winter sets in many species appear on the marshes in flocks. Some, such as the yellowhammer, come probably from the adjacent agricultural land; others are almost certainly of Continental origin and represent a continuation of the westerly movement up the Thames, which can be witnessed in progress along the north shore of Kent further east. In the diversified environment provided by the Stone Marshes very large numbers of such birds as starlings, various species of finches, redwings, skylarks and lapwings are sometimes found in winter when severe conditions on the Continent cause the hard-weather movements that seem to be particularly noticeable in December. At this season also rock pipits are a feature of the saltings, while a few are regular along the walls as far up the river as Crayford Ness.

The persistence of some of the smaller passerines has been so marked in spite of the intrusion of railways, rubbish dumps, cement works, rifle ranges and other disturbing factors that it is disappointing not to be able to write in similar terms of the ducks and waders. Even so, on the south side of the Thames, ducks are attracted to the flooded pits caused by the excavation of clay for the local cement works, and waders to the lagoons formed by the settling tanks of Littlebrook Power Station. However, at no part of the river within our Area are the conditions really estuarine, and the mud-flats, for example, never exceed 200 yards in width at low water; below Woolwich, they average perhaps 100 yards, while up-river they are naturally much narrower. The saltings also are of no very great extent and the largest stretch, Broadness Salt Marsh at Swanscombe,

Eric Hosking

Plate 11a. A reservoir under construction: a breeding ground of little ringed plovers

b. A gravel pit showing sandy spits with encroaching vegetation

C. B. Ashby

Plate 12. Little ringed plover

encompasses some 200 acres. There is thus relatively little feeding ground or freedom from disturbance by river traffic which, coupled with the absence of the secluded fleets and the mixture of open water and reedy cover found in the marshes further east, results in a marked shortage of surface-feeding duck. Until recently only the mallard had been proved to breed, and teal and wigeon do not normally occur even in winter in parties of more than twenty or thirty. Shelduck are sometimes seen in pairs and breeding was proved for the first time in 1954. Diving ducks in winter are more numerous, and both pochard and tufted ducks are regular visitors to the flooded clay pits below Dartford; in the winter of 1953–54, for example, there were up to 100 tufted duck and 262 pochard. The lack of open water is reflected in the scarcity of the coot, which is absent north of the Thames and on the south side breeds only on the flooded pits, in marked contrast with its abundance on the marshes of the estuary proper. It is the pits, an artificial feature of the environment, and not any relic of the natural surroundings, that mainly attract those wildfowl which still appear. Red-throated divers and smew are among the more frequent of the irregular visitors, while cormorants are not unusual in the early morning in autumn and winter.

The mud-flats are also too narrow at low tide to attract many waders on passage or in winter, and equally there are not sufficiently large stretches of undisturbed pasture to attract more than an occasional curlew or golden plover. Redshanks and lapwings, however, breed quite freely and up to ten pairs of the former have been found in recent years as near in as Ripple Level; in addition, a few pairs of snipe breed from Plumstead eastwards. With the advent of hard weather very large flocks of lapwings have been seen. Dunlin are no longer likely to occur on the shore in large numbers, though Horn (1921) had seen them, at a date not mentioned, "so numerous over the flat towards Purfleet as to give the impression of a drifting smoke-cloud." Common and green sandpipers have both wintered in recent years along the small tidal fleet on Stone marshes, and both are quite regular on migration.

Until 1952 other waders were occasional visitors only to the Littlebrook Power Station slurry tanks already mentioned, and in that year a turnstone, two little stints, two curlew sandpipers and a ruff were seen in the period September 16th–25th. In the two ensuing years there has been a much heavier autumn passage, including up to 4 little stints, 26 curlew sand-pipers and 14 ruffs (all in 1953), 9 little ringed plovers and peaks of 73 dunlin and 92 ringed plover. Ones and twos of several of the more un-usual waders have been seen on migration, while in winter a little stint was seen in December, 1954, an avocet stayed for nearly four weeks between late 1952 and early 1953, and in the hard spell of February, 1954,

270 dunlin and 10 knot were recorded. Other unusual species seen in that month included scaup, bar-tailed godwit, up to 50 bramblings at Stone, red-necked grebe and red-breasted merganser.

Gulls are present at all seasons, but naturally are most numerous in autumn and winter. A number of immature gulls of all five common species stay throughout the summer, principally below Dartford, and often rest during the day on the marshes or on the pools in the chalk quarries. Very few indeed roost at night on the marshes, and in winter there is a big evening flight to the lower reaches of the river.

Other features of the Thames and its environs below London include the breeding of swallows in the old gun emplacements and in disused military huts, regular visits by herons and the breeding of kestrels in factory buildings and ruined warehouses as well as in the more normal sites in trees and chalk pits. In recent years other raptorial birds seen have included short-eared owl, peregrine, buzzard and hen harrier. Carrion crows are common and the rubbish dumps on the north side are a favourite feeding ground, as they are also for many rooks and jackdaws. Turtle doves nest in numbers in the dense thorn thickets east of Erith, and occur less commonly as far up-river as Plumstead. Red-legged partridges breed on some of the arable land and are fond of the adjacent chalk quarries; these also attract many stock doves, while sand martins breed in the loamy overburden. Shallow pits in these quarries may act as a centre for a very mixed community including moorhen, coot, little grebe, mute swan, yellow wagtail, little ringed plover and summering gulls.

The migration associated with the Thames and the adjoining marshes is discussed in a later chapter, and if undue emphasis appears to have been laid here on the unnatural features of the environment this is but an inevitable reflection of the development of the land adjoining the Thames. Even so, the presence of the large colony of reed warblers and the persistence so near London as Greenwich of several species which normally favour wider open spaces is very striking and invites speculation as to what might have been there now if only an earlier generation had shown some interest in nature conservation.

THE WOODLANDS
by Dr. Geoffrey Beven

WOODS differ from parks and orchards in that the trees are close together, and their crowns tend to form a complete canopy shading the ground. There is thus a characteristic undergrowth or even bare soil from which grass is largely excluded except in the open glades. Although some changes have occurred in the last fifty years, Londoners are still able to visit many small semi-natural woods. With the great expansion of the built-up areas many woods have become isolated and the bird life thus indirectly affected, but the decrease in woodland has not been as great as that of the open and cultivated land. The close proximity of some woods to new housing estates, as at Elmstead Woods, near Bromley, has meant much trampling out of the undergrowth, and some trampling also occurs during the great week-end exodus from town to country. This lack of shrub-layer is characteristic of many London commons. Small private woods, no longer fenced, suffer in the same way. This results in a scarcity of some small birds, notably warblers and nightingales. Robins also are less numerous where shrubs are scanty and therefore scarce in the parks of central London.

Some types of woods, however, have increased in extent in the last fifty years. Especially is this so of the light open woodlands on sandy soils, where, since the reduction of grazing by animals on the surrounding heaths, birches have spread from existing woods. On the plateau of Wimbledon Common, owing to excessive cutting and grazing, nearly all trees had disappeared by about 1860. Grazing of cattle ceased in 1921 and considerable invasion of birch has occurred since (Rollings, 1934). There has been a similar colonisation of birch at Headley Heath and Oxshott, and on Chislehurst, Hayes and Keston Commons. On damper soils mixed oakwood, preceded by hawthorn, also invades grassland when grazing is discontinued, as for example at Bookham Common. Here there has been a marked encroachment of hawthorn on to the plains, a stage leading to climax oakwood. Similarly, Pear Tree Plain, Epping Forest, is being invaded by birch and oak scrub, since cattle grazing was discontinued a few years ago.

From another aspect, however, conditions have greatly changed since 1900, when Bucknill wrote of Surrey: "The county is patrolled by game-keepers . . . ". Then magpies, jays and sparrow hawks were scarce in the woods round London. Now, keepers are few, and magpies, carrion crows and jays are abundant, the last two species having also increased in central London. Most of the more rural woods have their sparrow hawks and they are also found in large woods well inside the limit of suburban London.

The types of woodland vary with the underlying soil and each has its characteristic birds. Species which are more or less common to all these woods include jay, chaffinch, blue and great tits, song thrush, blackbird and woodpigeon. Primarily a woodland bird in the breeding season, the robin is more frequent in those with good secondary growth such as haw-thorn. However, robins prefer the edges of woodland and some leave dense oakwood in mid-winter, returning in March or later. Hence they may start breeding after the robins of gardens and hedgerows (Lack, 1948). On the other hand, wrens are truly birds of the scrub and in woods are numerous only in those with undergrowth; they feed mainly in the herb and ground vegetation. Where there are larger trees, species such as mistle thrushes, green and greater spotted woodpeckers appear.

Large pine plantations are not a feature of the London Area. Pines, oaks and sweet chestnuts are associated at Black Park, and open birch and pine woods are found on the Bagshot Sands, as at Esher and Oxshott. There is almost no undergrowth in places, but where the pines are more openly spaced some scrub birch and even oak is springing up, and here are many willow warblers. With the pines the coal tit, goldcrest and tree creeper become more evident. The wood warbler occurs occasionally in pure pinewood but usually prefers some birch secondary growth. Cross-bills are scarce winter visitors to the mature pines and sometimes breed after "irruptions." Pure larch woods, with similar birds, occur sparingly as on Mickleham Downs.

Beech woods are frequent on the chalk of the North Downs between the Darent and Mole valleys. The beeches are very occasionally mixed with pines as at Cuckoo Wood, and with yew, box and sycamore about Norbury Park and Box Hill. They also grow locally on gravel, as in Epping Forest. There is one beech wood on Lower Greensand at Limps-field. Usually little or no secondary growth is present, the ground being covered with a thick persistent layer of dead leaves and perhaps moss and in autumn, beechmast. Where the canopy opens to admit sufficient light there may be a little grass. Wood warblers are characteristic of this habitat; they nest on the ground, feed in the canopy and sing much from the lower branches of the trees. Jays, hawfinches, chaffinches, bramblings nuthatches, marsh tits and woodpigeons all feed on the beechmast. During

Plate 13a. Richmond Park: the Pen Ponds

b. Richmond Park: many species, including redstart, jackdaw and kestrel, breed in the old oaks

C. B. As

Plate 14a. Perry Oaks sewage farm has been visited by thirty-three species of waders since the Second World War

b. Epsom sewage farm: an old-fashioned sewage bed much frequented by common and jack snipe

C. W. G. Pau

he colder months the yew is an attraction for the marsh and great tits, vhich carry off and open the seeds, and for blackbirds, mistle and song hrushes, which are fond of the fleshy red aril.

Of quite a different type are the lightly wooded heathlands of birch n sand or gravel. Situated largely south of the Thames, good examples 1ay be found on the commons and heaths at Headley, Wimbledon, Hayes, Ceston and Dartford, and also at Hampstead and Stanmore. Birch springs p in woods where the oaks have been felled, and patches may be found 1 localities like Epping Forest. Later, scrub oak may encroach on the irch woods and develop into oakwood. Where the trees are sparse, the ree pipit is conspicuous and nightjars may be found, but these birds are 1ore characteristic of commons with scattered trees. The secondary rowth, mainly of young birch, is thin. It is not surprising, therefore, that 1e two most frequent warblers are the willow and wood warblers, both f which nest on the ground. A few lesser redpolls are thinly scattered uring the breeding season but flocks are commonly seen in winter, often ith siskins, and feed on the catkins of the birches. Long-tailed tits, which re mainly birds of scrub, invade the woodland in flocks after having ested on the commons.

Oakwoods are the most important and widespread of the woodlands round London, as in the rest of lowland England. They are found mainly n clays and loams, e.g. London Clay and Woolwich beds, where the ominant tree is usually the pedunculate oak, although many others are resent including birch, hornbeam, sycamore and, to a lesser extent, beech nd ash. Good examples of the numerous oakwoods are at Broxbourne, Iadley, Ruislip, Stanmore, Ashtead and Bookham. Oak is mixed with irch at Harrow Weald, Whippendell and Darenth Woods. In Epping orest hornbeams are a conspicuous feature of the oakwoods, but hazel, hich is commonly mixed with the oaks south of the Thames, is relatively arce. The sessile oak is sometimes dominant on the sands or loams, as at ampstead Heath, Joyden's and Abbey Woods.

It is in the oakwoods that the richest variety of bird-life is found, and oubtless the reason lies in the variety of the trees and of the underlying getation. The secondary growth consists mainly of hazel, hawthorn, der, holly, ivy and saplings of the dominant trees. Bracken, bramble or uebells may dominate the ground vegetation. It must be admitted that ere is much to be learnt of the precise effect on the common birds of these fferent varieties of oakwood. We know, however, that the prevalence of ornbeams in Epping Forest is an attraction for hawfinches, which feed the fruit and were at one time so common that one observer found over hundred nests. They have also often been seen feeding below a small oup of hornbeams in Richmond Park. Where the woodlands are open and the trees are old with plenty of holes, redstarts may be found as in Epping and Hainault Forests. Open woodland with scattered birch and oak, such as Darenth Wood, is attractive to nightjars. Small numbers of woodcock find shelter in many woods, both damp and dry, but most of the few pairs that stay the summer are believed to be in the woods on the North Downs.

Tits are the predominant small birds of the woods. In oakwoods the blue tit is the most numerous, and in those at Bookham Common, for example, there are about twice as many as great tits in spring, and two or three times as many in winter. Some great and blue tits leave the woodlands in winter for the hedgerows and gardens. Whereas the blue tit feeds regularly in all vertical zones from herb layer to canopy, the great tit finds its food more commonly in the herb and shrub layers (Hartley, 1953). These two species form the bulk of the tit population in the spring but during August there is an immigration of long-tailed tits. The tit flocks begin to form in June and July and are composed largely of young birds of the year, many of the older blue and great tits appearing to retain their territories all the year round. Less frequent are marsh and coal tits, and the willow tit occurs thinly in damp woods. Nuthatches associate with the tit flocks in winter, together with treecreepers and goldcrests, while willow warblers may join them for a brief spell in the autumn. Treecreepers, nuthatches and, less frequently, goldcrests remain to nest.

Song thrushes are not characteristic of the dense woodland. They need an open feeding ground, preferably grassland, and thus occur mainly in open woodland or near the wood edge, many birds leaving the woods after the autumn berries have disappeared. Song thrushes have not acquired the blackbird's habit of turning over leaves in search of food, and their mortality is therefore higher when the ground is frozen. They are well outnumbered by blackbirds, the ratio of the two varying with the density of the woodland, being from two to ten blackbirds for every song thrush during the spring, and in the winter the proportion may be ten or even twenty to one (Nicholson, 1951). Spotted flycatchers frequent the open glades whereas the nightingales breed locally where there is dense undergrowth. The destruction of these thickets has doubtless been responsible for the retreat of the latter from the suburbs in recent years.

Blackcaps and garden warblers are characteristic of oakwoods, although the former seems to need tall song posts, afforded by canopy trees, whereas garden warblers may be satisfied with secondary growth for this purpose (Lack and Venables, 1939). Willow warblers are more numerous although really scrubland birds, and in the oakwood at Bookham Common are found to be more abundant where there is thicker hawthorn or hazel. On the other hand chiffchaffs occur much more sparingly there in spite of the presence of taller trees, which they like for song posts and feeding space. Bullfinches are widely distributed, and chaffinches breed in the dense oakwoods but leave them after the nesting season, returning in the following March (Beven, 1953).

Pheasants are still seen in the rural oakwoods and parks. Stock doves breed in holes in older trees, while woodpigeons nest in almost all the woods, greatly increasing in numbers there in the winter. The latter species feeds mainly on open ground, but when occurring in dense woodland keeps chiefly to the canopy (Colquhoun and Morley, 1943). Tawny owls occur where there are older trees with suitable holes for nesting. Both the green and greater spotted woodpeckers are found in all the more open types of woodland but the lesser spotted predominantly in broad-leaved woods. Jackdaws nest in tree holes but feed chiefly in open country. During May, however, many enter the forests to eat the moth caterpillars, which are then defoliating the oaks. This habit is shared by starlings which are not characteristic of woodlands at other seasons.

By way of summary, it is fair to say that London is surrounded by a variety of woods which, although typical of those of south-east England, may have been more modified by man than woods in other parts of the country. There is often a richer variety of trees, some of which are planted and others 'escapes' from gardens and parks. Nevertheless, so far as is known, the changes in the avifauna of these woods since 1900 do not seem to have been as great as might have been expected considering their proximity to the Metropolis.

Special references

BEVEN, G. (1953). Further observations on the Bird Population of an Oakwood in Surrey (Eastern Wood, Bookham Common). *L.N.*, 32 : 51-77.

COLQUHOUN, M. K. and MORLEY, A. (1943). Vertical Zonation in Woodland Bird Communities. *Journ. Anim. Ecol.*, xii : 75-81.

HARTLEY, P. H. T. (1953). An Ecological Study of the Feeding Habits of the English Titmice. *Journ. Anim. Ecol.*, 22 : 261–288.

LACK, D. (1948). Notes on the Ecology of the Robin. *Ibis, 90*: 252–279.

LACK, D. and VENABLES, L. S. V. (1939). Habitat Distribution of British Woodland Birds. *Journ. Anim. Ecol.*, 8 : 39–71.

NICHOLSON, E. M. (1951). Birds and Men. New Naturalist No. 17. London, Collins.

ROLLINGS, S. W. (1934). The Vegetation of Wimbledon Common. An Essay in Historical Ecology. *School Nature Study, 29* : 10–16.

AGRICULTURAL LAND

by H. F. Greenfield and W. D. Melluish

THIS CHAPTER is concerned with the birds of land devoted to any kind of agricultural crop, including grass, or under commercial horticultural crops, including orchards, and of any good-sized tract of rough grass that could be grazed whether it is or not.

Some idea of the proportion of our Area from which buildings have displaced agriculture has been given in the first chapter. When one remembers the alarming speed at which cultivable land disappeared under housing during the twenties and thirties, it is easy to underestimate the amount of land that remains in agriculture. It is, in fact, enormous. If inside our circle another is imagined at 15 miles from St. Paul's it will be found that at least seven-eighths of the belt between is used for agriculture or horticulture of some kind. Near Mill Hill a considerable acreage survives within ten miles of St. Paul's. In Middlesex, the only county wholly within our Area, there were, for example, in June, 1954, about 74,000 head of poultry, 29,000 pigs, 2,300 sheep, 7,000 cattle and 29,000 acres under crops and grass (Ministry of Agriculture returns). But in 1900 outside the ten-mile radius from St. Paul's agricultural land was interrupted only by villages and a few small towns, and a good deal remained within seven or eight miles of the centre. Middlesex returns for that year were: about 14,000 pigs, 20,000 sheep, 22,000 cattle and 112,000 acres under crops and grass, but at that time the statistics included the County of London, so the comparison is not exact.

The birds of agricultural land have never been so well watched as those of the reservoirs, sewage farms or London parks, but in recent years they have received more attention and two studies may be briefly mentioned as giving some indication of the bird population. In 1948–49 H. A. Bilby found 61 species in a census of some 618 acres in the Harlington district; the village area, including gardens, amounted to about 13%, orchards covered 12% and the remaining 75% was agricultural land mainly market gardening and under intensive cultivation. Of the 37 species which nested in 1949 all but eleven were found breeding in the orchards, and a total of 232 breeding pairs were identified, with a density of 3.8 pairs per ten acres. Near Mill Hill in 1938 Melluish made ten counts at roughly monthly intervals on about 64 acres of grassland forming part of a dairy farm; he found a population of some 41 species with a density varying from 2.5 to 19.1 birds per 10 acres, the average being 8.6 for the year. Counts at similar intervals carried out nine years later, after the war, showed how more intensive cultivation had affected the local bird population. By then about two-thirds of the ground had been ploughed and a rotation of crops sown, ditches had been cleared and hedges trimmed. The 1947 figures showed an increase, both in variety and strength, 48 species being observed with densities varying from 11.7 to 28.2 birds per ten acres and an average of 19.0. Of the additional species three were predatory, namely little owl, kestrel and sparrow hawk and the advent of arable fields had attracted black-headed, common and herring gulls, not previously recorded.

All common forms of agriculture and horticulture are practised in the London Area, except, of course, hill farming. Arable has to some extent replaced grass around London since 1939 owing to the drive for greater home food production, and in proportion to pasture there is probably more of it north than south of the Thames. Pasture in the Area varies as elsewhere, from fields of modern grass and clover strains to a few neglected meadows, sometimes waterlogged and abounding in coarse vegetation. Market gardening has almost certainly increased since 1900, and is practised mainly in a few north-eastern, south-eastern and western districts. Orchard and other fruit-growing as a sizeable commercial enterprise is concentrated in parts of Kent and West Middlesex, but on a smaller scale is more widespread in both suburbs and country.

At the present time, agricultural land in the London Area attracts about forty species of birds, which resort to ploughed land, stubble or pasture, rickyards and the vicinity of farm buildings mainly to feed, finding ample sustenance in the weeds, crops and their insect pests as well as in the small animal life that abounds in pastoral country. The strength of the considerable nesting population depends to some extent on the presence of hedges, small trees and buildings. These features are important, not only as song-posts and nesting sites, but also for the cover they afford birds against rough weather, raptors and other enemies. Among the hedgerows, especially those dignified by occasional trees, one finds nests of turtle dove, magpie, thrushes, wren, hedge sparrow, lesser whitethroat, yellowhammer, greenfinch and others which but for this shelter would probably not be attracted to breed on agricultural land. But, except in orchards, the density of birds is rather low during the breeding season compared with that of other wilder habitats such as waste land, scrublands and swamps or the more intensively tended parks and gardens. While some species may be found on farm land at all times of the year, others roam the fields only after the breeding season, or tend to confine their visits to grassland.

The bird life of arable land around London does not differ markedly from that of many other arable districts. In winter the flocks of finches and their kindred concentrate during the harder weather upon such spots as the surrounds of ricks and manure heaps or the sunny and sheltered ground adjoining hedges and woods. At harvest and for some time after, and when certain crops are sown, these species are more dispersed, though always in flocks however loose. The four commonest appear to be green-finch, linnet, chaffinch and house sparrow. There are fewer linnets in the London Area than in some parts of Southern England, but large flocks sometimes occur; for example, on arable, both 800 feet up in east Surrey and at a low elevation in west Middlesex. The brambling occurs with these composite flocks as well as with chaffinches only; as a rough general-isation, the poorer the beech-mast crop the more it is seen on arable land.

There is no evidence that these five species have much changed their numbers or habits on arable land since 1900. The tree sparrow, however, was reputed scarcer early in the century; the real difference may largely be in the number of observers able to distinguish it from the house sparrow. The two species often associate outside the breeding season, but many of the breeding haunts of the tree sparrow are amid pasture or in orchards or away from agricultural land as defined for this chapter.

The general distribution of the corn bunting is very patchy. In our area the bird's chief stronghold is on the Thames-side marshes, where it is found mainly on waste ground and rough grazing; in this environment it has extended its range considerably in recent years. On the Middlesex plain it is associated more with land cropped with cereals, clover or lucerne, but there are many fields of these without corn buntings. Although evidently more generally distributed earlier in the century, the species never seems to have been very common.

Several pasture-loving birds are of course also common on arable; the skylark and meadow pipit, especially in hard weather, are to be seen near, though seldom in, the mixed finch-bunting flocks; the yellow wagtail spends by no means all its time, while breeding or otherwise, on pasture; occasionally woodlarks and goldfinches occur on arable outside the breeding season.

The rook is a species very closely associated with cultivation, as grain forms an important part of its diet. Outward expansion of the Metropolis has greatly affected its distribution and one now has to look beyond the 10 mile circle to find a rookery of any size. For their feeding grounds rooks prefer the more open terrain and are seldom seen in small fields that are confined by hedges. When foraging on grassland or arable they are often joined by carrion crows, jackdaws, starlings and gulls.

The increase of ploughing in recent years has sometimes attracted lapwings to breed on newly furrowed land, but this is the very type of ground on which nesting is often unsuccessful because of farming operations, particularly harrowing. Such dangers are least on poor quality pasture and marginal land, where the shorter vegetation and lack of disturbance may materially assist the successful rearing of the young. A general decline in the numbers of lapwings in many districts is probably part of a much wider decrease due to a number of causes, and many stretches of plough which were once used regularly for nesting have now been abandoned. Around London this decline has probably been hastened by the dwindling of marginal land, particularly during and since the war.

In most rural districts there is an autumn influx of immigrant lapwings, and winter flocks are sometimes joined by golden plovers, whose habitats in our Area are (apart from sewage farms) more or less confined to extensive open fields, bare fallow or autumn-sown plough. One can now only find the golden plover regularly in a very few places, mostly north of the Thames, the largest concentration usually occurring on or near Radlett airfield, where there have been as many as 600 birds in a recent winter and 200–300 is not an exceptionally high count. Though the evidence is far from conclusive, the species was probably more widespread in the earlier years of the century.

Unlike the corncrake, whose loss is described elsewhere, both kinds of partridge have held their own during the half-century on such land as has remained truly agricultural; the red-legged is now and probably always was rather the fonder of arable. The quail, recorded more often since 1941 than in the rest of the century, bred near Rickmansworth in 1947 on a partly arable, partly grassland slope. In the Colne valley, as elsewhere, large numbers of herring gulls are sometimes seen on the plough in winter, but equally often they are on pasture. The common gull, on the other hand, though found on both, has perhaps a slight leaning towards pasture. The black-headed gull, so much commoner on agricultural and other land now than in 1900, is probably rather more often seen on arable than on grassland; its attractive habit of closely following the plough is well-known and unaffected by the general replacement of horses by tractors. There is ample evidence that gulls come inland more now than at the beginning of our period. To an ornithologist who walked the agricultural land of our Area in 1900 but not again till the fifties, this would be the most noticeable change in bird life. Nearly as noticeable would be the increase in the numbers of carrion crows and of the little owl, which was then a rarity.

In general, however, he would find the shrinkage of our agricultural land far more striking than the changes in bird life on that which remains.

The birds which prefer pasture, again, do not differ markedly from those of grassland in other lowland parts of England. Within a general liking for pasture, however, there are preferences, some very noticeable, for one kind of pasture over another.

The woodlark has recently become commoner and occurs on grazing land of the rougher kinds, but heath and downland are its major haunts. The whinchat and particularly the goldfinch need to be mentioned because not all pasture in our Area is kept to an ideal standard. Gold-finches in the breeding season are mainly garden and orchard birds with us, but at other times they have a patchy distribution, parties frequenting the grassland on which their favourite weeds grow. In certain districts, notably the Colne valley, are pieces of land interspersed with gravel pits, sewage-beds, refuse tips, etc., pieces which may not justify the cost of making them into good pasture. Here are many of our goldfinches in autumn and winter and some of our few whinchats in the breeding season.

Pasture which is rather damp as well as rough, for example Staines Moor or near the Thames estuary, is favoured by the yellow wagtail and the meadow pipit; while the spots chosen by our few breeding redshank and snipe (and occasional jack snipe in winter) are usually so damp that their agricultural value is small. The average standard of drainage of farm land has risen since 1939 and the records of the forties strongly suggest a fall in breeding numbers of both the last species. The redshank almost certainly did not breed in 1950 in so many places as are given in the summary of its status in the *London Bird Report* for 1939.

Good pasture—from the farmer's point of view—has a less varied bird life. The skylark, in our Area, is often found on it, so is the meadow pipit in winter and on passage, and the yellowhammer provided there are perches. In so far as they are birds of agricultural land and not of coppice, hedge and garden, the thrushes show some preference for the better over the poorer grassland; they also, of course, like bare plough.

The bird life of our horticultural land is of two widely differing kinds, that of orchards and that of ground under vegetable, flower and fruit crops. Where small fruit, flowers and shrubs are grown for sale, the bird life naturally resembles that of gardens. The commercial growing of vegetables may, according to its scale, attract either mostly garden or mostly field birds; extensive market gardens are arable land from a bird's standpoint and much the same species frequent them; if vegetables are allowed to seed or become weedy, linnets and goldfinches in particular are attracted.

Fruit trees, however, harbour a different selection of birds. Even when

C. B. Ashby

Plate 15a. The slurry pools on Stone Marshes are visited by many waders

b. The Thames at Dartford: there is little mud at low tide compared with the open estuary

C. B. Ashby

Plate 16a. One of the many chalk quarries in North Kent. (*C. Ashby*)

b. The steep south escarpment of the North Downs. (*C. B. Ashby*)

the trees are fairly young, properly sprayed and otherwise tended, birds more associated with woodland begin to haunt them, e.g. great and blue tit, bullfinch and hawfinch. As the trees mature these species increase; the goldfinch nests, in one district at least showing a preference for plum trees, and more birds characteristic of woods and otherwise incidental to agricultural land, such as magpies, woodpeckers, other tits and occasional treecreepers, come in. One or two of the last haunts of the wryneck have also been in such orchards.

It is not appropriate here to discuss the wide and relatively unknown subject of the good and harm birds do to agriculture. In any case there is no reason to suppose, for example, that the voracious woodpigeon is either more or less the farmer's foe in our Area than elsewhere. And whether or not all the insects a swallow eats are harmful to agriculture, it is sufficient to rejoice that our swallows do not appear to have been affected by modernisation of the buildings and the disappearance of the once familiar midden, and that a pair or more can still be found constant to most farmsteads each summer, when succeeding generations occupy their traditional nesting sites.

COMMONS, DOWNS AND PARKLAND
by R. C. Homes

WHEN DISCUSSING the birds of reservoirs and gravel-pits we were able to write of an expansion of the available territory and of the continued presence, and even increase, of aquatic birds, which are less affected than most by the spread of London. If we turn, however, to the commons, downs and parkland of our Area or, in other words, to the remnants of open land not used for agriculture, building or other development, we find that most of the typical species of such open, uncultivated country have decreased considerably.

The falling into disuse of commoners' rights has contributed largely to the transition of many of the true "commons" to scrubland, since the many grazing animals which formerly kept the grass reasonably short and checked the growth of the scrub are no longer to be found. As Peterken has written in the *London Naturalist* for 1952: " It is difficult, at times, to decide whether to describe a locality as heathland or mixed scrubland and our Area contains many examples of varied stages of this transition from heathland to scrub." Typically, the drier heaths are dominated by the common ling (*Calluna vulgaris*) or by the bell heather (*Erica cinerea*), while gorse (*Ulex europaeus*) is a conspicuous feature of the larger associated growth. Although this habitat still exists in several parts of Kent and Surrey it has suffered so greatly from heath fires, public trampling and the exigencies of the last war that no very extensive stretches remain in our Area. When the heather is replaced by bracken (*Pteridium aquilinum*) and rosebay willow-herb (*Chamaenerion angustifolium*) on the drier parts and by purple moor-grass (*Molinia caerulea*) on the damper soils as at Epsom and Esher Commons, a scattered growth of scrub, usually with birch and hawthorn predominant, appears and various stages of this transition are typical of large parts of many of the localities called "commons" on the map and which will be termed "scrubland" for our purpose. When the process has been continued for some years, the birch scrub may become an open wood with scattered oak trees or, at a later stage still, the oak may replace the birch as the dominant species and parts of the habitat become true woodland.

The tremendous growth of London in the first half of this century has involved the destruction of many habitats and it is inevitable that open stretches of uncultivated land should have borne a large share of the burden. Downland, in particular, has many features which make it suitable for surburban development and, even where the buildings are well spaced with large gardens, the damage is soon done so far as the bird communities of open land are concerned. At the same time many large estates have been surrendered to the builder with the consequence that open country has been replaced by rows or clusters of detached and semi-detached houses.

Building spread furthest and most rapidly in the late twenties and the thirties, when housing estates were multiplying fast. From an ornithological viewpoint the respite gained during the last war from the hands of the builder was offset by the results of the call for greater food production, and many of the surviving expanses of parkland, commons and heath came under the plough, some to be lost perhaps for good, others to degenerate in a few years into rough grassland. A countryside which in 1900 contained many small towns and villages separated by open ground still contained in 1950 many open spaces, but these were mostly surrounded by built-up areas and streaked by railways and arterial roads.

The gradual disappearance of the type of country we are considering was partly arrested by the foresight of the London County Council, through their sponsorship in 1935 of the conception of the Green Belt, which was given legal form three years later. Many places, not necessarily in public ownership, were to be permanently protected against building with the object of providing a barrier to the continuous expansion of London. The "belt" is chiefly at a radius of 13 to 15 miles from the centre of London, but, coupled with National Trust properties, includes some districts a few miles further out and embraces such well-known tracts of country as Cassiobury Park, Epping and Hainault Forests, Dartford Heath, Hayes and Wickham Commons, Selsdon Wood, Banstead and Epsom Downs, Banstead, Walton and Headley Heaths, Box Hill, Esher and Cobham Commons. Other stretches of downs and scrubland have been preserved as golf-courses, the effects of which are discussed later.

The importance of the Green Belt as a factor in helping to preserve what remains of the bird life cannot be overstressed; although parts of it have been sacrificed to the pressing post-war needs for housing development, it is still a safeguard against the more random extension of building and is especially important where the area preserved from development is sufficiently large to support several pairs of the more local species. The result of building in the past has often been to reduce the undeveloped country that remains to such small proportions that the scarcer species rapidly dwindle to numbers which are no longer large enough to withstand exceptional losses from other causes. Even where open spaces remain as yet undisturbed by building or agriculture, their nature and attractiveness to birds has changed greatly. Not only has the population of Greater London expanded alarmingly, but the enormous growth in the cult of the open air associated with the hiking movement in the early thirties resulted in much greater numbers of people tramping over the commons, downs and heaths around London. While this may well have been the origin of the greatly increased interest in natural history and nature conservation, it has undeniably been a disturbing factor to wild life. As Professor Abercrombie has said in his Greater London Plan, 1944: "Heaths and commons require equal care; they are much affected by intensity of use . . . but let their wildness be trampled underfoot and no chance given to regeneration and they become dreary wastes like Mitcham Common." Even though the cause in this particular case was as much wartime development and the use of part of the common as a corporation dump, the axiom is only too true.

The effect of all of the increased disturbance is most serious for those birds nesting on or very near the ground; nearly all the birds most characteristic of heaths and commons come into this category. They include such species as yellowhammer and reed bunting, skylark, meadow and tree pipits, whitethroats and chats, Dartford and grasshopper warblers and nightjar. Linnet, bullfinch, red-backed shrike, lesser whitethroat and turtle dove belong to the same community but usually nest at a slightly

safer height. Exceptions to the height of nesting may be fairly frequent
for yellowhammer and linnet in particular, but in general the distinction
holds good.

North of the Thames the Area has never within our period been so rich
in this type of habitat as the southern half, and Stanmore Common, for
example, is open woodland rather than heath or scrubland. At Ruislip
birds have had to contend with a great increase in human disturbance,
due in part to the construction of a lido at one end of Poor's Field. Among
the breeding species, the red-backed shrike, not being a ground nester, has
so far managed to survive, as it has also on similar land at Bentley Priory,
Stanmore and near Mill Hill. In spite of the disturbance the woodlark,
which has increased generally in recent years, has been gained here as at
several other open spaces, such as Epping and Hainault Forests, both of
which include considerable stretches of rough grassland. Apart from this
welcome gain, which may or may not be permanent, the story of the
ground-nesting birds north of the Thames is not a happy one, and grasshopper warbler, stonechat, whinchat and nightjar have all declined in
numbers.

In 1907 Kendall found the whinchat commonly north of Wembley
Park, and the red-backed shrike bred in the Kingsbury district. While
building would be quite sufficient explanation for their disappearance from
these parts, it does not explain why the meadow pipit a long time ago and
the whinchat quite recently have left other less disturbed districts, and
both species seem to breed much less plentifully than they once did in
south-east England. Doubtless reduction in the amount of waste ground
and the greater disturbance of such undeveloped districts as do remain are
contributory factors, while the stonechat which had established itself
locally on grassy railway embankments, possibly as a result of earlier
destruction of the more natural habitats, suffered disastrously from the
severe winter of 1946–47. It may be mentioned here that the winters of
the forties were much more severe than their predecessors, reversing a
trend towards milder conditions in northern Europe that has been
described by several writers.

In the forties also, increased ploughing-up during and after the war
contributed to the difficulties of the more local birds of the heaths and
scrubland community, and at Upminster Common, for example, linnet,
reed bunting, yellowhammer, red-backed shrike, stonechat and a few
warblers have suffered from this cause, although the skylark has been
unaffected by the change. Even when ploughing was abandoned the land
became covered with long grass and the vegetation has not yet reverted
to its original nature.

South of the Thames the same problem exists. No longer are there any

C. B. Ashby

b. Oxshott Heath showing natural regeneration in the pine wood

M. D. England

Plate 17a. Greater spotted woodpecker: a much increased species during this century.

C. B.

Plate 18a. Bookham Common: the oakwood, with secondary growth

b. The pollarded hornbeams of Epping Forest are a favourite haunt of redstarts and hawfinches

John Ma

extensive stretches of heather in our Area and, instead, bracken, purple moor-grass, or in drier places like Headley Heath rosebay willow-herb, cover the ground. Elsewhere birch scrub has steadily increased its hold, as on parts of Epsom and Arbrook Commons. On Walton Heath it was the severe winter of 1939-40 which sealed the fate of the Dartford warbler; now part of their former territory has fallen to the plough. Before the last war Walton Heath and Ashtead, Bookham and Epsom Commons between them supported a varied community containing reed buntings, stonechats, grasshopper warblers in good numbers, red-backed shrikes and nightjars, but even in the thirties the gorse was being eliminated by heath fires, and building development was stretching out over the fringes of Ashtead Common. With the advent of war 114 acres of Walton Heath, 111 acres of Epsom and 166 acres of Ashtead Common came under the plough, and now the stonechat has gone while only a few pairs of the other species remain. The decrease of gorse has been a serious factor in many other localities, notably for stonechat, linnet and yellow-hammer.

Wimbledon Common deserves special reference not only because of its extent and proximity to London but also because it embraces a mixture of heathland and grass heath, which despite much trampling still shelters several pairs of woodlarks, and such typical species as yellowhammer, sky-lark and meadow and tree pipits, while in the thirties even the Dartford warbler succeeded in breeding. In its mixed birch woods where the tran-sition to the climatic climax is more advanced, hawfinch, wood warbler and sparrow hawk have all bred in recent years. It is regrettable that this extensive common, with the adjoining Putney Heath, is being increasingly affected by the development by public authorities of housing estates on sites facing the common which were once privately owned, with the con-sequent threat of much greater disturbance. At the time of writing, clearance of undergrowth and the filling-in of ponds and gravel pits is unfortunately still proceeding under official supervision, and inevitable though this tidying-up process may be in some places, it recalls the fears of Professor Abercrombie mentioned earlier in this chapter.

The value of bracken, in particular, in providing nesting cover to such species as stonechat, whinchat, woodlark, tree and meadow pipits, and yellow and reed buntings has been stressed by Collenette when writing of Richmond Park (L.N. for 1936, p. 44). In the early spring before the new shoots have grown to any height, withered fronds of the previous year provide not only nesting sites but also that small element of protection from trampling that allows birds some chance of breeding success even on ground open to the public. Where bracken, however, becomes too extensive, as has been the tendency on some of the commons, it ceases to attract birds and results in a decline in those species which nest on or near the ground.

On the Kent commons of Chislehurst, Hayes and Keston there has been a reduction in the amount of gorse, heather, short grass and even bracken to the advantage of birch scrub, while as in Surrey and north of the Thames the few remaining stretches of open, uncultivated country are much isolated by building, so that re-colonisation by lost species is made more difficult. Stonechat and whinchat have gone, red-backed shrike and nightjar remain in reduced numbers, and skylark and meadow pipit both suffer from the change from heath to birch scrub.

Although in general the commoner birds of scrub and wood benefit at the expense of those of more open country, it is remarkable that, for some other reason unknown, the woodlark has increased and spread in recent years in spite of being a ground-nesting species. Many of the barer open spaces were transformed by wartime activities and on Blackheath, for example, several pairs of yellow wagtails were breeding in 1947, after which their breeding ground was converted to football pitches and speed-way tracks, while in 1946 two pairs of wheatears nested there, for the first time in the London Area since 1930.

The reluctance of birds to abandon traditional haunts has been well illustrated at Mitcham Common, where stonechats held on as long as any-where and several pairs of red-backed shrikes still breed despite consider-able disturbance, especially from bird's-nesting boys. In the last few winters up to three short-eared owls have frequented the common, which retains an extensive area of scrub that has several times been visited by great grey shrikes, birds which at this season are seen with some frequency on a few of the heaths and downs remaining. Nomadic parties of redpolls and sometimes siskins, occur on the birch-clad commons. Redpolls breed spasmodically on the heaths but are associated in spring just as much with the large private gardens that often adjoin heathland, as at Oxted and Limpsfield.

So far we have discussed the outer commons and heaths, while the parks of central London have already been fully treated in the chapter on Inner London. There remain the inner open spaces which deserve some mention even though their birds are now more typical of a suburban bird community. The best known of these open spaces is Hampstead Heath the southern end of which is less than four miles from Charing Cross Once the resort of bird-catchers, it was sufficiently unspoilt in the early part of the century to have nightjars breeding regularly until about 191 and as recently as 1954 no fewer than 89 species were seen. Although it ha now lost as residents most of the species we are considering in this chapter in recent years a pair of skylarks bred on the derelict gun-site from 194 to 1952 and a pair of yellow wagtails in 1952. Tree pipits, suspected of breeding in several previous years, definitely did so in 1954, when there were also five singing yellowhammers although there was no proof of nesting. Among the more unusual visitors to the Heath in the last few years have been white-fronted goose, buzzard, short-eared owl, hooded crow and ring ouzel, while intensive watching in recent years has revealed the breeding of a pair of swallows in an old deer-shed in Golders Hill Park in 1952 and of redstarts in Ken Wood in 1954.

Although this chapter is not primarily concerned with woodland birds we cannot leave the Heath and Ken Wood without mentioning that about twelve pairs of blackcaps, five of whitethroats and eight of chiffchaffs still breed so close to the centre of London. Garden warblers, for some reason not clear, disappeared after 1950, lesser whitethroats which bred annually until 1946 have since nested only erratically, while a pair of wood warblers bred again in 1951 and 1954 after regular nesting had ceased some years previously.

Another open space in the inner suburbs, Wormwood Scrubs, has received little attention from ornithologists, but up to 46 skylarks were feeding there in the winter of 1950, only some five miles from Charing Cross. There were twelve there throughout the season of 1951 and young were seen. Yellow wagtails were breeding in 1950, where there were 4–5 pairs, and also in 1951. Two partridges were present in April and June of that year and at the end of September there were seven.

Many of the inner 'Commons' south of the Thames have suffered greatly from the clearance of undergrowth and the encroachment of building on the surrounding playing fields and allotments. Now most of them resemble open parkland with short grass, and are much disturbed. On Wandsworth Common, for example, about 4½ miles from Charing Cross, linnets, skylarks and meadow pipits, which were all breeding in the late twenties, have now disappeared although at least one pair of linnets was nesting as recently as 1948 in the grounds of the nearby Springfield Hospital. Tree pipits also bred on the adjacent Furzedown until 1906, about which time skylarks were nesting on all the larger fields around Tooting. While the ground-nesting birds have gone, and also the large colony of rooks which left Burntwood Lane about the time of World War I, willow warblers and an occasional pair of whitethroats still breed at the time of writing. The other nesting birds of the district are now those typical of the suburbs which are discussed elsewhere.

Downland is absent from our region north of the Thames, as the twenty mile radius does not reach the Chilterns, but to the south there were formerly extensive open chalk downs as near London as Croydon. The downs nearest to London, as at Waddon, Purley and Sanderstead, which were once expanses of rolling grassland with rough hedges and hawthorn scrub, are now largely built on, although some open stretches have been saved from the builder by golfing interests. They may then retain ground nesting birds, such as skylarks and meadow pipits, while on some golf courses woodlarks seem to find the close-cut "fairway" for feeding and the "rough" for nesting an attractive combination. A few species like red-backed shrike and linnet may nest in the scattered bushes, but the courses are usually too much trampled over for the more local stonechat and whinchat. Just as birch has dominated many of the commons, so it has spread on some of the lower downs, and Park Downs, Banstead, which had few trees of any kind early in the century, now have a copse of birch with a few oaks and beeches; wheatears have gone and tree pipits increased. A decline in undergrowth, here as in other places where local councils have decided to "improve" their districts, has resulted in the loss of the nightingale, blackcap and other birds requiring low cover.

On the relatively narrow summits of the North Downs there has been less change, for there is no proof that within our period stone curlews or hobbies have been residents although the latter is sometimes associated elsewhere with clumps of trees on downland. Wheatears, however, did breed in limited numbers in several places but have now long since disappeared except as passage migrants. The birds went before the increased disturbance became pronounced, and all the chats have declined in our Area, in common with a general decrease in south-east England. On the other hand, magpies and little owls have increased enormously, and the former is now especially numerous on the slopes of the downs. The increase of the magpie and of the carrion crow and jay may be a contributory factor in the decline of ground-nesting species. Within this century another of the Corvidae, the hooded crow, formerly a common winter visitor to the downs, has vanished except as a vagrant.

Generally speaking, on our part of the North Downs the extent of open ground which is not devoted to agriculture allows no comparison with the much more spacious South Downs, and it is the heathland on the northern dip slope that is of more ornithological importance. Nevertheless, it was at the foot of one of the steeper escarpments that a few pairs of cirl buntings were found with most certainty in our Area, while in the chalk quarries large colonies of jackdaws and stock doves have long been established. On both the agricultural southern slopes and the fringes of the heath on the northern side flocks of finches and yellowhammers are conspicuous in winter.

Of the undeveloped country under discussion only parkland remains to be considered, and this it is sometimes difficult to define. Characteristically, however, there is an almost complete absence of scrub, bushes or other undergrowth, as a result of grazing by animals or regular clearance by man, but groups of old trees are well spaced out in a pastoral setting, thus differentiating it from ordinary grazing land. Typical species include jackdaws, tree pipits, nuthatches, mistle thrushes, woodpeckers, tawny and little owls, stock doves and, more locally, redstarts. In Essex, where so much of the land is devoted to agriculture, the parks of South Weald, Thorndon and Navestock, for example, introduce a pleasant change in the landscape and attract a different fauna partly because of the ornamental lake so often found within the boundaries of such estates. These parks have shared in the general increase of the woodlark, which until recently was almost unknown in Essex, but some other typical birds of parkland such as nuthatch and nightjar are not numerous.

The effect of the Inner London parks has already been discussed. It is impossible in a limited space to mention all the other parks of interest but probably the most famous within our boundary is the Royal Park at Richmond, extending to well over two thousand acres and including several enclosed wooded sanctuaries amidst undulating grassland with clumps of venerable oaks. Here a few pairs of woodlarks were resident long before they became more widely distributed, and four or five pairs were breeding in 1950. Several ground-nesting species, such as tree pipit, reed bunting, stonechat and whinchat were all at one time a feature, and even wheatears bred in the early years of the century. Now, with the increased popular use of the park, the chats have gone, though the other two species remain and those associated with old trees, such as the nuthatch, redstart, woodpeckers, owls and kestrel, all continue to flourish. In one of the sanctuaries there was for many years a successful heronry which in 1939 contained 61 nests; unfortunately, disturbance during the ensuing war drove away many of the birds and in the last ten years or so there have never been more than 23 nests. Similarly, on the nearby Ham Common woodlarks have come and reed buntings persist, but stonechats and whinchats have both vanished. As in many other districts close to London magpies have appeared recently and carrion crows and jays have increased.

MIGRATION
by E. R. Parrinder

THE SPREAD of London has had a disastrous effect upon many of the resident birds but, paradoxically, the concomitants of the growth have made the Area one of the best in Britain, away from the coast, for watching bird migration. The necessity of providing the human population with water, and disposing of its sewage, has led to the creation of artificial sanctuaries where migrants, especially ducks and waders, can break their journey to rest and feed. There can be no doubt that but for the reservoirs and sewage farms most of these birds would pass over.

The purpose of this chapter is to discuss the kinds of movement which can be seen in London and the influence of the natural and man-made refuges which make the existence of such movements apparent. In general, only those birds which appear every year, in spring, autumn or winter, are mentioned, although London receives its share of irregular visitors and vagrants—the occurrences of these occasional migrants are detailed in the specific notes.

Our knowledge of migration in London, as elsewhere, comes from three main sources: from the direct observation of migrating flocks (now known as visible migration), from the observation of seasonal changes in the bird population and from the recoveries of ringed birds. The first well documented account of visible migration in the Area, or indeed from any inland part of Britain, was that of F. D. Power who, between 1874 and 1909, watched from a suburban garden in Brixton, less than five miles from the centre and well built-up even in those days. Power recorded that on fair mornings in the second half of October, especially after one or two days of WNW. wind, flock after flock, varying in size from half a dozen birds to upwards of fifty, would pass over his garden in a westerly direction, usually between 7.30 a.m. and 10.30 a.m. Chaffinches exceeded all the other species put together and next to them in numbers were larks, starlings, rooks, greenfinches and bramblings. Power emphasised many times that these huge migrations were only visible with westerly, especially north-westerly, winds, although he gave some evidence of chaffinches flying so high as to be almost out of sight when the ground wind was from the east or south-east.

It is a curious fact that visible migration over the built-up areas on this scale was not recorded again until near the end of our period; indeed there are very few notes even of small-scale movements until the late 1920's. It is not suggested that diurnal migration did not take place over London in the interval, but no one seems to have had the interest and persistence of Power to look up in the sky in the early hours of October mornings, when the wind was blowing from the north-west. In October, 1925, Professor E. H. Warmington saw two small parties of chaffinches flying over central London and in the next two or three autumns occasional flocks of chaffinches, meadow pipits and skylarks were recorded flying over the central parks, mostly in a westerly direction. In 1948, W. G. Teagle noticed a pronounced north-westerly migration of chaffinches over the Green Park, St. James's Park and Kensington Gardens between October 6th and November 3rd. The peak was in the second half of October, 525 birds being counted in half an hour on October 15th and about 330 in the same period on October 20th.

In the following year, L. Baker and E. R. Parrinder began an intensive watch for visible migration from a roof-top in Trafalgar Square and from then onwards London ornithologists once more became aware of the vast autumnal movements that Power had described, half a century earlier. Since 1949, simultaneous watches have been kept in most autumns from points in the centre and in the inner and outer suburbs on both sides of the Thames. These observations have confirmed those of Power with some interesting differences.

It is now clear that the visible migration is on a broad front, although of some species, notably the starling and the chaffinch, larger numbers are sometimes seen on migration over the centre of London than over the outskirts; it is probable that the general direction of the Thames valley is followed, but there is no indication that any of the flocks keep closely to its winding course. Power's statement that with easterly winds the movement was scarcely, if at all, noticeable remains broadly true for the finches, but starlings are now seen with the wind in almost any direction and skylarks have been more frequently observed with easterly than with westerly winds. On fair, cloudless days with light, easterly winds, flocks of chaffinches, recognised by their characteristic flight, have been seen over Trafalgar Square at so great a height as to be almost out of view; Deelder (*Ardea*, 37: 1–88) has shown that in such conditions chaffinches emigrate at a great height from the Dutch coast. The effect of Continental weather conditions on migration over London has yet to be studied and might give valuable indications of the origin of our visitors.

It is difficult to compare the numbers of each species seen by Power, in thirty-five years of watching, with those seen in the last few years. Continuous north-westerly winds, which Power insisted produced the best visible migration, have been conspicuously absent in recent Octobers. But chaffinches still seem to be most numerous, although starlings, which were third on Power's list, are close behind. The peak figure for chaffinches was obtained on October 14th, 1950, when 715 were counted passing over Trafalgar Square in two and a half hours. They flew low over the rooftops in small parties of up to 40 birds and nearly all were heading west or just north of west. Starlings appear to travel in larger parties and there were three flocks of over 100 in a total of 741 counted in just under two hours on November 3rd, 1951.

Of the other finches, small numbers of bramblings and greenfinches, separately or accompanying the chaffinches, have been seen on the days of heavy migration and a few goldfinches have also occurred. Next to chaffinches and starlings, the most frequently observed day migrants over London, apart from hirundines and swifts, are meadow pipits and sky-larks. Meadow pipits arrive early, towards the end of September, and their migration continues intermittently throughout October to early November. Although meadow pipits are also seen on a broad front, the maximum figures in recent years (114 in two hours past the Albert Bridge and 346 in one hour at Swanscombe) suggest that they may prefer to follow the Thames. Power did not observe large scale movements of either meadow pipits or skylarks in this century but he refers to great migrations of skylarks in the 1880's and 1890's. Only relatively small numbers of either species have been seen in recent autumns, but it may be that the weather conditions have not been suitable for seeing larger migration— at least on the days when watch has been kept.

The most striking apparent change in the pattern of visible migration over London since Power's day is in the movements of the Corvidae, especially rooks, and woodpigeons. Of rooks, Power wrote: "Large immi-grant flocks are to be seen in most years in October; they take the same route as other winter visitors, viz., WNW., and, like them, seem to require the wind to be blowing from that quarter". Jackdaws were sometimes seen with the rooks and in October, 1909, 700 passed over the Brixton garden. Eagle Clarke, in *Studies in Bird Migration*, mentioned rooks among the species taking part in a vast migration which he saw over Bermondsey on October 22nd, 1896—a day when, according to Power's records, the wind was NE. to NW. In recent years the only records of rooks over central London have been a flock of 50, with 250 jackdaws, flying NW. over Bloomsbury on October 12th, 1952, when the wind was NE., and six over the same place on October 25th, flying SW. with the wind.

Power did not mention the passage of woodpigeons, but recent observations from the rooftops of central London have disclosed a considerable autumnal movement. On October 21st, 1950, for example, ten flocks, totalling 266 birds, were counted over Trafalgar Square in just over an hour; on the same morning, 450 passed over Finchley and 1094, in about a dozen flocks, over Epping Forest. Large movements were also seen in November, 1951, and November, 1952. Most of the flocks were flying in a westerly direction, but some parties flew NE. or even SSE. The reasons for these contrary movements and whether they link up with the movements which are known to take place on the coasts of Sussex and East Anglia requires further study.

Among other species which have been observed flying over the built-up areas, regularly but in smaller numbers, are pied and grey wagtails, and lapwings. Both wagtails have been seen most frequently from points near the Thames and it is probable that they follow the river. The movements of the lapwing are too complex to be discussed here in detail. Power only had three autumn records of their migration over Brixton and there have not been many more in recent times. There is a fair amount of visual evidence, however, of the mid-summer lapwing movements, apparently originating on the Continent, mentioned by Spencer in *The Lapwing in Britain* (1953). Power gave two examples of movements in June and July and a number of observers since have noted similar passages; in 1943, for example, K. E. Hoy noted that in June and July of that year, as in the two previous years, there was a marked westward migration of lapwings over Epping Forest. The recovery in North London in August of a lapwing ringed as a young bird in Northern Bohemia three months earlier is an interesting indication of the distance which these mid-summer migrants may have travelled.

The movements so far described have been those which can be seen every autumn, if the weather here, and presumably on the Continent also, is favourable. There is little doubt that most of the visible migration is on a front at least as broad as the London Area and the fact that it has been recorded more often in the built-up than in the rural districts is because flocks, or even single birds, going over streets and rooftops are more obviously on migration than those over fields and woods. More co-ordinated watching, in this country and abroad, will need to be done before we can be certain of the origin of the migrating flocks or of the distance which they have travelled on the morning of their arrival over London. But as the standard direction is westerly it is evident that the movements are a continuation of the westerly movements in the Thames Estuary, first described by Eagle Clarke in his classic *Studies in Bird Migration* (1912). The passage over London normally begins at about one hour after first light and continues for about two hours: the peak is certainly not later than the peak arrival time at the North Foreland (about 70 miles to the east) given by Dr. Lack in his paper on "Visible Migration in 1952" (*B.B., 47:* 1–15). It seems likely, therefore, that the flocks seen over London have not flown direct from the Continent but have made their landfall earlier, perhaps on the previous day. The final destination of the migrating flocks is not yet known, but Dr. Snow has shown (*Ibis, 95:* 242–270) that there is a fairly general westerly or south-westerly movement of diurnal migrants across southern England in the autumn and at least some of the birds continue on to Ireland.

It might be expected that a return movement of winter visitors would be visible over London in the spring, but, in fact, very little has been recorded, either by Power in his 35 years of watching or in more recent times. It may be that the birds return by a different route or that such small numbers are involved that they pass unnoticed.

The most easily observed of all aerial migration over London, as elsewhere, is the great passage of hirundines and swifts which occurs each spring and autumn. The movements are not confined to the early hours but often continue all day. They extend over a longer period than for other day migrants and the directions taken are different from those of the winter visitors.

In the spring from mid-March to the end of May or early June, and in the autumn from July until October, parties of swallows, martins and sand martins can be seen on passage from anywhere in the Area, including the heavily built-up centre. The movement is on a broad front, although there is evidence that the courses of such rivers as the Thames, Lea and Colne are followed where they are parallel, or nearly so, to the standard direction. The migrations of hirundines are notoriously complex and subject to the wind and weather and it is not possible to analyse here the many varied directions of flight which have been recorded. Over most parts of the Area by far the greatest numbers travel, as they did in Power's day, in a north or north-westerly direction in the spring and in a southerly direction in the autumn. The notable exception is on the Thames marshes below London where the passage appears to be westerly on both migrations and it is presumably a continuation of the westerly movements up the Thames Estuary (Gillham and Homes, 1950). Although there are a few records of westerly movement across London, mostly in the autumn, it is clear that most of the vast numbers which come up the Thames must turn off before reaching London, but the only direct evidence of where this may occur comes from J. F. Burton who has seen swallows, in autumn, flying south on reaching the Darent. Apart from its shorter duration, the migration of swifts follows a very similar pattern to that of the hirundines, including the westerly movements in the lower Thames.

The visible passage of diurnal migrants has been described in some detail because, apart from the invaluable observations of Power, comparatively little was known about it until recent times and there are still many gaps to be filled in. But, of course, by far the greatest number of birds migrate at night; their movements are invisible, but the calls of such species as redwing, curlew and even ducks may at times be heard coming from the night sky, even over the heart of London. Evidence of the vast movements in progress is provided by the changes which take place in the bird population. In the spring the main changes are the return of the summer visitors and the passage through the Area of birds on their way farther north; in the autumn the disappearance of the summer residents, the southerly movements of the passage migrants and the immigration of winter visitors.

The return of the summer residents is as undramatic, yet full of the auguries of summer, as it is elsewhere in the country. Cuckoo, chiffchaff, blackcap and garden warbler all appear in their accustomed haunts and we can only guess that the last part of the journey was a steady, bush to bush, movement up from the coast rather than a direct approach in the night.

The spring passage cannot compare with the autumn for the variety of species nor for the number of individuals taking part; it is more hurried and those birds which pause to rest and feed in the London Area do not stay so long as they do in the autumn. As a consequence, there is less opportunity for the "week-end" ornithologist to see birds which arrive, and probably also depart, during the week. Nevertheless, even that part of the spring passage which is observed at the week-ends is by no means inconsiderable.

In the spring, as in the autumn, the man-made reservoirs, gravel pits and sewage farms, all necessary adjuncts of a great city, provide quiet resting, feeding and roosting places for passage migrants. These artificial sanctuaries are mainly grouped in the river valleys of the Thames, Colne and Lea, but there is one small area which is especially favoured, both by the bird and the bird-watcher. This is the corner of Middlesex just south-west of London Airport which contains two vast reservoirs, three or four flooded gravel pits, an area of water meadows and one of the best sewage farms, ornithologically, in the country. A walk through this area on almost any day from mid-March to the end of May is certain, so far as anything is certain in the study of migration, to produce evidence of the great movements which are taking place. In the latter half of May, 1950, for example, a walk on one or two days would have produced white wagtails, a Sandwich tern at Poyle gravel pits, two black-tailed godwits, a greenshank and both common and green sandpipers on Staines Moor, up to 16 sanderlings (some in summer plumage) and a great flock of 120 black terns at Staines reservoirs, while at Perry Oaks sewage farm there were shelduck, ringed plovers, a turnstone, more common and green sandpipers, half a dozen dunlin and a ruff. The spring passage of black terns in 1950 was unusually heavy, small and large flocks being recorded from all over the Area between May 11th and 24th; the numbers at Staines were the highest in the country.

All the waders mentioned above, except the black-tailed godwit, are regular spring passage migrants to the Area, although usually in smaller numbers than in the autumn. Even the black-tailed godwit is not so uncommon as it was and birds were seen in the Area in four springs in the years 1947–52. Curlew and whimbrel are regularly seen flying over, or heard calling at night. Wood sandpiper, spotted redshank, knot and little stint all occur occasionally but the better time for seeing these and the rarer waders is the autumn.

Black and common/arctic terns occur regularly on the spring passage, principally at the larger reservoirs, although single birds or small parties have been seen at many of the smaller waters. In some springs exceptional movements occur in the London Area as well as in other parts of Britain. Recently, there were big spring passages of black terns in 1946 and in the three years 1948–50, and of common and especially arctic terns in 1947.

The through passage movements of passerines are less easy to observe than those of waders and terns because in the country areas it may be impossible, unless there is a large concentration, to distinguish the itinerant birds from the residents. It is here that London bird-watchers have an especial advantage because although the heavily built-up districts are by no means avian deserts, as the chapter on Inner London has shown, the number of species which nest there is small and strangers are easily observed. Moreover, the sheer size of the conurbation means that the oases of park or bombed site, are perhaps more likely to be visited than similar areas in smaller cities, beyond which the birds can see. So we have the paradox that our knowledge of migration through London would be considerably poorer were it not for the vast agglomeration of bricks and mortar.

A keen observer in the spring of 1950 could have seen (or heard), by visiting the most likely places in the quieter periods of each day, wheatears and whinchats in the bombed areas of the City, a redstart in the Kennington Road and another in Kensington Gardens, a nightingale in Regent's Park, sedge warbler, blackcap, garden warbler, whitethroat and wood warbler in one or other of the Royal Parks, a tree pipit in the College garden of Westminster Abbey and pied, grey and yellow wagtails in the City. All the warblers which nest in Britain, except the grasshopper and Dartford

warblers, have been recorded in the spring from Inner London. The ones
mentioned above are fairly regular, as are willow warbler, chiffchaff and
lesser whitethroat. Even the sedge warbler is occasionally heard singing
by the edges of the park lakes and until 1928 the reed warbler appeared
in Kensington Gardens in most springs—since then it has become much
rarer. Despite almost annual reports in the press, the nightingale is uncommon in the centre and the one in 1950 was the only proved occurrence
in recent years.

In London, as elsewhere, the return movements of many species begin
in late June, almost before the spring passage is over. In July redshank,
dunlin, green and common sandpipers and other waders begin to arrive
at the reservoirs and sewage farms. But the evidence of migration which
can be seen in July is a trickle compared with the flood in August and
September. Far more birds, and more species, are involved than in the
spring; the movement is much less hurried and individuals may stay days
or even weeks before passing on. As a general rule, the peak periods
lie between mid-August and the third week of September and between
these dates London bird-watchers see much more evidence of migration
than in most other inland districts—and more than on many coastal
marshes.

The account which follows of the autumn passage through London is
largely based upon observations made over the last 25 years; prior to this
much smaller numbers were recorded, even of many of the commoner
species, while other species which are now regular were recorded only
rarely, if at all. It seems likely that most of these differences are due to the
great increase of bird-watchers rather than to changes in migration habits
—but this subject is discussed more fully in the introduction to the waders
section of the specific notes on pages 169-70.

To begin with the grebes; it is probable that the flocks of dabchicks
which assemble on certain of the shallower reservoirs, and of great crested
grebes on the larger deeper reservoirs, consist of birds on passage. Of the
rarer grebes, only the black-necked appears with unfailing regularity; the
increase in its numbers in the last decade, both on passage and in the
winter, is certainly genuine because its main strongholds, the reservoirs
at Staines and Hendon, have always been well watched.

The cormorant is another species which has increased on migration in
recent years. It is now seen in the autumn and winter on the Thames
below Dartford Creek and above Kew and on most of the reservoirs and
larger gravel pits; migrating flights are sometimes recorded—for example,
two small parties flew over Staines reservoirs on September 16th, 1950,
and flocks of 20 were seen on the next day and on September 19th.

The movements of the ducks have been fully described in the specific notes and in the chapter on the reservoirs; the species whose passage migration can regularly be separated from the arrival of winter visitors are teal, garganey, shoveler, pochard and, less frequently, shelduck. All of these can be seen at the reservoirs, especially Staines, while teal and garganey also occur at the sewage farms and by marshy rivers, as on Staines Moor, and pochard are frequently seen at the larger gravel pits.

In an area as built-up as London it is not to be expected that much will be seen in autumn of the passage of birds of prey. Buzzards are not infrequently reported, however, especially over Epping Forest and the North Downs. Peregrines and merlins also occur fairly regularly; the fact that peregrines are not infrequently seen in Inner London is presumably a reflection of their predilection for pigeons—they have been seen to attack the pigeons outside St. Paul's, in the Tower and elsewhere. It is probable that kestrels and sparrow hawks also pass through but it is impossible to tell genuine migrants from dispersing local birds.

Perhaps the most exciting evidence of migration through London is the autumn passage of waders. Most of the 25 or so species which regularly visit the Area are likely to come down at any place which has a semblance of their normal feeding habitat, but they will not stay unless there is a tolerable freedom from disturbance. Thus, although about 15 kinds of wader have occurred in Inner London at one time or another, very few have been seen on more than one day and only one, the common sandpiper, is at all regular. But many of the reservoirs, gravel pits and sewage farms, as well as the remnants of the Thames marshes and foreshore, do provide the essential requirements—water with a feeding margin, preferably muddy and with some vegetation as cover, and sanctuary from shooters—which enable individuals to stay until the migratory urge moves them on.

It is evident, from the records, that much of the wader movement through the Area is on a broad front, as it is in other inland districts of England. To take the greenshank as a random example, over the years 1948–1952 inclusive it was recorded in the autumn from three parts of the Thames marshes, from four reservoirs, two sewage farms and two gravel pits in the Thames and Lea valleys and from five other localities close to the Thames—including Kensington Gardens. But in the same period it was also reported from ten scattered places as far away from the Thames as Watford and Hainault in the north and Beddington in the south. Moreover, the birds which give the loudest and most familiar calls, especially curlew, whimbrel, dunlin, redshank and greenshank, have frequently been heard at night passing over districts as far apart as Mill Hill, Harold Wood and Caterham. Glegg, in his paper on " The Thames as a Bird Migration Route" (*London Nat.* for 1928) conceded that there was some degree of over land migration of waders but suggested that "so many interesting birds would not have been seen had it not been for the fact that the reservoirs are contiguous to the river". Except perhaps for the common sandpiper, however, there is no evidence that any waders regularly follow the Thames. The fact is that most of the reservoirs and gravel pits are, of necessity contiguous to either the Thames or the Lea but those which are not, as at Ruislip, Aldenham and Hendon, are still attractive to waders and were more so before boating was allowed. The sewage farms at Edmonton, Brooklands and elsewhere, well away from the Thames, were famous haunts of waders before they were made unsuitable. Another pointer to the suggestion that abundant food and freedom from disturbance are more important than closeness to the Thames is the fact, discussed in the reservoir chapter, that the numbers and variety of passage waders always increase when the water level of a reservoir is lowered and a greater feeding area exposed.

Although it is worth looking for waders in the autumn by any stretch of water with a feeding edge, the largest numbers are seen, as in the spring, in S.W. Middlesex, especially at the Staines reservoirs and Perry Oaks sewage farm. In the autumn of 1950, for example, green and common sandpipers, one or two greenshanks, up to 17 little stints, 20–30 dunlin, up to 17 curlew sandpipers and a maximum of 12 ruffs could be seen at Perry Oaks throughout August and September. Ringed plovers, in flocks totalling 45–60, were recorded between August 20th and September 8th. In the same two months the farm was visited by a few turnstones, wood sandpipers and sanderlings and by a black-tailed godwit, a pectoral sandpiper and a Baird's sandpiper. These last two American birds were apparently brought in by westerly gales which seem also to have been responsible for the appearance, in the same third week of September, of grey phalaropes at the Brent and King George VI reservoirs and of two Sabine's gulls at the old reservoirs at Staines.

These rarities do not, of course, occur every autumn but the almost daily watch which is now kept at some of the reservoirs and sewage farms in the Area has increased the chance of unusual birds being observed— pectoral sandpipers were seen again in 1951 and 1952, and in 1953 a lesser yellowlegs and a buff-breasted sandpiper turned up at Perry Oaks and both stayed long enough for every interested London ornithologist to see them. Even waders with such specialised habitats as the dotterel and stone curlew are occasionally to be seen in London. A flock of ten dotterel was found on the gravelly edge of London Airport on August 26th, 1950. Stone curlew are most likely to occur on downland or on such open spaces as Richmond Park, but in 1952 one was picked up in a children's sand-pit at Kilburn—an extraordinary example of a bird's capacity to find even the smallest patch of ground less unfamiliar than streets and pavements.

With the great increase of watchers it is now becoming clearer that the passage of waders, and of other species, takes place as a series of waves, or wavelets, rather than as a continuous stream. The movements of ruffs in the years 1950 and 1951 illustrate this and also that the incidence of the movements is not constant from year to year. In 1950, the autumn passage of ruffs began on July 9th with two at Hamper Mill and two at Perry Oaks. No more were seen until August 8th when up to three were at Perry Oaks for two weeks. A larger wave, with a maximum of 12, occurred between August 26th and 30th and then up to nine (not necessarily the same birds) were seen during all September and up to October 9th. In 1951, no ruffs were seen until August 17th and then only single birds until the end of the month. In the first three weeks of September, however, parties of up to six were at Perry Oaks and up to 12 at Ponders End sewage farm, in the Lea valley. Thereafter, only one or two were seen at irregular intervals until the passage ended about October 21st.

Not only do the peak periods of wader migration through London vary from year to year, but even in the same year the waves of different species do not always coincide. Thus although the peak for ruffs in 1952 was August 5th, that for ringed plover was on the 10th, dunlin on the 15th and for curlew sandpiper on September 17th. Clearly, meteorological conditions are not the only factors involved.

Of the gulls, the lesser black-backed is seen in London as a regular passage migrant and it is interesting that until 1925 it was most often recorded in the spring. It is now frequently observed in both seasons but the largest numbers occur in the autumn, when large flocks may be seen on playing fields, aerodromes and other open spaces as well as along the Thames and at the reservoirs and sewage farms. Like the waders, the terns pass through in waves which are heavier in some years than in others; recently there have been exceptional passages of black terns in 1946 (associated with north-easterly winds) and of common/arctic terns in each of the three years 1948–1950. Both little and Sandwich terns are regular on passage but in much smaller numbers; the Sandwich tern appears to have become more frequent in recent years. The fact that in the autumn terns are most often seen over the reservoirs in the Thames valley, especially at Barn Elms and Staines, has led some ornithologists to suppose that they come up the Thames from the estuary, where large westward movements take place annually. But, as discussed in the specific notes, very few terns appear to penetrate up river beyond Dartford and it seems more likely that the passage through London is on a broad front in a north-south direction. In support of this supposition is the account (*vide L.B.R.* for 1949) of common/arctic terns at one of the Staines reservoirs on September 4th; 20 were seen at 11 a.m. and they were joined by fresh arrivals from

C. B. Ashby

Plate *19a*. A typical birch common
b. The woodlark increased enormously in the 1930's

M. D. England

Plate 20a. Wimbledon Common, only seven miles from Charing Cross
b. Bookham Common: the plain

the north until by 12.30 p.m. at least 114 were present—shortly afterwards the flock dispersed and by 1 p.m. only 10 remained.

The passage movements of those passerines which mostly travel by day were described at the beginning of this chapter. Evidence of some of these movements, especially of the wagtails, hirundines and swifts, can usually be seen at the reservoirs and sewage farms. The concentration of yellow wagtails sometimes reaches large numbers; for example, 300–350 were counted at one of the Lea valley reservoirs in August, 1951. Very little is known of the passage of tits through the Area. Power, writing of his suburban garden, said that both great and blue tits, which he thought to be foreign immigrants, passed through in October but the only other reports which suggest a passage are more recent and come from Inner London. Although both great and blue tits nest in the central parks and squares, increases in their numbers are more noticeable than elsewhere and autumnal increases have been noted fairly frequently. An unusually large influx occurred between September 23rd and October 28th, 1949; five species took part, with blue tits predominating, and a party of 14 long-tailed tits was followed westwards on foot and by bus from St. Paul's to Fetter Lane.

The return passage of the warblers is always difficult to observe inland because most are silent and even in Inner London only the chiffchaff, willow warbler and whitethroat are recorded at this season with any regularity. Two ringing recoveries, both of sedge warblers, give an indication of the direction of this largely unseen autumn passage—both were found in August and one had been ringed six weeks earlier at Bedford, 44 miles north, and the other two months earlier at Driffield, 185 miles north. The chats and flycatchers, because they are more conspicuous, are seen more frequently. Both wheatear and whinchat pass through the parks and bombed sites but larger numbers are seen on sewage farms and on the higher ground in Surrey. Spotted flycatchers sometimes appear in flocks of 20 or more, even in the central parks. Pied flycatchers are more often seen singly, in woods or on wooded commons, but there was a remarkable passage through Regent's Park, Green Park and Kensington Gardens in 1951 with a maximum of 15 in one small area of Regent's Park on September 3rd.

While the autumn passage is still in progress the winter visitors to the London Area begin to arrive. With its vast acreage of water—rivers, canals, reservoirs, lakes, gravel pits and sewage farms—it is not surprising that London has for long been famous among ornithologists for the number and variety of water birds which can be seen in the winter months. The most numerous, of course, are the ducks of which at the peak period in January there may be as many as ten thousand individuals of a dozen or

so species. There are few places in Britain where one can be so certain of
seeing, in a single afternoon, such birds as goosander, smew, gadwall and
goldeneye. The normal and hard weather movements of the ducks, and of
the grebes and divers, have been fully discussed in other chapters and in
the specific notes and will not be repeated here. To judge from the ringing
returns it is likely that most, if not all, of the wintering ducks come from
abroad, especially Scandinavia and the Baltic countries, and not from
other parts of Britain. Gaggles of geese, usually whitefronts, occasionally
fly over during hard weather but there are very few undisturbed feeding
grounds in the Area and they have rarely stayed for more than a few hours.
Whooper and Bewick's swans are also unusual winter visitors.

Of the birds of prey, buzzard, hen harrier and merlin are all occasional
winter visitors. The peregrine is seen more frequently and has wintered
in the Staines district since 1948.

The resident population of moorhens and coots is noticeably increased
in the winter and coot, especially, appear on the reservoirs and other
waters devoid of cover. In most winters there are a score or so of reports
of the water rail, from a variety of places ranging from gravel pits and
sewage farms to golf-courses, ponds and even, in 1936, the coal bunker of
the Houses of Parliament.

By comparison with the autumn, waders are hard to find in winter at
the sewage farms and reservoirs. Oystercatchers, ringed and grey plovers,
turnstones, curlews, godwits, greenshanks and knot have all been recorded
but by no means regularly and in very small numbers. Curlew, redshank
and dunlin may be seen, especially in December and January, on the
Thames marshes below Erith but they only penetrate higher in severe
weather. The most abundant and widespread wader in winter is the common snipe, which frequents the marshy ground in the river valleys and at
the sewage farms; flocks of 200, and occasionally considerably more
are not unusual in cold weather. Jack snipe, usually in small
numbers, are also regular and in most recent years both common and
green sandpipers have wintered on the Thames marshes and elsewhere
Although it is unusual for more than a score of woodcock to be reported
the fact that 41 were shot in one wood in 1936 suggests that they are much
overlooked. The golden plover is a scarce visitor to the Thames marshes
but it occurs in considerable numbers in some parts of the Area, mostly
north of the Thames. It is particularly fond of the grassy areas between
aerodrome runways where flocks of 500 or over are not infrequent.

Those Londoners who can remember the beginning of the century
whether they are bird-watchers or not, must be aware of the great change
which have taken place in the winter distribution of the gulls. These
changes are described in detail under each species and there is only space

here for a brief summary. In 1900, black-headed gulls had been established as regular winter visitors for less than a decade and although they came to London in some numbers they were largely confined to the main river valleys. The common gull seems to have been very uncommon except perhaps on the Thames below Dartford, the greater black-backed gull was scarcely ever seen, at any time of the year, and the lesser black-backed only occurred, in very small numbers, as a spring passage migrant. The herring gull was recorded as a regular but not very numerous winter visitor. At the end of our period, black-headed gulls are present all the year round and in the winter, when their numbers greatly increase, they scavenge for food in all parts of the Area. The common gull has become a regular visitor, both to the Thames and to playing fields and grasslands in the outer districts; flocks of up to 300 are not an unusual sight. Greater black-backed gulls were still rare visitors as late as the 1920's but since then, and especially in the last ten years, they have increased remarkably. On January 29th, 1950, 235 were counted from a launch along the 20-mile stretch of the Thames from Barnes to Woolwich; flocks of up to 400 have been seen assembling, prior to roosting, at Walton reservoir and the Hampton filter beds. The lesser black-backed is now seen more frequently on the autumn passage than in the spring and has recently increased in winter. The status of the herring gull has perhaps changed less than that of the others, but it is certainly more numerous now than in 1900 and it is also more widespread and visits rubbish dumps and sewage farms as well as the river and reservoirs. Recoveries in the Area of black-headed, common and herring gulls ringed abroad show that these species, like the ducks, mostly emanate from the Scandinavian and Baltic countries although some of the black-headed gulls come from Central Europe.

Of the rarer gulls, the little gull occurs in small numbers on the autumn passage and there are now one or two reports each winter of the glaucous gull, until recently a vagrant to the Area.

Of the winter visitors other than water birds, the London Area shelters as wide a variety as other inland districts of southern England. Among those reported regularly are short-eared owls, fieldfares, redwings, goldcrests, meadow and rock pipits, great grey shrikes, siskins, redpolls and bramblings. Details of the migrations of these and other visitors will be found in the specific notes. There are three winter records of the blackcap and one each of whinchat, garden warbler (the first in Britain), whitethroat (the second in Britain), willow warbler and chiffchaff. It may be significant that only the whitethroat was away from the built-up districts.

Hard weather in mid-winter is often accompanied by large-scale immigrations into the Area. In the cold spell of 1938, for example, many thousands of skylarks were flying west over London throughout one day and on the following days they were reported in the squares and streets all over central London including Piccadilly and Oxford Circus. Thousands of redwings also passed over the centre and both redwings and fieldfares and several of the finches invaded gardens in the inner suburbs in search of food. A few bramblings stayed for several days in Ladbroke Square. In the same period both brent and pink-footed geese were seen and the numbers of all the ducks in the Area increased considerably—three smew even appeared on the Serpentine and two on a small pond at Beddington. Slavonian, black-necked and red-necked grebes were seen and there were unusual movements of some of the waders—a dunlin picked up dead at South Kensington was identified as belonging to the Lapland race.

ROOSTS AND FLY-LINES

by S. Cramp, E. R. Parrinder and B. A. Richards

THIS CHAPTER deals with those species whose communal roosts in the London area are of particular interest and importance—the starling and the feral pigeon, mainly in the centre, the house sparrow throughout the built-up areas, the woodpigeon on islands in the parks or rural woods, the pied wagtail on suburban buildings and in reed-beds, and the rook, carrion crow and jackdaw in woods in the suburbs and the country. The nightly gatherings of the gulls on London's reservoirs have already been discussed, and any notes on roosting habits of special significance among other species will be found later under the specific headings.

One of the most spectacular changes in London bird life in this century has been the growth of the starling's habit of roosting in the centre of the Metropolis. The packed ledges in and around Trafalgar Square and the dramatic aerial evolutions as the birds arrive are now familiar and famous, but fifty years ago the habit had scarcely begun. The early history of the starling roosts has been detailed by Fitter in *London's Natural History* and *London's Birds* and only a summary need be given here. Before the 1890's the starling was referred to as nesting in the central parks and leaving for the country at the end of the summer, and no writer of this period gives any indication of the existence of urban roosts. In November, 1894, however, T. D. Pigott wrote to *The Times* to say that starlings (he estimated the numbers at more than a thousand) were coming in from the suburbs to roost in the trees on Duck Island in St. James's Park. Hudson, writing in *Birds in London* in 1898, said that from the end of June starlings were roosting communally in the trees on the islands in Battersea and Regent's Parks, Buckingham Palace gardens and the Serpentine. He described it as a growing habit, but stated that "at the beginning of October most of the birds go away to spend the winter in the country". There seems little doubt that the habit of roosting communally in the centre of London was begun by resident British starlings, and not by the Continental immigrants, which do not arrive in this country in numbers until October.

The habit of roosting on buildings, and of continuing to do so through-out the winter, seems to have begun before the First World War, but there is no reference in the literature which enables us to be more precise than that it began some time between 1898 and the winter of 1913–1914. The reason for this major change is not known with certainty. The spread of London, making the journey to the country roosts even longer than to the centre, was probably one of the factors which induced the starlings to continue roosting in London even after the leaves had fallen. We now know that the big change-over each year from tree to building roosts does occur at about the time when the trees are losing their leaves: a minority of the birds, however, continue to roost in trees throughout the winter.

Virtually no field work was carried out on the roosting of starlings in London until 1925, when E. M. Nicholson made a survey of the Inner London roosts and the fly-lines to them, the results of which have not been published. Up to this time it was commonly believed that the starlings came into London in a few enormous flocks and were probably Continental immigrants which had spent the day feeding at sewage farms and on playing fields. Nicholson showed that the roosting starlings were the resident birds of the suburbs and he described how the individual birds collected at a local rendezvous, then flew in towards London in small flocks, picking up others as they went. The next major work was Fitter's comprehensive paper "The Starling Roosts of the London Area", published in the *London Naturalist* for 1942. In this all known roosts, past and present, were listed and an approximate boundary given to the 'catchment area' within which starlings fly in to London to roost. In 1949 the Ornithological Section of the London Natural History Society began a three year census and trap-ping programme in an attempt to solve some of the many problems which remained: this task involved the ringing of over 5,000 starlings in Trafalgar Square at night and in suburban gardens by day, and frequent counts of the birds using all the central roosts. The remainder of this summarised account of the roosting of starlings is based upon the results of the 1949–52 inquiry, which are being prepared for separate publication.

The periodic counts showed that starlings roost in the centre of London throughout the year and that the number using the roosts never falls much below ten thousand. In 1950, this bottom level was reached by late April when most of the breeding pairs are roosting in their suburban nesting holes. The birds still using the central roosts were mostly males, probably largely non-breeding first-year birds, together with some adults returning to the communal roost after their young had hatched. Most of them used the buildings around Trafalgar Square, although some roosted in trees along the Embankment and elsewhere. The young from the first brood appeared to make the nightly journey from the suburbs to the central roosts almost as soon as they were fledged. Before the end of May thousands of young birds were roosting in the trees on Duck Island, in St James's Park, and this new roost gradually attracted the birds from Trafalgar Square until in early June less than a thousand remained on the buildings. From June until mid-July each flock of starlings dropped straight into the trees on arrival, and it was possible to estimate their numbers by stationing observers around the lake. The average of these counts in 1950 was 90,000 birds. In the second half of July, when the young from the second and late broods had also been fledged, three important changes occurred: the spectacular massed flights began; the birds started to gather on the buildings (and once on the minute hand of Big Ben, preventing it from striking nine o'clock) before going to the island; and a roost of about 20,000 strong was started in the trees of Finsbury Circus, in the City. This roost was used by birds from the eastern sector, but many from the western sector also went to it, passing over Duck Island and Trafalgar Square. It lasted until September; there has been a similar July to September roost in Finsbury Circus in other years and the reason for its short existence is not clear.

Between July and October complex movements took place which could not be assessed numerically because of the difficulty of counting birds in trees in full leaf. The numbers roosting on buildings in Trafalgar Square increased slowly but there was no major change-over until the fall of the leaves in November. Meanwhile the birds roosting in trees transferred from St. James's Park and from Finsbury Circus to the trees along the Embankment. Other smaller tree roosts were started in Trafalgar and Leicester Squares and in several places on the south side of the river.

Although some birds continued to roost in trees throughout the winter, the majority had transferred to the buildings by early December when the leaves had all fallen. By then counting was again possible, and an enormous decrease in the roost population was disclosed—in 1950, total numbers were down to just under 40,000, less than half of the summer peak. This drop was too steep to be accounted for by normal mortality alone and the subsidiary causes are still not known. There seem to b three possibilities: (1) that some juveniles had moved away from London; ringing recoveries, discussed in the species account, show that this does happen but that there is also an influx of young birds from the north and east; (2) that birds were drawn off to new roosts in the rural districts started probably by Continental birds arriving in October; there was some evidence of this, but the numbers involved did not appear to be large; (3) that a considerable proportion of adults began to roost in their nesting holes as early as November; this seems unlikely, but further observations are needed.

One thing is clear—there is no truth in the belief once held that the central roosts reach their peak in October. This was a convenient theory when it was believed that most of the roosting birds were Continental immigrants. It probably arose from an observational error: in October, the time when starlings are coming in to roost each evening coincides with the time when the streets are full of people going home from work and the starlings are noticed more then than in any other month of the year.

From December until March the fall in numbers was much less and could be accounted for by normal mortality. The big drop (from 26,000 to about 10,000 in 1950) occurred in the last few days of March and the first two weeks in April when most of the breeding birds ceased travelling to the central roosts and stayed at home to sleep in their nesting holes. Shortly before and during this period many birds were arriving over Trafalgar Square in pairs and individual sexual pursuits largely replaced the communal aerial evolutions.

The observational evidence that the great majority of the starlings which roost in central London are British residents rather than Continental immigrants is borne out by the recoveries from the 3275 birds which were ringed at the Trafalgar Square roost in 1949–1952. At the time of writing, 297 recoveries have been reported and only fourteen of these have been outside the London area—eleven within Britain and three in Holland. The proportion of Continental birds which use the central roost is evidently extremely small but it seems likely that individuals or small flocks are occasionally "drawn in" by the flocks of resident birds flying towards the centre.

The accompanying map (Fig. 3) shows the places of recovery of the 283 starlings which were found within the London area. It will be seen that the majority are in the inner and outer suburbs, six to fourteen miles from the centre, and only a few fall outside the boundaries of the catchment area drawn from the observation of flylines. These boundaries are properly zones rather than fixed lines and are subject to minor changes at different times of the year and from year to year. Their delineation on the map is intended to give an approximate picture of the feeding range of London

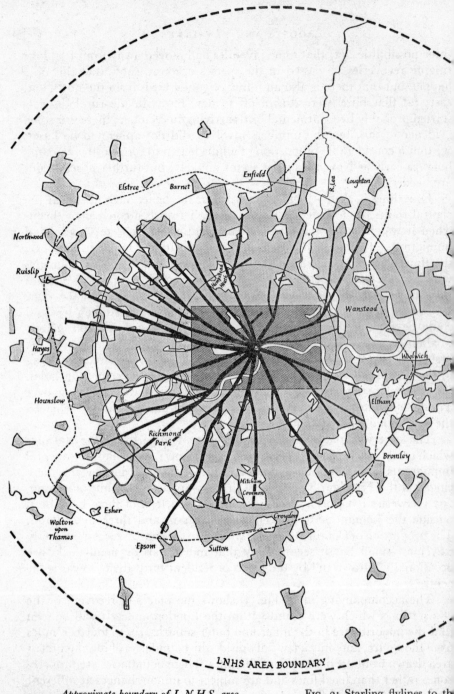

FIG. 2: Starling flylines to the central London roosts

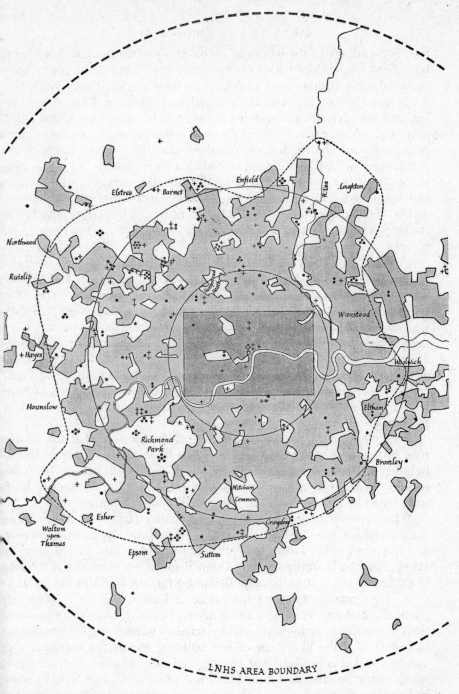

+ *recoveries in winter (Oct.–March)*
• *recoveries in summer (April–Sept.)*

FIG. 3: Recoveries of starlings
from the central London roosts

roosting starlings in the winter of 1950. Many of the fly-lines (see Fig. 2)
have been known for at least twenty years but although the routes have
persisted some of them have undoubtedly been extended since Nicholson
made his second survey (also unpublished) in 1932–1933. Then the gathering area was described as varying between half-a-mile and eleven miles,
with a probable average of less than six miles. Now, both observations
of fly-lines and the ringing returns show that the extreme limits of the
gathering area have been extended to at least fourteen miles. This extension
is mostly to the north-west and south-west—the direction of London's
furthest sprawl. This increase in the gathering area is probably the reason,
rather than an increase in population density, for the larger number of
starlings which now use the central roosts than at the time of Nicholson's
surveys.

Another important change in comparatively recent times has been the
concentration of the major building roosts to the ledges in and around
Trafalgar Square. The large roost at the British Museum was deserted after
the spring of 1931, and the once famous roosts in the City, on St. Paul's
Cathedral, the General Post Office and the Royal Exchange, seem to have
been largely abandoned in the early years of the second war—possibly as
a result of the disturbance caused by the incendiary raids. The changes
at the smaller tree and building roosts in central London listed by Fitter
(1943) are too uncertain and complicated to discuss in detail here, and the
reader is referred to the full report of the 1949–52 starling enquiry to be
published.

One of the most interesting features of the roosts is that the chosen
trees or buildings are most often in the best lit and busiest streets. Flood-
lighting, as during the 1951 Festival, has no noticeable effect. Even the
neon signs are used as perches, and on one occasion a number of birds
were burnt by a short circuit in a sign in Trafalgar Square.

There is no evidence that the starlings do any harm to buildings, other
than the mess caused by their droppings, but agitation by building owners,
and questions in the House have at various times caused the Ministry of
Works and the Westminster City Council to declare war on the roosting
birds and to attempt to dislodge them. So far, the starlings have always
won. It is possible to move the birds, at least temporarily, from any
particular building by such means as fireworks, which cause more nuisance
than the starlings, or by low tension electrified wires, which are expensive
to install. But the liberation of one building means the occupation of
another, and it is unlikely that any method short of mass extermination,
which would be cruel and unjustified, will prevent starlings from roosting
in London.

Although the central roosts are used by the majority of the starlings living within the boundaries shown on the maps, a number of smaller roosts have been recorded in the autumn and winter, even in Inner London, in trees and on such places as church steeples. Some of these, such as the girders under the Albert Bridge, have been occupied for many years and appear to be used by local birds. Why some birds should roost locally while others fly to the central roost is another mystery of starling behaviour.

Relatively little is known of the seasonal roosting behaviour of the resident starlings living outside the 'catchment area'. Fitter (*L.N.,* for 1942) listed many roosts in the outer suburban and rural areas, mainly in trees or hawthorn thickets, but most of these were occupied in the autumn and winter only, when they probably consisted largely of Continental birds. Less than a dozen outer roosts have been recorded as in use between April and September, and the summer roosting behaviour of the country starlings needs further investigation.

On the ledges of many buildings in central London the feral pigeons can be seen roosting with the starlings. They also use the stone figures and ornaments on buildings, and for years some twenty birds have roosted on the brickwork ledge of a tall chimney in Northumberland Street, attracted presumably by the warmth. Normally the pigeons roost thirty feet or more above the pavement, but some on a Bloomsbury hotel may be seen sleeping only a few feet above the heads of the passers-by. Numbers on any one building are not large; the highest recorded figure being 138 on the National Gallery in September, though most roosts are much smaller. Many feral pigeons, however, roost out of sight, in the church towers, ruins etc., which form the centres of their colonies. Although in London they regularly perch on trees in some of the parks and squares, there are so far no records of their using trees for roosting.

House sparrows, like starlings, may roost in their nest-holes or join communal roosts. Before flying to the roosts they often gather in trees near to their feeding places, and it is not always clear whether observers have distinguished between these gathering-places and true roosts. As early as 1868 Shirley Hibberd mentioned a number of places in central London where gatherings of sparrows could be heard chirping in the mornings and evenings, though he did not say that these "chapels", as they were then known, were actual roosts. Excluding instances where confusion may have arisen, there remain a number of definite records of communal roosts of house sparrows. As examples may be mentioned the plane trees outside Southwark Cathedral, where in February, 1937, H. J. Burkill saw over 1200 birds roosting and where in 1949 and 1950 a much smaller number shared the roost with starlings, and the plane trees near Temple Station where P. A. D. Hollom noted a large roost in March, 1931.

Only a fraction of the communal roosts in central London have been reported, however, as may be seen from a survey of the roosts in some 3½ square miles in Westminster, Holborn and St. Pancras, carried out by S. Cramp between July, 1949, and May, 1950. In this small area 24 communal roosts, ranging in size from 20 to over 2,000 birds, were found. Even this total was almost certainly too low, for sparrow roosts, which are less noisy and usually much smaller than those of the starling, are easily missed, particularly in the late summer and early autumn, when the leaves provide effective cover and all those discovered then held less than 50 birds. Except for one roost in a creeper in Russell Square (which is said to have been used every autumn for at least fifteen years), all were in planes. Later in the year many of these small local roosts were deserted, and the sparrows resorted to larger roosts, also in planes. The two most notable were along the Victoria Embankment and in Euston Square, both of which held over 2,000 birds at their peak. Most of these larger roosts lasted throughout the winter, but the fluctuations in the numbers of birds using them showed that many sparrows must change their roosts from time to time.

In April, there was a sharp and general fall in the numbers of sparrows using the roosts, though a handful of birds, presumably non-breeding, were to be found there late into May. In fact, communal sparrow roosts have been reported in the London area in every month of the year. Several of the roosts were shared with starlings, which occupied the upper branches while the sparrows slept lower down, usually to within twenty feet of the ground, though at one roost some were as low as ten feet. Many of the sparrows flew singly to the roosts, most in parties of ten and under, though flocks of 27 and 50 birds were counted. No sparrows were seen flying more than 1.4 miles to a roost and the great majority travelled only a few hundred yards.

Outside the central area, however, house sparrows probably fly greater distances to their roosts, for much larger numbers have been recorded using them. P. W. E. Currie estimated that several thousand sparrows were roosting in scattered bushes of hawthorn and gorse on Banstead Downs in December, 1950, while at Motspur Park, in the same month, B. A. Richards found a roost in a hawthorn thicket said to have been occupied for over twenty years which appeared to hold several thousand birds. Collenette (1937) states that a sparrow roost in Richmond Park held some 2,700 birds in January, 1936, with about 2,500 as late as March 22nd. Other roosts have been found in various parks and in the lopped planes along busy streets, as in Paddington and Lambeth. In 1928 F. Howard Lancum described the long-standing habit of some London sparrows of roosting on the flanges of electric standard lamps, with their backs to the lights.

There have been few instances of communal roosts on buildings, though many sparrows roost in their nest-holes, which are frequently in buildings, throughout the winter. It is difficult to estimate the proportion of birds doing this, but it is not small; indeed, in some large colonies, such as Bloomsbury Square, where the nests are in the ventilation holes of an office block, the majority appear to do so. In these situations the nest is kept in good repair during the winter, and this has sometimes led to erroneous reports of unseasonable breeding.

It has been said earlier that the feral pigeon has never been recorded as roosting in trees in London. Its relative, the woodpigeon, however, always roosts in trees, though in London it uses buildings for perching, singing and, less frequently, nesting. The striking increase of the wood-pigeon in central London dates from the late eighties of the last century, and the communal roosts there seem to have begun soon after. In 1902 some two hundred woodpigeons roosted regularly on the islands in the lake in Battersea Park, a site which is still in use. The island in the Serpentine in Hyde Park has also been used for many years. Dr. Carmichael Low counted the roosts on a number of occasions in 1925 and 1926, finding a maximum of 776 birds in early January, and at the beginning of 1935 A. H. Macpherson reported that some hundreds were roosting there, with several thousands more in the trees in nearby Kensington Gardens. He noted a rapid fall in numbers towards the end of February and it appears that these large communal roots are abandoned during the spring and summer. The latest date for any roost in Inner London is April 10th and the earliest September 28th. Woodpigeons have also been reported roosting on many occasions in Regent's Park since February, 1930, when L. Parmenter counted 1231 birds, and again they used the trees on islands or near the shores of the lake. A few of the St. James's Park woodpigeons roost on Duck Island, but the majority fly south-west to roost in Battersea Park, as C. S. Bayne discovered as early as 1932. There has been a small scattered roost in the planes along Victoria Embankment in recent years, but apart from this there are few records of Inner London roosts outside the parks.

Elsewhere in the Area woodpigeon roosts have been most frequently reported from parks in the suburbs and outskirts, and remarkably few have been recorded in the rural districts. Richmond Park has been used in many winters, with about 2000 birds in December, 1938, while large numbers were seen roosting at Bushy Park between 1933 and 1941. In Ken Wood, R. S. R. Fitter found birds roosting in 1936 and 1938 (when over 300 were counted), and G. Taylor states that they still use it, often sharing the trees with carrion crows. Large numbers were seen roosting at Copse Wood, Ruislip, in 1937 and this roost was probably again in use in 1949

The roost of pied wagtails in the heart of Dublin is well known (*B.B.* 24: 364 *et seq.*), but there appear to be few other records of urban roosting by this species. In London several roosts have been located in the built-up areas, usually in the suburbs not too distant from suitable feeding grounds. Those nearest to the centre have been in Balham High Road, where in February, 1937, D. Seth-Smith saw at least 150 birds in holly trees in the garden of a house, and outside Golders Green station where they were observed gathering in willows near the busy cross-roads in 1933. In 1948 pied wagtails were seen congregating at dusk on the roofs near Ealing Broadway station, and a small roost was found in 1950 in a plane tree at Hanwell Broadway, not far distant. A roost in pollarded planes along the main London Road at Thornton Heath, originally discovered in 1937 was still in use in 1950. In the autumn of 1949 C. B. Ashby followed the birds from their feeding grounds at Beddington sewage farm to this roost and estimated that their numbers increased from about 125 on August 16th to at least 293 on September 4th. In the more rural parts of the Area many roosts have been reported, mainly in reed-beds, though willows, limes, laurels, gorse and even a field of artichokes have also been used.

Most of the carrion crow roosts reported have been in the suburbs or the outskirts of the built-up area. The larger roosts tend to be "traditional" and the occupation of some of them may date back to well before our period. At Ken Wood carrion crows have been roosting since the twenties at least and probably much earlier. This roost is occupied all the year round, but reaches a peak of 70 or 80 birds in late October (G. Taylor *in litt.*). At a roost on an island at Walthamstow reservoirs, first recorded by R. W. Pethen in 1921, fairly complete counts were made in 1922 and in several years during the thirties, which showed that while numbers were highest in late autumn and winter (with a maximum of about 100 birds) from 30 to 50 were often present throughout the spring and summer. There is a large roost at Monk's Orchard, near Beckenham, and G. E. Manser recorded two or three hundred crows flying in that direction in December 1950. Many of these came probably from the nearby sewage farm at Elmers End. Similarly, at Beddington sewage farm the daytime population uses a roost on the Oaks estate at Woodmansterne. Counts made here by C. B. Ashby gave a winter peak of over 200 in February, 1949.

Other carrion crow roosts for which less complete information is available are—Bushy Park, up to 100 in the winters of 1936–37 and 1937–38; Perivale Wood, about 70 in 1950; Hamper Mill, about 100, with a few rooks, in 1950, and Oakhill Park, East Barnet, where forty or fifty birds were seen flying to roost in October, 1936. Essex roosts have been reported from Chingford Plain, Hainault Forest and Cranham Wood. In Richmond Park crows were "apparently roosting" in Sidmouth Plantation in 1940.

and in December, 1950, R. W. Hayman counted 150 assembled prior to roosting in the Park. In February, 1933, however, L. Parmenter witnessed a movement of crows out of Richmond Park at sunset in the direction of Kew Gardens, where he had counted 23 birds roosting in March, 1929.

The roosts of rooks and jackdaws are in more rural situations and this is perhaps the reason why fewer have been reported in the Area. They far exceed in size those of the carrion crow, some of the largest containing many thousands of birds. Here again some of the roosts have been in use for many years. W. B. Alexander, writing in 1939, stated that the roost in Gatton Park had been in use for at least fifty years, but it was abandoned towards the end of 1949. In February, 1947, a rough estimate gave a figure of about 5,000 birds, with jackdaws outnumbering rooks by about five to three. Fly-lines to this roost were noticed over Kingswood, Walton Heath, Reigate Hill and Redhill Common, and jackdaws from Richmond Park have been shown to fly in the evening over Motspur Park and Banstead, almost certainly to join this roost. In March, 1950, about a thousand jackdaws were counted on this fly-line, probably representing the whole of the park's daytime population. Part at least of the population using this roost now goes to one at Smallfield, outside our Area.

The only other large roost within our Area south of the Thames is at Titsey. It draws birds from the Addington, Warlingham and Westerham districts. Large numbers of rooks and jackdaws from the Darent valley around Lullingstone, Eynsford and Shoreham have been traced to a roost at Kemsing, which is just outside our Area, and birds from the Leatherhead district also appear to fly beyond our borders. North of the Thames the major roosts are at Oxhey Woods, Bricket Wood and Cuffley Great Wood in Hertfordshire, and Copped Hall in Essex. Smaller roosts in Essex are at High Beach, Stanford Rivers and Upminster Common. At the last of these, rooks have been seen to fly in from the Kent side of the river.

Part Two

SYSTEMATIC LIST

BLACK-THROATED DIVER, *Colymbus arcticus* L. Scarce winter visitor.

The black-throated diver has been recorded about 26 times, mainly on the larger reservoirs. Although one or more have appeared in most recent years, they are still not seen in every winter in spite of increased observation. In February, 1937, however, when there was a widespread and remarkable influx of divers and grebes, there were four, and possibly five, birds on different reservoirs in the Area (*B.B.*, 30:370–4 and *L.B.R* for 1937: 1–2). Two were seen at Molesey from February 2nd–21st; one at Walthamstow from February 6th–20th: one seen at Staines on January 31st and February 14th may possibly have been one of the Molesey birds. Another, which appeared on Lonsdale Road reservoirs, Barnes, on February 1st remained in the district until June 5th, by which time it was in full breeding plumage. On March 12th of that year also one was seen on a reservoir at Hampton.

In 1948 an oiled bird appeared on Staines reservoirs on January 10th and remained there until February 8th. On March 9th one, which was probably the same, was seen on the Thames at Hammersmith, and subsequently at Lonsdale Road reservoir until April 12th. It was then caught and taken to Barn Elms where it eventually died on April 18th. Post-mortem examination showed that it was heavily infested with internal parasites.

Others have been seen at the reservoirs in the Lea valley, and at Barn Elms, Molesey and Staines, in Richmond Park in 1908, at Caterham in 1909 and at the Rickmansworth aquadrome in 1949. Davis (1907) reported two which had been shot in the Dartford district, where recently two were seen on a flooded clay pit in February, 1952, and one in February 1953.

GREAT NORTHERN DIVER, *Colymbus immer* Brünnich. R are winter visitor to the reservoirs.

The great northern diver has appeared in the Area just over twenty times. Eleven of the records fall within a period of twelve years, from 1927 to 1939 inclusive, during which there were only two years, 1928 and 1933, when great northern divers did not visit the Area. Outside this period one was seen at Staines reservoirs from December 25th, 1905 to January 1st, 1906, and the remainder in the winters since 1949–1950 inclusive. Most of the birds have been on the deeper waters in the northern part of the Lea valley reservoirs, at Staines and at Walton, but on the shallower reservoirs there have been three at Barn Elms, two at Brent and one at Elstree. They have usually been seen singly, but in the winter of 1930–31 there were three at Staines, although not all at the same time.

The longest visit was by one at Staines reservoir from December 15th, 1951 to May 18th, 1952, and the earliest was on October 23rd, 1934.

RED-THROATED DIVER, *Colymbus stellatus* Pontoppidan. Occasional winter visitor and passage migrant.

There have been over fifty records of the red-throated diver since 1900, but although some of the birds have stayed in the Area for considerable periods, several of those seen have been oiled and no less than eighteen have been found dead. Red-throated divers essentially prefer the sea to fresh water for feeding and it is almost certain that they only stay inland when weakened by oiling or some other cause.

There are records for all months from November to June inclusive, the earliest of these being of a bird which stayed on the Thames at Twickenham from November 1st–15th, 1939. Birds seen in the spring are probably often genuine passage migrants, and one on Staines reservoir from May 2nd–5th, 1929, was in full breeding dress. It was seen again as late as June 9th by D. Gunn. There was one at Staines in partial summer plumage on September 12th, 1953.

The red-throated diver has visited some twenty different 'waters' in the Area, including not only the reservoirs but also gravel pits at Ruxley and Sewardstone and park lakes at South Weald, Thorndon and Wanstead. Five birds have remained for a month or more, the longest stay being on the Pen Ponds, Richmond Park, from February 13th to April 27th, 1921.

At clay pits on the Stone Marshes at least five have been shot in recent years because of alleged damage to fishing interests.

There are three records for Inner London, all on the Serpentine: 1934, one from mid-March to April 25th; 1941, one from January 27th to February 2nd; 1948, one seen on February 9th was found dead on the 11th.

GREAT CRESTED GREBE, *Podiceps cristatus* (L). Present throughout the year, breeding on most of the large waters where vegetation supplies anchorage for a nest. Many of the breeding waters deserted in autumn, when there is a concentration on the larger bare, concrete-banked reservoirs; although many leave the Area entirely, large flocks in winter are not unknown. No marked passage in spring at the reservoirs.

The British population of great crested grebes reached probably its lowest ebb soon after the middle of the last century, when there were perhaps not more than 42 pairs in the whole country and none in the London Area. Since that time, numbers have increased with hardly a setback. By the beginning of the present century some 150 sites were occupied by 300 or more pairs, and now the total population in Britain in the breeding season is probably between 1500 and 2000 pairs, including non-breeders.

Seen against this general background, the contribution of the London Area to the increase was negligible at the outset, and by the turn of the century grebes were recorded as nesting only in Osterley Park, on the Pen Ponds and in Gatton Park. This state of affairs was no doubt partly due to lack of many suitable sites, but thereafter the spread was more rapid. Ten years later the bird was nesting, or had nested, on four waters in Essex, two in Hertfordshire, three in Middlesex and four in Surrey. By 1921 these figures had increased again by one in Kent, two in Middlesex and three in Surrey, i.e. in the parts of these counties within our province.

In 1931 a detailed census was undertaken in June and July and gave 68 pairs at 22 sites out of a total of about 1160 pairs in all England and Wales. Their distribution is shown in the following table:

	Number of pairs	Waters occupied for breeding	Non-breeding birds on reservoirs	Total number of birds
BUCKS	2	1	—	4
ESSEX	27	4*	30	84
HERTS	6	3	—	12

*Lea Valley Reservoirs counted as one water.

	Number of pairs	Waters occupied for breeding	Non-breeding birds on reservoirs	Total number of birds
KENT	—	—	—	—
MIDDLESEX	15	6	34	64
SURREY	18	8	25	61
	68	22	89	225

Another count in June, 1935, showed a very similar total to 1931, as far as breeding waters were concerned; the count for the larger waters was incomplete. There is relatively little information for the next decade, but at the end of the war access to reservoirs was once more permitted and, in 1946, London grebes were again counted as part of a wider census organised by the British Trust for Ornithology. In this year the national census gave a total similar to the pre-war figures, but the London contribution had increased by over fifty per cent., with a total of about 350 birds.

From January to March, 1947, the most severe, persistent frost for many years was experienced, and in the succeeding breeding season grebes in the London Area, as in the country generally, showed a drop of nearly 20 per cent. More remarkable, the whole of this loss was more than made good in a single season, and the figures for 1948 exceeded by nearly 10 per cent the previous peak of 1946.

Following another marked increase in 1949 there was a jump of one-third in 1950 to a total of 557 birds, of which 242 were on gravel pits and 140 on the large, deep reservoirs where breeding is impossible. The number of pairs positively recorded as breeding was 149, but it is not certain how many of the remainder were non-breeding birds. A decline in 1951 and 1952 was followed by an even higher total of 627 in 1953, this time 305 being on gravel pits, which also harboured over half the pairs actually proved to be breeding. Middlesex held 203 of the total number of birds and in several recent years has had more grebes in June than any other county.

Thus in the London Area the summer population of grebes has increased in rough figures by over 75 per cent. since the war and by over 250 per cent. since 1931, while in 1900 there was only a mere handful. It is safe to say that this remarkable increase could not have occurred without the formation of the great number of artificial waters, both reservoirs and gravel pits, now existing in the Area. For nesting it is the gravel pits which have made the greatest contribution, and many of them have only come into existence within the last twenty or twenty-five years. Two were in use as breeding sites in 1931, but very many more were excavated during the war and by 1946 they provided 123 of the 178 waters visited in the course of that year's survey.

The reservoirs of the Metropolitan Water Board normally provide no opportunities for grebes to breed, except round the wooded islands of some of the Walthamstow group. In the 1931 enquiry, however, three cases of attempted breeding were quoted, two of them on the top of concrete banks (B.B., 26: 185–6). Subsequently, one or two pairs tried to breed at the Lonsdale Road reservoirs in the years 1941-45, the nests being attached to booms placed in the water as a war-time measure. In 1949 a pair at Hampton attached their nest to weeds rooted on the bottom of the distributing reservoir; the first clutch was destroyed by rising water but a second nest was built and three chicks hatched.

With the great increase in the breeding population during the last twenty years, one would have expected a corresponding rise in the numbers which assemble on the large reservoirs in autumn as the breeding sites are abandoned. In fact, there is no evidence of any rise in the total numbers, and there may have been a slight fall. On October 22nd

1938, 743 grebes were counted on the principal reservoirs in the Lea and Thames valleys, and by this date numbers at Littleton and Staines were substantially below their autumn peak. The more important waters were counted again in 1953 but at a much earlier date, approximately 500 birds on September 6th comparing with 521 on the same waters (excluding King George VI reservoir not then built) on the 1938 date already quoted. The wide variation in times of maximum numbers at different waters in any one year, and in the Area as a whole in different years, makes comparison very difficult, especially as relatively few counts have been made in post-war years compared with the long series for some years in the thirties. It seems certain, however, that the very marked increase in the breeding birds of the country as a whole has not been accompanied by any corresponding rise in the size of the autumn flocks in the London Area.

It is perhaps significant, therefore, that the great crested grebe sample census has shown that the summer population of northern and central England has decreased, and was lower in 1946–50 than in 1931, while in southern England the population has increased and by 1950 was nearly double that of 1931. The inference is that there is a general, definite southward shift of the whole population at the end of the breeding season; that the autumn and winter assemblies on the London reservoirs are not drawn from the local breeding stock but from birds from farther north, where numbers are now lower than in pre-war years; and perhaps that when the London breeding birds leave the breeding waters, they go right away and their first stage carries them well outside the London Area. This last point is supported by events in spring when the return to the breeding waters is not preceded by an increase in the birds recorded on the reservoirs. It is interesting to note, moreover, that eighty birds were seen at Staines in 1906, when the species was well established farther north although few pairs were yet breeding near London.

In autumn the grebes show a clear preference for the large deep reservoirs and the passage birds are little attracted to the many gravel pits which support such a high proportion of the breeding population. Gatherings of over 200 birds at a single reservoir or group of waters have included the following:

King George V reservoir		213	*August* 13,	1953
Littleton	,,	330	*September* 29,	1934
,,	,,	291	*August* 26,	1935
Molesey	,,	257	*November* 13,	1937
Staines	,,	260	*September* 5,	1937

In some years numbers build up quite early in July, and in 1952 there were 82, all adults, at Staines on the 5th, rising to 151 by the 27th, and in the following year there were 121 at King George V reservoir by July 11th. These are presumably all non-breeding birds or ones that have failed to rear young. On the other hand there have occasionally been large concentrations in the winter months.

In Inner London great crested grebes are occasional visitors to the waters in Hyde Park and Kensington Gardens.

RED-NECKED GREBE, *Podiceps griseigena* (Boddaert). Occasional visitor to reservoirs, Thames and other waters, mostly between October and March.

The first record for the red-necked grebe for this century was of one at Highgate Ponds in February, 1913; the second, nine years later, was at Barn Elms. Since then about 61 birds have been reported, of which 25 have been at the Lea valley reservoirs, 13 at Staines and King George VI reservoirs, seven at Barn Elms, three at Brent reservoir, two each on the Thames, in Kensington Gardens, at Elstree and on Stone marshes, and one each at Island Barn reservoir and on ponds at Cheshunt, Mitcham, Springwell and Wimbledon. Most of the waters mentioned, with the notable exception of those at Staines, are relatively shallow.

Occasionally two red-necked grebes have been reported in company, but most have been alone. Arrivals have been reported in every month from September to March, most frequently in January followed equally by November and February. Some of the birds are obviously on southward passage in autumn or early winter, while the appearance of others is evidently due to unfavourable conditions at sea as at the end of January and in early February, 1937, when many species that normally winter at sea were driven inland following a severe N.E. gale and very low temperatures in the region of Denmark and the Baltic (*B.B.*, 30: 373–4).

Occurrences that can safely be attributed to spring passage are two only: a bird in the Lea valley from March 30th to April 6th, 1935, and one at Barn Elms on March 28th, 1953, which was in almost full summer plumage and was frequently heard to call. Red-necked grebes have seldom remained more than two months, the longest stay being at Walthamstow reservoirs from January 4th to March 28th, 1936. Exceptionally, in 1930, one appeared at Staines in summer and stayed from July 13th to August 8th.

SLAVONIAN GREBE, *Podiceps auritus* (L.). Occasional winter visitor and passage migrant to reservoirs, lakes, Thames, between September and April. Two summer records.

The first recorded visit of the Slavonian grebe to the London Area in the present century was on the Thames at Richmond on February 16th, 1917, and twice subsequently off Chelsea Embarkment (*The Field*, 139:385). No more were reported until 1924, when A. Holte Macpherson saw one at Staines reservoir on March 9th and another at Barn Elms in October. Bucknill (1900) mentions two London records before our period—a bird seen at Charlton in 1870 and another at East Molesey in 1876. Five records in fifty-four years probably do not represent the true state of affairs but it is evident from the writings of Glegg (1929 and 1935) and Ticehurst (1909) that the Slavonian grebe was virtually unknown as a London bird before 1925.

Since then Slavonian grebes have been seen on about fifty occasions, one or more appearing in most years. Their time of arrival has been spread fairly evenly from September to March, none staying for much over two months and most of them only remaining a few days. They have been observed at the Lea valley reservoirs in fifteen different years, at Staines in thirteen and Barn Elms in seven. Elsewhere they have been seen on one or two occasions, among other places on the less artificial reservoirs at Brent, Elstree, and Ruislip, at Rickmansworth Aquadrome and in Hyde Park and Kensington Gardens. In 1937, when small numbers of divers and grebes appeared throughout the country (*B.B.*, 30:370–4 and *L.B.R.* for 1937:1–2) up to four Slavonians were seen on a gravel pit at Mitcham from January 31st until the end of March and there were single grebes at Sunbury reservoir and on the Serpentine, where one stayed for two days. The only other records for Inner London are of one on the Round Pond, Kensington Gardens in late November, 1934, and another on the Serpentine on April 27th, 1950. The largest parties have consisted of four birds—at Staines in November, 1930, and at Mitcham in 1937.

Slavonian grebes have been seen on three other occasions in April, and there was one at the Walthamstow reservoirs on June 16th, 1934. In 1948 a female in full breeding plumage was seen at Poyle gravel pits on April 25th. On May 29th this bird was watched while it was diving for water-weed and attempting to build a nest, as described by T. Bispham in *British Birds*, 41:351. It stayed until June 1st and one, probably the same, was seen on Staines reservoirs from June 6th to August 2nd and again from August 29th to September 21st.

BLACK-NECKED GREBE, *Podiceps caspicus* Hablizl. A visitor in all months, most regular and numerous in late summer and autumn.

At the opening of the century the black-necked grebe was known around London only as an irregular visitor in ones and twos, a desirable addition to the collector's cabinet. From 1922 to 1934, however, it occurred in almost every year and was classed by Glegg (1935) as an irregular visitor which had been recorded in all months save June and was apparently increasing. This trend was continued until the war, and where the records had previously been only of one or two birds together, or very exceptionally three, small parties were now appearing. By 1939 the *London Bird Report* was commenting on an "unusually large number" on the big deep reservoirs at Staines between July and December, up to seven or eight being seen.

When regular observation was resumed in 1945, the autumn was notable for a flock of 21 at Staines in September. This number has not been exceeded, although flocks of up to fourteen and fifteen have occurred there in several years. Black-necked grebes may appear in any month. In winter and spring there may be parties of up to half-a-dozen or so at Staines and perhaps occasional birds elsewhere, but in the last fifteen years they have become known principally as regular visitors in summer and autumn, whereas the Slavonian and red-necked grebes are essentially irregular visitors in winter. In some years the little flocks of black-necked grebes at Staines appear as early as the end of June but the numbers are usually highest from August to October. Some probably stay for several months but this can only be guessed except when a few remain in a constant party, as for example the six or seven which were reported at Staines on seven dates between November 5th and December 3rd, 1950.

Although the black-necked grebe is now regular at Staines, it is still erratic in its appearances on the other reservoirs and elsewhere, ones and twos occurring briefly in a few localities each year. Occasionally they are seen on the Thames, or on ponds such as those at Godstone or on Bookham Common, on gravel pits, or even on the park lakes of Inner London.

LITTLE GREBE, *Podiceps ruficollis* (Pallas). Resident, breeds regularly on undisturbed waters where there is sufficient cover. Autumn and winter flocks sometimes up to sixty or more on shallower waters, and exceptionally over a hundred. Infrequent on large, open reservoirs.

Around the beginning of our period information on the breeding status of the little grebe is very sketchy. In Inner London the first pair is thought to have nested in St. James's Park about 1883 and little grebes are believed to have spread from there to the other London parks, so that by 1898 W. H. Hudson in *Birds in London* was able to describe them as being as well established as the moorhen and the woodpigeon.

More evidence of their distribution in the breeding season was forthcoming in the years between the wars, although it relates mostly to Middlesex and Surrey. Among a number of Surrey localities a notable colony is at Fetcham Mill Pond, where P. H. T. Hartley estimated in 1931 and 1932 that about twelve pairs bred. Since the partial drainage of this area and conversion of parts to cress beds numbers have been much less. This pond is particularly favourable for observation and in the clear water around the spring as many as twelve dabchicks may be seen and their progress below the surface watched as clearly as if they were in an aquarium. Among the other places in Surrey where little grebes have bred fairly regularly are various gravel pits, particularly those at Beddington which have now been filled in.

In Middlesex, the reservoir at Ruislip, which has natural banks, has been a stronghold of the little grebe for the past twenty years, and many have bred at the south end of Elstree reservoir, though not since 1946. Elsewhere in the Area little grebes breed on many ponds and in the quieter reaches of some of the rivers, but many of their haunts are now artificial ones such as the numerous gravel pits and the shallower pools in the beds of some of the clay and chalk pits along the south bank of the Thames below Erith. In general, though there has been some shifting of the breeding population of little grebe due to changes in their favoured habitats, they still breed successfully, particularly in the south and west, where many reed-fringed ponds have been created by gravel workings, and on some of the streams and ponds that have suffered least at the hand of man.

In the built-up areas isolated nests have occasionally been found on the Fox reservoir at Ealing, at Wimbledon and Highgate, and on the Leg of Mutton Pond on Hampstead Heath. The lake in the grounds of Buckingham Palace was for long a favourite site, probably because the birds were undisturbed—a pair bred there as recently as 1949—whereas in St. James's Park the periodical cleaning of the lake interferes with the supply of food and nesting materials, and breeding is now only erratic.

After the breeding season little grebes gather into flocks, particularly at the Brent reservoir, where the shallow water and marginal vegetation are an annual attraction. The numbers often reach 50-60 and exceptionally in 1953 there were 112 on September 19th and 121 on October 11th. Flocks are seldom seen on the deeper reservoirs, and the other localities where they may appear include gravel pits, ponds and other shallow reservoirs, notably at Fetcham, Mitcham, Walthamstow and Dagenham Breach, and at the Pen Ponds in Richmond Park. There is no evidence of the origin of these birds.

PETREL, *Hydrobates* or *Oceanodroma*

F. J. Holroyde saw a small white-rumped petrel in flight and on the water on the Thames between Waterloo Bridge and Blackfriars Bridge on January 15th, 1947, but was unable to identify the species. A bird which was picked up in Battersea Park on November 24th, 1949, and was taken to the P.D.S.A., Wandsworth Road, S.W. was described in the *Evening Standard* of the following day as a "stormy petrel". No exact description of this bird is available and its true identity must remain in doubt.

LEACH'S PETREL. *Oceanodroma leucorrhoa* (Vieillot)

Until 1952 gale-blown Leach's petrels had been reported on six occasions. A dead bird picked up in Cassiobury Park in November, 1905, was identified by W. Bickerton (*Trans.* Herts. N. H. S., 13 (I):49). A bird which had been wounded by shot was found at Wade's Hill in December, 1907 (Hanson, *L.N.* for 1926:41). One which was "taken" at Honor Oak Park station on September 13th, 1942, was identified by W. E. Glegg as female. On the fringe of the Area one was found dead at Gerrards Cross on December 24th, 1949 (Smithells, *Country Life,* 105:94). In the same year single birds were seen on two occasions at Staines reservoirs and satisfactorily identified in the field; one on January 7th, by A. E. English and H. R. Mead-Briggs, and one on November 13th, by C. A. White and W. N. Mitchell.

In 1952 there was a remarkable wreck of Leach's petrels in the British Isles (*B.B.* 47:137–63); in our Area, seven were found dead between October 28th and November 14th, and two were seen alive on November 3rd at Brent and Staines reservoirs respectively. A live bird was picked up in Romford on November 2nd, 1954.

STORM PETREL, *Hydrobates pelagicus* (L.)

A storm petrel was seen at Staines reservoirs at close range by E. E. Green and C. A. Walter on November 11th, 1950, and excellent descriptions were given. This was the first certain record for this species in the London Area during this century.

MANX SHEARWATER, *Procellaria puffinus* Brünnich

The Manx shearwater is another of the maritime species which sometimes become victims of gales at sea, being blown far inland to be picked up either dead or exhausted. The four recorded in the Area have all been in September: one found alive at Honor Oak on September 23rd, 1930; one in Clapham in 1946; one at Barn Elms on September 8th, 1953, and a badly oiled bird found on a pond on Mitcham Common about the same time.

MADEIRAN LITTLE SHEARWATER, *Procellaria b. baroli* (Bp.)

A male was picked up exhausted at Welling on August 20th, 1912. It was identified by R. Lydekker (*Country Life,* 33: 107, cf. also *B.B.* 6:314).

FULMAR, *Fulmarus glacialis* (L.)

Mrs. W. I. Brewer had good views of three fulmars flying north-east over Crayford on September 4th, 1954.

GANNET, *Sula bassana* (L.). Rare vagrant.

Outside the breeding season the gannet is essentially a bird of the open sea, and its presence inland is usually the result of strong winds. Twelve have been recorded in the London Area, two in May, one each in June and August and the rest in winter. Of these, four were seen in flight, or swimming, apparently undamaged, six were caught or found alive, one was shot and one found dead. Those in flight were all seen over water—one at Waterloo Bridge on January 28th, 1941, the others at Staines reservoirs on June 18th and September 13th, 1950—and one was associating with the swans on the Round Pond in Kensington Gardens on October 14th, 1952.

Of those which were stranded on the ground one hit overhead wires at Stratford in November, 1911, one was found in a cottage garden at Kenley in November, 1927, and was identified by H. W. Shepheard-Walwyn, a reliable ornithologist (*Daily Mirror,* 2.11.27) and another was picked up in a cornfield at Hayes, Middlesex, on August 6th, 1948 (*Hayes Gazette,* 13.8.48). The remaining records include one in February, 1937, at High Barnet (*The Times,* 23.4.40), two at the end of May—one at Wandsworth in 1930 and one in Epping Forest in 1941—, one at Hampton reservoir in late October, 1949, and one on November 30th, 1934, at Harlesden (*B.B.,* 28:312).

CORMORANT, *Phalacrocorax carbo* (L.). Regular visitor to the Thames, reservoirs and larger gravel pits. Recorded in all months but mainly in winter. Some evidence of a passage movement in mid-September.

The cormorant appears to have been almost unknown in the Area before 1919, and there are only occasional records, usually of single birds, for the 1920's. During the thirties they began to appear with greater frequency at the reservoirs of western Essex and south-west Middlesex, and yet in 1935 Glegg still regarded the species as "an unusual and irregular visitor" to Middlesex. On September 18th, 1931, a party of twenty-seven was seen at Queen Mary Reservoir, and these birds were evidently on passage, to judge from similar observations made at Staines in 1950.

Pinioned cormorants kept in St. James's Park from 1888 until the First World War do not seem to have attracted wild birds to the lake. Nesting took place but we are not told what became of the offspring, which presumably were left full-winged. Another pinioned pair, introduced in 1923, nested for the first time in 1931, and breeding continued for a number of years. As the young were not pinioned, many of the records for Inner London after 1932 can be attributed to the wanderings of these park-bred birds, but wild cormorants did sometimes pay visits and occasionally alighted on tall buildings. Two rested on Big Ben in June, 1928, while three years later another passed a few August evenings on the cross of St. Paul's. In 1933 a cormorant, believed at the time to be a wild one, mated with a bird hatched in St. James's Park, and in 1936 C. S. Bayne gave the number of full-winged cormorants in the Park as eleven, this total including two newcomers, one of them a ringed bird. By January, 1943, the two pinioned birds were dead, but cormorants continued to visit the lake for a few years afterwards, usually in autumn. Pinioned birds were introduced again in 1949, but were destroyed in the following year because they were found to be eating the ducklings.

In the London Area generally there was a remarkable increase in the number of records after 1946, with birds occurring on gravel pits at Hamper Mill and Rickmansworth, at the Brent, Walthamstow, and Ruislip Reservoirs, on and by the Thames particularly above Kew Bridge and on the clay pits below Dartford Creek, and at several localities in south-west Middlesex. Cormorants are now regularly seen at Syon Park from autumn until early spring, numbers of them perching in the riverside trees. As shown by Glegg (1938) there is nothing to support the suggestion that in 1936 a pair nested on Syon Marsh and reared young. The species is now a regular winter visitor to the Thames Valley reservoirs, especially those at Molesey and Staines, and a few sometimes stay on into the summer. In 1950 up to eight roosted on a buoy on the King George VI reservoir, and on December 26th, 1952, I.C.T. Nisbet discovered a roost of 2 birds in tall trees near Yeoveney, close to the Bucks/Middlesex border. Up to 30 were seen regularly on the reservoirs about that time and in the following winter, with a maximum of 43 on Staines Moor on February 15th, 1953.

Migration was noted on three dates in September, 1950, parties of 18 to 20 were seen passing over Staines reservoirs in a south-easterly direction. A bird ringed at Rhossilli, Glamorgan, on June 14th, 1930, was recovered at Staines on August 23rd of the same year.

At least two birds closely resembling the Southern race, *P. c. sinensis,* have been seen, one by P. A. D. Hollom at Littleton reservoir on March 19th, 1950, and another by I. C. T. Nisbet at King George VI reservoir on April 4th, 1952.

SHAG, *Phalacrocorax aristotelis* (L.). Irregular visitor, occurring mainly in winter but occasionally at other times.

There are few records of the shag before 1930, the first being of one shot at Aldenham in 1909 (*Trans.* Herts. N. H. S., 14:201). On January 12th, 1926, there was one in Wapping Basin, and in December of the same year Glegg (1929) saw one at the Lea valley reservoirs.

In the thirties records became more frequent, but after 1947 there were none until February 17th, 1953, when a young bird which had been ringed on the Farne Islands in 1952 was recovered at Morden, Surrey. In 1954, during a prolonged frost in February, shags were seen singly by Lambeth Bridge in Inner London on the 2nd, in a Brentwood garden on the 5th and in the Lea valley on the 9th. A second bird appeared there on the 15th.

Although the majority have been on the Thames, especially on the tidal stretch between Hammersmith and Isleworth, shags have been found on several of the large reservoirs as well as on smaller waters at Hamper Mill, Riverhead and elsewhere. Possibly some have been storm-driven, such as the three found in a nursery garden at Hoddesdon and exhausted ones picked up in the inner suburban districts of Balham and Hornsey. There have been ten in Inner London, including four on the Serpentine.

Most records have been of single birds but there have been a few small parties, such as three on the Thames at Chiswick in February, 1938, five on Ruislip reservoir in April the same year, and nine on the lake in Osterley Park in February, 1935. In 1937 three immature shags frequented the Thames near Barnes railway bridge during April and May, and at least one stayed until June 28th.

A shag recovered at Rickmansworth in December, 1936, had been ringed on the Bass Rock in July of that year.

HERON, *Ardea cinerea* L. Resident, passage migrant and winter visitor; breeds and flourishes in six main heronries, some within a mile of densely built-up areas. A regular visitor to the park lakes of Inner London, and parties of up to twenty or more occur on the reservoirs and elsewhere.

About 200 pairs of herons now nest annually within 20 miles of St. Paul's. This is nearly half the total for the Thames drainage area. Since 1945, when they were fewer, they have been settled in heronries at Wanstead Park, Walthamstow reservoirs and Little Parndon in the Lea valley, in Richmond and Kempton Parks near the Thames, and at Gatton Park in Surrey.

The oldest heronry is at the lake in Wanstead Park, where up to 70 pairs have nested regularly in tall elms and were a populous and long-established colony as far back as 1834 (Glegg, 1929). An anti-aircraft gun was used in the park during the First World War and a few pairs which then began to nest four miles away on an islet in Walthamstow No. 5 reservoir were doubtless from Wanstead. The numbers there did not seriously decrease, however, until the thirties and the transfer of most of the colony to Walthamstow which then occurred was the result of increasing human disturbance.

At Walthamstow the herons nest in complete sanctuary and in much the same numbers as at Wanstead in its heyday. Nearly all the nests are in dense thickets of large hawthorns thrusting up from an untrodden wilderness of elder, lilac, rose-briars and brambles. In places the nests cluster three or four to a tree, with new nests built on or beside the whitewashed remnants of old. The heronry at Little Parndon higher up the Lea began with five pairs in 1945, and has regularly held thirteen or fourteen nests in very high trees since 1950. It is probably the lost heronry from Hunsdon, two miles away in Hertfordshire, which was last heard of in 1939 with a strength of eight or nine pairs.

The heronry in Richmond Park started with a single pair about 1880. The colony increased to thirty or forty nests by 1909 and reached a maximum of 61 in 1939. Two bombs were dropped among the nesting trees in 1941 when over fifty pairs were in residence; the next year some of the trees of the plantation were felled and nine of the forty nesting pairs deserted. By 1944 several displaced and prospecting pairs had nested by the Thames at Syon Marsh and on Tagg's Island, and a new and flourishing heronry had become established at Kempton Park (*vide L.B.R.*, 10:23). This was started by one or two pairs in 1942, rose to twenty pairs in its second year, and increased at a rate of about ten pairs a year until by 1951 there were 93 occupied nests and it became the third largest in the country. Meanwhile the old site in Sidmouth Plantation was still being disturbed, so that the colony fell to eleven pairs in 1946 and evidently most transferred to Kempton. Here they nest unmolested in a variety of trees and are protected by game preservation. This site is within five miles of Richmond Park and rather less from a heronry which became extinct at Burwood Park, near Hersham, after 1942. Fifteen or twenty pairs had nested at Burwood Park since at least 1925, and birds from this colony may have resorted to Kempton, accounting in part for its rapid expansion.

The small heronry in Gatton Park started with one pair in 1930. The early settlers failed to go beyond the threshold of three or four pairs until 1943, when there were seven. A slight increase during the war years may have been the result of an intake of birds displaced from elsewhere, but certainly at Gatton they were not free from disturbance and more than half of the eleven nests in 1948 were robbed or destroyed. A colony which existed in Black Park, Iver, from about 1868 continued with 12 to 30 pairs until 1925 but was reduced to six in 1928 and became extinct. From time to time single pairs have nested sporadically, as for example those in 1950 and 1951 at Osterley Park, the first since a colony existed there from c.1550 to some time prior to 1872. Lockley (1936) referred to a colony at Syon House, but this was disclaimed by Glegg in *B.B.*, 30:249)

The effect of hard winters on the nesting of herons has been discussed by W. B. Alexander in his series of papers in *British Birds* "The Index of Heron Population." It was shown that the severe winters of the early years of the war, and the exceptionally cold and prolonged spell in early 1947, were followed by general reductions in the numbers of nesting herons. Using Alexander's method, a London Index may be calculated on the basis of the average nesting population in the six years to 1938, during which period the fluctuations were small and the population of London herons "normal" and probably not very different from the early years of the century. The figures during the years of change may be related to this standard as a percentage, and a diagram prepared similar to that in *B.B.*, 44: 124.

This shows that the effects in the London Area were broadly similar to those in the rest of the country, with considerable falls in breeding population after the worst of the winters. But whereas the Index for the country generally only returned to par in 1951, the London Index had recovered from the cold spells of the early forties by 1945, and in the years following the reverse of 1947 steadily built up to a substantially higher figure. Lack (*B.B.*, 39:205) asks: "If the heron can increase in one year from 79 per cent, to 92 per cent. of par why, when the population is at par, cannot it increase in the next year in the same proportion?" This is just what has happened in the London Area, with the Index rising in 1951 to 155 per cent. of the pre-war level; only now, in 1952 and 1953, is the "density-dependent mortality factor" becoming evident (*vide B.B.*, 46:102). The London Area would seem to be especially favourable to herons in that it offers them freedom from persecution, and a less severe winter climate than many other parts of Britain. Alexander's analysis in *B.B.*, 41:147 shows that in the summer of 1948, when herons were at their lowest ebb, the 16 per cent. reduction of the Thames area was very considerably less than the overall drop of 40 per cent.

The approximate numbers of occupied nests early in the century, and the minimum numbers since 1945, are given in the following table:

	1900/ 1912	1945	1946	1947	1948	1949	1950	1951	1952	1953	1954
WALTHAMSTOW	—	68	62	52	49	59	67	67	58	52	69
WANSTEAD	c.60	6	9	4	5	4	4	4	4	7	6
PARNDON	—	5	(5)	5	4	3	13	12	14	13	13
RICHMOND	20/30	39	11	10	11	12	12	18	20	23	13
KEMPTON	—	39	52	52	57	71	81	93	88	87	85
GATTON	—	8	(8)	(2)	11	7	8	10	12	10	10
IVER	12/30	—	—	—	—	—	—	—	—	—	—
MISCELLANEOUS	2/27	—	—	1	3	—	1	1	1	1	—
TOTAL	94/147	165	147	126	140	156	186	205	197	193	196

The attachment of some London herons to the neighbourhood of their home heronries is illustrated by two recoveries: an adult ringed at Hersham in May, 1934, was recovered within two miles in July, 1936; and a bird ringed as a nestling at Hersham was found eight years later at the heronry of its birth. The dispersal of young herons soon after fledging is shown by the recovery of another Hersham nestling, and two from

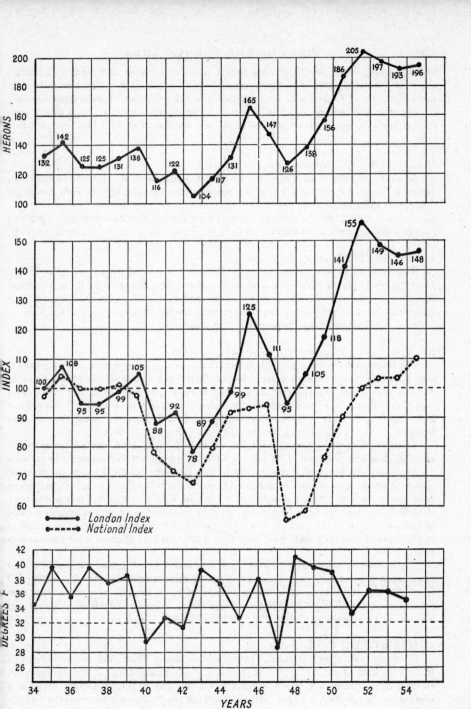

FIG. 4
The heron population of the London Area

Walthamstow, which moved in their first autumn and winter to Sussex, Cambridge-shire and Norfolk; while two from Virginia Water were retaken within two months in the Colne valley. Conversely, six ringed as young in Kent and Cambridgeshire were recovered in the London Area in their first autumn and winter, and two others after several years. A heron ringed in Slesvig in June was found at Mill Hill four autumns later.

[NIGHT HERON, *Nycticorax nycticorax* (L.)]

A heron, believed to have been of this species, was seen by R. H. Ryall at the Brent reservoir on April 25th, 1951, but as the observation was made in poor light it was not considered quite conclusive.

A ringed night heron, which had escaped from the London Zoo, frequented gardens and raided fish-ponds at Watford during April, 1935 (*Trans.* Herts. N. H. S., 20:282).

LITTLE BITTERN, *Ixobrychus minutus* (L.)

Two little bitterns appeared in 1954. An adult was seen by J. L. F. Parslow at Nazeing gravel pit on May 30th, and an immature, first identified by B. A. Marsh on August 20th, stayed at the Pen Ponds in Richmond Park until at least the 24th, during which time it was seen by many observers. One in similar plumage was reported by B. S. Milne at Beddington sewage farm on the 27th and 29th.

BITTERN, *Botaurus stellaris* (L.). Rare winter visitor.

The bittern has occurred more than twenty times during the period under considera-tion, mostly between December and March. There have also been records for October and November, and one of a bird found dead at Poyle gravel pit by Lord Hurcomb on April 17th, 1948 which "had evidently been shot a week or two previously". Birds have been reported in each of the counties represented in the London Area, the numbers being:— Surrey 7; Middlesex 5; Bucks. 1; Herts. 5; Essex 2; Kent 4.

The Area does not possess any extensive reed-beds of the kind which bitterns would normally frequent, but most of the records have come from wet and swampy places, with a certain amount of suitable cover, such as can be found on the Thames marshes, at sewage farms and gravel pits. Occasionally, however, birds have been found in unexpected situations. One was found entangled in a bush in Kew Gardens in December, 1921 (*Kew Bulletin*, 1936: 60–64). In March, 1947, bitterns were seen in a suburban garden at Carshalton and in the grounds of a college at Strawberry Hill. During the winter of 1948 one was found on a main road near Oxted and was kept alive for some months at a nearby farm.

Many of the occurrences were at times of very severe weather, and it is probable that at such times bitterns are forced away from their more normal habitats by shortage of food. During and shortly after the great frost of 1947, for instance, there were four records of single birds:— Beddington sewage farm, February 1st; Ruxley gravel pit, March 2nd; Carshalton, March 18th; Strawberry Hill, March 21st.

WHITE STORK, *Ciconia ciconia* (L.)

On May 11th, 1930 Maj.-Gen. Dudley Ridout saw a white stork on the ground in Richmond Park (*Field*, 155:773). At the time it was thought that it was probably an escaped bird. Professor E. H. Warmington also saw one in bright sunlight flying in a south-westerly direction over Mill Hill on April 6th, 1938. There is no reason to suppose that this was not a genuinely wild bird, and this constitutes the first record for the county of Middlesex.

Reference should be made, however, to the experiment of 1936 when, under the aegis of the Haslemere Educational Museum, a number of young storks were released at a place on the Kent Marshes. When the birds left this area in August, 1936, they spread out along the south coast and to the Isle of Wight. The last reports to be received concerning them were from Cornwall on October 7th, 1936.

MANDARIN DUCK, *Aix galericulata* (L.)

The mandarin is an imported species which for some years has bred freely, not far beyond the limits of our Area, in wooded country around Virginia Water and Windsor Great Park. Here it finds a congenial habitat of close woods, threaded by small streams, where old oak and other trees afford holes for nesting and acorns and fruits for food. This thriving colony is believed to have been formed by birds which escaped from the collection of Mr. Alfred Ezra at Cobham. The presence of mandarins on the River Bourne, near Virginia Water, was first noted by Derek Goodwin about 1929.

Despite this breeding colony so near to London reports of the presence of mandarins in our Area have been surprisingly few. Dr. G. Carmichael Low saw one at Staines reservoirs on November 18th, 1928, and another on the Round Pond, Kensington Gardens, on January 9th, 1940. A drake in Regent's Park on April 13th, 1954, had not come from any of the Royal Parks.

In the spring of 1946 boys investigating a hole in an oak tree near Thorpe, on the fringe of our Area, put off "a funny sort of duck", and found eight or nine eggs inside, all of which they took. A blown egg from this clutch was recovered in 1947 or 1948, and was identified at the Natural History Museum as a mandarin's egg. Goodwin, who has given us this information, considered that the mandarin almost certainly did breed in the neighbourhood of Thorpe, and in 1953 R. W. Hayman found a female with seven young on the Surrey side of the Thames near Runnymede, a few hundred yards outside our boundary.

MALLARD, *Anas platyrhynchos* L.

A common resident, breeding freely even in the parks and in Inner London. Numbers enormously increased in winter.

In 1900 the reservoirs already constructed occupied less than a fifth of the present surface area of those now controlled by the Metropolitan Water Board; they included all the Walthamstow reservoirs except Banbury and Lockwood but not Littleton and Staines which are among those that now shelter the largest numbers of mallard at peak periods. The influence of the reservoirs in making the London Area a haven for mallard has been tremendous, and already in 1906 Kerr was writing of flocks of several hundreds at the Staines reservoirs, which had only been completed four years earlier. Previously in that district only small flocks visited the Thames in severe winters.

Although no figures are available to prove it, there can be no question that the mallard has enormously increased as a winter visitor since the beginning of the century, and it is probable that it has also increased in the breeding season. For a species which frequents small waters throughout the district counts confined to the reservoirs and larger lakes obviously give an incomplete picture, but undoubtedly many of the mallard which feed on the small ponds and ditches shelter by day on the open waters, so that the numbers on these do reflect the changes of the population as a whole, if we except the birds which have become tame and relatively sedentary on waters freely accessible to the public.

The size of flocks reported on occasion in the late twenties and early thirties suggests that no very marked permanent change has taken place since then. Counts of about 1000 at Littleton in September and at Staines in October, 1931, and of about 1500 at Littleton in January, 1930, compare with more normal annual peaks of six or seven hundred. Since 1945 with the resumption of systematic observation, the biggest flocks reported have been of about 1100 birds at Staines in November, 1950, and a few less at the end of January, 1952. Otherwise the maximum size of flocks is almost exactly the same as twenty years earlier.

The number of winter visitors is bound up closely with the severity of the weather, numbers increasing when there is widespread and severe frost further north and tending to be low when unusually hard conditions in previous winters may have seriously depleted the stock. From the census of ducks on all the larger waters it appears that the winter population of mallard in the years following the exceptional conditions of early 1947 was at an unusually low ebb, but that it had more than recovered by the winter of 1949-50. Though, as we have seen, the larger waters by no means account for all the mallard in the Area, we can say that the winter population on the principal waters (listed on page 45) is of the order of 3,500-4,500 and reached over 5,200 on January 27th, 1952, when there was severe freezing-up further north.

Part of the mallard's success as a London bird is undoubtedly due to its indifference to man when not directly molested. Thus, while owing to cats and other predators ground-nesting in London is very unlikely to succeed and the use of holes in trees is quite normal in the parks, the ducks have no hesitation in leading their broods across busy streets or in nesting in unusual situations such as roof gardens, flower-boxes, the timbers of the temporary Waterloo Bridge, a Dutch eel-boat moored opposite Billingsgate market, on barges in the Surrey docks or in the static water-tanks used by the fire service during the last war. The presence of ducklings in these tanks at the side of such busy thoroughfares as Victoria Street has been one of the more surprising features of London bird life. Twenty-one ducklings hatched from one hole in a tree in Regent's Park in 1947, with two ducks subsequently in attendance on the young, while the influence of the reservoirs is well exemplified by the presence in 1950 of twenty-eight broods in the Barn Elms, Lonsdale Road and Ranelagh district. Glegg (1939) suggested that another factor in the success of mallard around London was their association with captive or domestic birds, and certainly at times it is impossible to separate the wild birds arrived for the winter from the resident birds that have become almost fearless of man.

Mallard breed freely along the Thames and wherever there are reservoirs, ponds, marshy ground, gravel pits or sewage-farms in the vicinity. The influence of man in providing artificial habitats is thus a powerful factor in maintaining the population, and large concentrations of breeding birds are reached in some of the suburban parks. Under normal conditions nests are placed on wet ground or under the shelter of bushes, but quite frequently they are in pollard willows or oaks, where they have been seen as much as 25 feet from the ground.

Cramp and Teagle (1952) have discussed the dispersal that takes place in Inner London in early spring in search of breeding sites. By July the birds have collected again on the main sheets of water, and about the end of this month numbers begin to increase quite apart from the concentrations of residents. This process continues in August, and by September gatherings of many hundreds are recorded on the larger reservoirs, notably at Littleton and Staines. At this stage the influence of the Thames must be stressed, and between Kew and Richmond, which is the most favoured stretch, close on six hundred mallard were counted on October 23rd, 1949. It is quite normal for numbers to fall off in late September or in October before the arrival of the winter flocks. The subsequent fluctuations depend on weather factors, which may be operative far outside the London Area, so that in some years little change is noticeable between late October and early March, whereas in others freezing-up further north may cause a sudden temporary influx.

In the six winter counts of some two or three thousand mallard each in 1938-39 Homes (*B.B.*, 36:49) showed that the percentage of males varied only between 51% and

53%. Twenty-six subsequent counts in winter from 1948–54, covering totals ranging from 1600 to over 3500, gave percentages of from 49% to about 55%. The ratio of the sexes from the time when these are clearly separable to the beginning of the breeding season is thus to all intents and purposes equal.

Despite the interest shown in ducks in recent years very little is on record of their feeding habits in the Area. That birds from St. James's Park do flight some distance is suggested by the presence of wheat grains in the gizzards of ducks which have been shot, though these may possibly have been obtained from the docks (Höhn, *L.B.R.*, 12:36–8), Flighting certainly occurs regularly at the Lea Valley reservoirs, and some mallard visit sewage farms and small ponds at night for feeding. They have also been seen feeding on algae at Barn Elms, but on present information there is no indication of the extent to which the reservoirs provide them with food, a problem which cannot be solved without extensive shooting. Certainly, in the parks, bread and other food offered by the public must form an appreciable part of their diet.

A habit of mallard that is probably commoner in the London parks than elsewhere is their persecution of house sparrows, which on several occasions they have been seen to seize and drown. Twice at least the victims have been swallowed (*Royal Parks Report*, 1929:4).

TEAL, *Anas crecca* L. Mainly winter visitor and passage migrant, and fourth most numerous duck in the area. Up to five pairs bred regularly at Ruislip from 1934 to about 1941, but otherwise very few records of breeding.

Movements of teal in Western Europe have been studied by Lebret (*Ardea*, 35 (1/2) 79–131) who has shown that there are three peaks in the British Isles, in the second half of August, the second half of October and in November or December. Exact dates naturally vary from year to year but, in general, flocks in our Area seldom reach a hundred in number before the second half of September, a notable exception being one of about 250 at Staines on September 3rd, 1929. Flocks of 2–300 may appear at any time from mid-September onwards, but it is usually December before the majority of the wintering birds arrive. The largest flocks at the principal localities have been as follows: Littleton, 400 on December 31st, 1929; Staines, about 600 on December 19th, 1948, and 650 on January 22nd, 1949; Island Barn Reservoir, Molesey, about 450 on February 7th, 1954.

The various duck censuses since 1937 have shown totals for teal of up to 853 of which all but eleven birds were on the reservoirs. Smaller flocks of up to a hundred or so regularly haunt the older gravel pits, sewage farms, cress-beds and parts of the Thames, particularly around Chiswick Eyot. Even so the above figure was a high one and it is doubtful if total numbers in the Area often much exceed a thousand. As already noted the preference of the bigger flocks for large, bare sheets of water, and of the smaller parties for partly overgrown gravel pits and similar localities with plenty of cover, contrasts strongly with the scarcity of teal on waters of intermediate size (cf. *L.B.R.*, 13:49–50). It follows that teal are most numerous in the Thames valley, but the smaller winter flocks occur regularly in the Colne valley and at various localities along the Wandle. In the Lea valley they are seldom numerous and the largest flocks recorded have numbered about 120 on two occasions.

Flocks of up to a hundred have been seen feeding on flooded fields in the Rainham district or visiting Berwick Pond at night, but little information is available on the feeding habits in the Area. Certainly the largest flocks on the Thames reservoirs can feed but little by day and must obviously disperse at night to nearby sewage farms and other suitable places for feeding. Only occasionally do teal visit Inner London and, compared with the other duck that visit the Area in numbers, they show few signs of becoming tame.

Numbers tend to drop appreciably in the second half of February or early March, in which month new flocks pass through on migration, a gathering of about 300 having been seen at Island Barn reservoir on March 27th, 1937. More characteristically, little parties or small flocks of twenty or so are seen at widely scattered localities. The percentage of males in flocks or totals for the Area of over a hundred birds ranges normally from 52% to 60%, with a slightly higher proportion in some large flocks. Comparison with details of smaller flocks shows a fairly consistent predominance of males in about the above proportion.

It was not until 1930 that teal were first proved to have bred in the Area, and then a pair nested near Cobham. In 1931 young were seen near the western border of Middlesex and in 1933 a nest was found at Ruislip. In the following year four pairs bred in the same locality and other pairs are thought to have done so between Northwood and Harefield. Breeding continued here until about 1941, part of the information being based on the unpublished records of G. K. McCulloch. In 1951 a nest with eggs was found at Epsom sewage farm. It is highly probable that a few pairs of teal have bred more often and in more localities than these records suggest, as pairs or solitary males have been seen with some regularity in the western parts of Middlesex, the Weybridge district and in the Lea and Roding valleys.

GARGANEY, *Anas querquedula* L. Unknown until 1927, increasing on spring passage until 1939 and regular in small numbers since 1945. Also noted in autumn, mainly in Middlesex. Has bred once in Middlesex and Surrey and may have done so regularly since 1946 in Essex and Middlesex.

The garganey was first recorded in the Area in 1927, when a male was seen in Richmond Park on March 17th (Collenette) and another in Kelsey Park on April 10th (*Field*, 149:676). In 1931 a pair was seen at the Middlesex end of Elstree reservoir and on May 10th a nest was found with twelve eggs, which were subsequently deserted. There is a possibility that young were reared later that year, but in 1932 a female only was seen. Apart from this one instance of breeding, the years 1928–39 produced eight spring records of from one to three birds (two in Essex, two in Middlesex and four in Surrey). In autumn, two were seen at Brooklands sewage farm in 1937.

Since the Second World War there has been a huge increase and birds have been recorded annually in Essex and Middlesex, in most years in Surrey and three times in Hertfordshire. In the Rainham district of Essex one to two pairs were seen every year from 1946 to 1952 and, in view of the regularity of breeding in the marshes of the Thames estuary, there seems every likelihood that they have nested or attempted to do so. In 1950 two adults were seen between August 23rd and 29th with seven young able to fly. In the Lea valley there were three pairs on March 20th and 27th, 1948.

In south-west Middlesex garganeys have similarly been of regular occurrence in spring since 1945, and from 1946 onwards have been present not only on passage but also in the breeding season, with a maximum of five males on May 9th, 1948. Again it seems more than likely that birds have bred but no proof has been obtained.

On the Thames and south of the river garganeys have appeared in several localities in spring, including a party of ten at Barn Elms on March 18th, 1947. In 1951 there were two pairs on flooded land at the Walton gravel pits on June 2nd, and in 1952 a duck was seen on the River Wey at Weybridge with two small young not yet able to fly. In the same year a pair stayed until June on Ruxley gravel pit in Kent.

The only Inner London record is of three on the Serpentine on March 12th, 1954.

In autumn the largest party contained 14 birds, seen at Old Parkbury and Moor Mill in August, 1953. Extreme dates are March 6th and October 31st.

Plate 21a. Great crested grebes are as common around London as anywhere in England: Gatton Park. (*G. L. Ackers*)

b. Drake smew with black-headed gulls and tufted ducks, a common association on the reservoirs. (*F. P. J. Kooijmans*)

Plate 22a. The wood sandpiper is a scarce but regular autumn visitor, especially to Perry Oaks. (*G. des Forges*)
b. The greenshank is a more frequent visitor on passage. (*G. des Forges*)

GADWALL, *Anas strepera* L. Very scarce vagrant up to 1932 when captive birds spread from St. James's Park. Has bred more or less regularly in the Barnes area since 1936 and at Beddington in a few years in the late thirties. Slightly larger numbers in winter but never numerous.

The earliest records of gadwall in our Area are of single birds at Navestock on November 7th, 1920, at Aldenham on February 7th, 1925, and at Staines on October 29th, 1931. Apart from these there were no other reports before 1932 except for the remarkable case of a drake which appeared on the Round Pond in Kensington Gardens in the winter of 1920–21 and was seen every subsequent winter for nine years, becoming a permanent resident in the later years.

In the autumn of 1932, after fifteen young had been reared in St. James's Park and allowed to grow up full-winged, the lake was drained and subsequently birds were reported in October from Staines, Godstone and Kensington Gardens.

The knowledge that full-winged birds had escaped may have discouraged many people from reporting their presence, and it was not until the autumn of 1935 that gadwall were recorded with regularity at Barn Elms, another 46 young at least having been hatched in the meantime in St. James's Park. Until 1939 the number at Barn Elms never exceeded ten but from then on the annual maximum has never been less than 20 or more than 42. Breeding took place at Barn Elms in 1936 and has been observed annually either there or at Lonsdale Road in all years since 1938 when observation has been possible. Elsewhere, breeding has only been noticed at Beddington, where a pair nested in 1938–39 and possibly in one or two previous and some later years.

Nowhere else have gadwall become regular even in small numbers, although a single drake was seen at Godstone in every year from 1932 to 1939. In the five other reports from Essex, three from Kent, eight from Hertfordshire, slightly more from Middlesex and isolated occurrences in other parts of Surrey, no flock exceeded thirteen in number. Even in the Barn Elms—Lonsdale Road district and the adjoining reaches of the Thames, where gadwall are regular, there are seldom over three pairs in the breeding season. They increase in autumn, and in some years the numbers then and in spring may exceed those in the heart of winter. The continued existence of the small colony at Barn Elms, where nests are made on the grass-covered causeways between the reservoirs, is a great source of interest to London ornithologists.

WIGEON, *Anas penelope* L. Winter visitor and passage migrant, large flocks being practically confined to Staines reservoirs. Stragglers may occur in summer but there is no suggestion of breeding.

A very large proportion of the wigeon that visit the London Area collect on the reservoirs at Staines, where until the winter of 1950–51 there was an average winter maximum of about 200, with numbers rarely exceeding 300. Nowhere else, except occasionally at Littleton, Barn Elms and in the Molesey district, have flocks of over a hundred been reported. It is possible that in the first quarter of the century, when reservoirs were so little visited, there may have been larger numbers, for W. A. Todd records in the *Zoologist* for 1909 that as many as two hundred had been seen at Barn Elms after severe weather. Despite much more intensive observation in the second quarter of the century the largest gathering reported for Barn Elms or Lonsdale Road reservoirs has been of about forty birds, and this was quite exceptional. There is some suggestion also that wigeon may have been commoner in the early years in the Lea valley, while Cornish (1902) had seen thirty to forty in Wanstead Park.

The only locality, apart from Littleton and Staines, where flocks of wigeon now occur regularly is at the Molesey group of reservoirs where in recent years upwards of a hundred have spent the winter, with a maximum of about 170 at the adjoining gravel pits on

February 7th, 1954. At times, especially in hard weather or on spring passage, parties may occur in other localities, and in recent years they have tended to be seen more often in the Chiswick reaches of the Thames. The status of the wigeon on the eastern side of the Area, where the boundary crosses the Thames at the Swanscombe marshes, is more obscure, as only recently has this district received much attention. The presence of about thirty birds there on October 27th, 1950, is, therefore, of some interest, but the Thames itself at that point is not wide enough to safeguard any large numbers from disturbance.

The earliest arrivals are normally of a few birds some time in September, but there is a passage at that time and occasionally in recent years it has been more noticeable. Thus about 150 wigeon were seen in the Staines district in late September, 1948, and forty-four on October 1st, 1949, while twenty flew over the Thames at Bermondsey on September 24th, 1941. Most often there are no flocks of any size before December, though exceptions do of course occur, notably a flock of 277 on October 30th, 1948. The largest flock yet recorded was one of 700 at Staines on December 19th, 1933, and since then numbers have only twice exceeded three hundred.

Except for shoveler, the wigeon are concentrated more at one or two localities than any of the other ducks, and frequently during the regular censuses of duck the numbers away from Staines have accounted for less than twenty per cent of the total. The reason for this is not very clear, though it is probably a result of the wigeon's feeding preference for pasture, for with the increased building development and concentration on the market gardening type of agriculture the other large reservoirs have little suitable undisturbed pasture close at hand. The birds undoubtedly prefer the large reservoirs to the smaller waters, because they can be further from any disturbance, and at Staines they not only feed on the grassy banks, but also have easy access to the banks of the Colne and the water-meadows on Staines Moor. The flock at Molesey in the last few years has also spent much of the day cropping the grass on the causeways.

The flocks frequently retain their winter composition until the middle of March, while small parties are seen regularly until late April, a few odd birds remaining occasionally into May or later. Despite the presence of three pairs at Staines throughout the breeding season in 1951 there is not yet any suggestion of breeding, though in view of a first breeding record for Berkshire in 1950 the possibility should not be overlooked.

PINTAIL, *Anas acuta* L. Exceptional visitor 1900–25, annual subsequently in very small numbers, principally in winter and on spring passage.

The early records of the pintail are almost exclusively from Essex and are of one or two birds in four winters between 1910 and 1926. In that period the only other reports are of a pair in Richmond Park on March 23rd, 1907, four birds at Barnes reservoirs on February 22nd, 1924, and one at Walthamstow reservoirs on September 12th, 1925. From 1926–30 one to two birds were seen every year in Richmond Park and from 1926 onwards pintails were reported annually in Middlesex. It was not until the winter of 1938–39 that odd birds were first seen regularly on the Thames and reservoirs in the Barnes district, while there was only one further record in Essex before the last war—four to five birds at the King George V reservoir in February, 1937.

No party larger than five was seen anywhere in the Area until the hard winter of 1946–47, when after regular reports of a few birds on the Thames, five pairs were seen at Walton reservoirs on March 2nd and twenty-six birds on March 8th. There are no other records of more than ten birds together, and in the Essex, Kent and Hertfordshire sectors there were until 1954 only occasional reports of one or two at a time. Rather more were seen in 1954, including eight flying over the Lea valley on January 31st.

In recent years pintails have increased markedly in winter in the south-east of England, and it is rather surprising that they have remained so scarce in the London Area.

SHOVELER, *Spatula clypeata* (L.). Up to about 1934 an annual visitor in very small numbers, mainly on autumn migration. Has subsequently increased considerably as a double passage migrant and partial winter visitor in west Middlesex and north-west Surrey, but largest numbers still seen in autumn. Has bred Bucks (once), Middlesex in 1935 and probably annually since 1948, and during the thirties possibly in Surrey.

For many of the ducks there is not sufficient evidence to show when their status has changed in the Area, but there is no question that the shoveler increased very considerably both on passage and as a winter visitor in the middle thirties. In 1900 Bucknill wrote of the species as "a rare winter visitor which has only been recorded in the county (Surrey) on a few occasions." For Essex, Glegg (1929) could only say that it was seen almost annually in limited numbers on inland waters during spring and autumn passage but that the largest party numbered six, while for Middlesex he wrote in 1935 that the shoveler was an annual visitor in limited numbers, but "it has no claim to be described as a winter resident, and is never numerous, the numbers ranging from one to twenty-one birds".

Though in Essex twelve is still the largest number seen in our part of the county, the above figures were soon exceeded considerably in Middlesex. Some thirty birds stayed throughout the winter of 1937–38 at Staines and during the autumn or early winter passage a flock of 88 was seen at the Island Barn reservoir, Molesey. This water had previously been little watched and prior to this winter the largest recorded flock in the Surrey part of the Area numbered ten. Staines, however, had been watched for some years, and in the last winter before observations were stopped by war-time restrictions a flock of 81 was recorded on October 8th, 1939. With the resumption of observations a further increase in the numbers in autumn was shown by flocks of 100 on October 15th, 1944, and a peak of 269 on September 2nd, 1945. Though the height of this movement was followed by a pronounced drop in numbers in most years, fresh arrivals also began to appear during the early winter months, reaching up to 200 at times and staying at the same level until about the turn of the year. Numbers are normally much lower in the second half of January and early February, but late in this month or more often in early March there is a marked return movement, most pronounced in 1949 when as many as 184 were seen on March 5th. Parties of twenty to thirty or so are still to be seen in April.

In spite of this pronounced increase during the last fifteen years of our period shoveler are still almost confined in any numbers to the Staines reservoirs. Although smaller flocks of twenty or thirty, and occasionally more, were occurring regularly on the Molesey group of reservoirs up to 1946, in more recent years very few have been seen there. Little has been recorded of their feeding habits in the Area that would explain why there are still so few seen in the Lea Valley and elsewhere. The only note of interest in this connection was made by A. J. B. Thompson when the large flock of 269 was seen at Staines. The birds were seen flying in from another part of the reservoir to feed busily where the water from the north basin was siphoning into the southern one. The food had not attracted the mallard or teal, and only grebes and a few pochard and tufted duck were among the shoveler.

Parallel with the increase on passage and as a partial winter visitor there have been a few definite breeding records and many more instances of drakes being seen alone in the breeding season or of small parties which probably included young reared locally. Dr. Sloane Chesser informed H. Bentham that he had seen and shot young at Beddington in 1932, while in most years from 1931 to 1939 birds were present in the breeding season at Brooklands sewage farm, including over twenty on July 17th, 1939, after four drakes had been present on June 1st. North of the Thames, Dr. Carmichael Low saw a duck with three young at Langley on June 21st, 1930. A female was seen with one young at

Littleton in 1935 and a year later there were ten drakes on June 10th. In 1939 ducks were seen with broods at Littleton and Staines. Since 1948 up to three pairs have bred in most years in the Perry Oaks-Staines district, and in 1952 as many as 10–12 pairs were present in the breeding season. In Essex, young were seen in 1951 at Berwick Pond, Rainham, and adults have been seen there and at a gravel pit in the Lea valley in other recent summers.

RED-CRESTED POCHARD, *Netta rufina* (Pallas). Very rare visitor; recent records may be due to escapes from central parks or Woburn.

The first red-crested pochard seen in the Area was a drake at the Lea valley reservoirs on February 16th, 1924 (*B.B.*, 17:310) and there are believed to have been others on the east coast at the same time (Glegg, 1929).

The species has been kept from time to time among the waterfowl in St. James's Park and, although its full history there is far from clear, it is known that in 1933 three young were hatched, of which two survived, and that two more were reared in 1936. Then, in 1950, several pairs were introduced into Regent's and St. James's Parks, young being reared and left unpinioned, and in the following winter a drake was seen at Barn Elms. Young reared in subsequent years have been left full-winged, and as many as twelve have been seen on the Round Pond in Kensington Gardens.

In view of the 1933 hatching it is significant that the second record away from Inner London was in 1934 when single birds were seen at Staines on April 26th and May 10th. The only others seen before the introduction in 1950 were at Beddington on November 23rd, 1940, in Kensington Gardens on February 14th, 1941, and at Barn Elms Reservoirs on May 2nd, 1946.

Since red-crested pochards have also been kept in captivity at Woburn, near Birmingham and elsewhere, there is inevitably a strong suspicion that all these birds were escapes, but it may be significant that the species has spread in recent times on the Continent. It now breeds in Germany, and since the early forties in Denmark and Holland, where large flocks (once up to 500—*B.B.*, 45:105) have been seen in winter. This suggests a westward movement of the German population and there is no reason why some of these birds should not reach this country.

SCAUP, *Aythya marila* (L.). Exceptional visitor before 1923, subsequently of almost annual occurrence in numbers not often exceeding eight. Single birds quite frequent in Inner London.

In the early years of the century, when tufted ducks were still a rarity in the south of England, scaup were reported in Richmond Park on March 27th, 1904, but in the light of the increasing reports of tufted in the next few years the identification is doubtful. A female, however, was shot on West Thurrock marsh in October, 1905, and the skin was preserved in the Stepney Borough Museum. The next certain record is of a bird in the Lea valley on December 31st, 1921, and it was not until the winter of 1923–24 that the scaup became a regular visitor. Two females were seen on the Round Pond on October 30th and remained for at least ten days, and single birds were seen at Staines, on the Serpentine in Hyde Park and in the Lea valley, where a drake remained from March 8th, 1924 to February 13th, 1926.

From 1923 onwards scaup occurred annually in the London Area except in 1927, and in all months except June, if the bird which stayed two years in the Lea valley is excluded. Only in three winters have more than eight been seen together, and both were notable for exceptionally severe spells. On January 8th, 1939, E. H. Gillham saw 17, including at least eight adult males, at Swanscombe at a time when many other ducks occurred in unusual numbers. In the winter of 1946–47 small parties were present for several months along the Thames and on the adjacent reservoirs west of London, the largest count being of 26 on February 23rd, 1947. During another severe spell in February and March, 1954, there were at times as many as 20 at Littleton, and up to five at several other localities.

Even though a few are now reported annually, scaup are still erratic in their appearance, and in the Lea valley, for example, they were seen in numbers up to eight in every year from 1929 to 1934, but seldom since. In the Hertfordshire sector there have been four records at Elstree reservoir, Hamper Mill and Stockers Lake, and in Kent they have appeared since the war at Danson Park, Ruxley gravel pit and Stone marshes, not more than four birds being concerned on any occasion. Middlesex and Surrey records have been rather more frequent.

Ones and twos have occurred frequently in Inner London since 1923 and often become very tame in association with tufted ducks; in recent years they have tended to make longer stays of several months. Very occasionally odd birds are seen in the second half of September, but more usually they are not seen before December and stay until late March, April or sometimes even May. Exceptionally, two were seen in Inner London on July 23rd, 1926.

A juvenile ringed at Lake Myvatn, Iceland, on August 6th, 1947, was recovered at Lonsdale Road, Barnes, on March 5th, 1950.

TUFTED DUCK, *Aythya fuligula* (L.). A resident and very common winter visitor that has increased enormously during this century. Breeds in limited numbers in several places, probably more extensively in the last twenty years.

Before 1900 the tufted duck was a rather scarce winter visitor. Cornish (1902), when recording over fifty at Barn Elms in that year, said that they had so far not appeared in any numbers either on the Surrey ponds or in Middlesex. In 1908 the average number in winter at Barn Elms was about twenty, while a year previously a flock of thirty at the Brent reservoir was the largest that had been seen there even though they were regular in smaller numbers (Kendall). A flock of ninety was seen in Battersea Park in 1905 by J. E. Barnes (*Field*, 105:277), and the species was seen for the first time in Richmond Park in 1905, at Dartford in 1907 and at Gatton Park in 1908.

Although tufted ducks were introduced to St. James's Park in the middle of the nineteenth century (Glegg, 1935 and *L.B.R.* for 1938), nothing further is known of their status there until 1913, when full-winged birds were nesting freely in the London parks. By this time the tufted duck was spreading rapidly in the British Isles. In our Area one pair bred in Dulwich Park annually from 1901-04; at the Walthamstow reservoirs the first pair bred in 1905, and by 1914 there were three nests on one small island—breeding also occurred in this period in Victoria Park about 1912, at Connaught Water, Finsbury Park and Winchmore Hill 1913 and at Snaresbrook 1916. Young were seen on a gravel pit at Hampton Wick in 1918, and regular breeding began at Kelsey Park, Beckenham, in 1920. The spread continued, but in many cases breeding was erratic.

The Walthamstow reservoirs have remained the chief breeding haunt outside Inner London, and as many as twelve broods have been counted in a season. Further up the Lea valley six pairs, and three separate families, were seen on Cheshunt Marsh in 1953, and tufted ducks have bred intermittently at other gravel pits. In Middlesex nesting was almost confined to London itself until the thirties, and there are still very few breeding pairs. Several gravel pits have been used in Hertfordshire commencing in 1936, and two pairs bred on the Middlesex part of the Elstree reservoir in 1933. In Surrey nesting began at Godstone in 1922 (max. 5 pairs in 1928), at Barn Elms in 1925 (max. 5 pairs), in Richmond Park in 1927 or possibly three years earlier (max. 6-7 pairs 1937-38), in the Beddington district on a series of gravel pits in 1929 (max. 8 pairs in 1939), at Gatton Park in 1930 (12 pairs in 1935), and has taken place erratically at several other sites including Wandsworth Common in 1927. In 1953 ten pairs, compared with the usual one–three, bred in Kew Gardens. Isolated records from Kent come from Chipstead ballast-pit, Ruxley and Greenwich Park, where a female once laid in a mallard's nest. The distribution of breeding records is closely correlated with the presence of suitable gravel pits, and as a result of several being filled in at Beddington no tufted duck have bred there since 1945. That many more would do so at the reservoirs if there were islands to provide a degree of safety is suggested by the history of the colony at Walthamstow reservoirs, where a series of islands does provide freedom from disturbance. Even so, nests are not infrequently found in the long grass bordering the banks of some of the reservoirs.

In Inner London tufted duck bred regularly in Hyde Park and Kensington Gardens from 1924 until at least 1938, but not again until 1954 when three broods were seen; forty-nine ducklings were counted in 1933. Regular breeding of unpinioned birds in St James's Park is recorded since 1925, and there were a hundred ducklings on the lake in 1929. Over eighty young have been counted in several subsequent years. Other sites used erratically include Buckingham Palace gardens and Regent's, Southwark and Victoria Parks.

The numbers of tufted duck in winter have also increased considerably since the early years of the century, when flocks of twenty, thirty or fifty were thought noteworthy. They were commonest at that time in the Lea valley, where most of the earlier reservoirs were situated, and ten years after the construction of the main Barn Elms reservoirs the numbers seen there were still small. There is no evidence to show when large flocks first began to occur, but in 1929 there were nearly 500 on one of the Walthamstow reservoirs on March 10th and about 410 at Molesey in September. A year later there was a count of about 600 at Staines, and in 1932 about a thousand were seen at Walthamstow. Until the winter of 1938–39 these remained the largest numbers recorded, except at Molesey where there were 864 on October 13th, 1937, and at Barn Elms where about 730 were counted in January, 1935.

In the course of a monthly census on the chief waters in the Area in the winter of 1938–39 over 3000 tufted duck were counted in the middle of January and February and even more had probably been present earlier as, after a sudden spell of very severe weather before Christmas, the numbers at Barn Elms alone had reached 1400–1500. Restricted opportunities for observation during the war prevented any comparison with the hard winters in the next few years, but big flocks were seen on the Thames itself when the reservoirs were presumably frozen over. Although there are a few earlier notes of flocks on the river—notably 25–50 near Battersea in February, 1917, and about 80 by Lots Road power station in January, 1928—the regular occurrence of large numbers on the Thames seems to date from the winter of 1939–40, as despite the greater concentration of observers after the closing of the reservoirs to the public it is difficult to believe that such large flocks would have gone entirely unnoticed before. The greatest numbers seen on the river in this period were 700–800 off Chelsea on February 14th, 1942, a mixed flock of 830 diving ducks off Hurlingham on February 29th, 1944 (in mild and open weather), and a conservative estimate of 2500 upstream from Chiswick Eyot on January 28th, 1945.

Another winter when snow and later unbroken frost lasted for an unusually long period came early in 1947, and the arrival of large numbers of tufted duck was shown by a count of 2200 at Barn Elms on December 22nd, 1946. With the freezing of all the smaller areas of water the diving ducks concentrated at the Walton reservoirs, where there were over 3500 tufted duck on February 25th. By March 2nd there was the phenomenal sight of 6000 divingducks of which over half were of the present species. The conditions at this time were quite exceptional, and a more normal picture is presented by

ie monthly censuses in the four subsequent winters, as a result of which it appears that
n average winter population for the major waters in the Area is 2500–3000. This figure
oes not include St. James's Park, where as many as six hundred tufted duck have been
:en and where it is usual for there to be three to four hundred in winter.

The contrast with the flocks of fifty or less early in the century, to which we have
lready referred, needs no stressing. The increase in numbers after the breeding season
iay be apparent as early as July, and by the end of September there may be several
undred at Staines and smaller numbers elsewhere. This increase continues usually at a
ow rate, and it is not until late December or early January that the really large num-
ers appear. Unless the weather is particularly severe some leave again before the
iiddle of February, and by the end of March there are probably less than a third of the
eak numbers. A fortnight later only a few hundreds remain.

The proportion of drakes in the censuses for the whole Area ranges normally from 50
> 60 per cent., but varies considerably on different waters. When tufted duck were
oundant every winter at Molesey, the proportion of drakes was sometimes as high as
3 per cent. and in mid-winter was usually well above the average for the Area. It is not
ifrequent for flocks of drakes to move independently with the result that percentages
om any one locality are apt to be misleading. Generally speaking, there is a small
reponderance of drakes in most totals of over a thousand, but this does not always hold
ood and females are often in the majority in March when the males may move off in
lvance.

The distribution of the tufted duck is linked far less with the Staines reservoirs than
iat of most of the ducks. While it is the second commonest duck in the Area and is more
idespread than any other except mallard, there is a strong suggestion of a preference for
ie shallower waters, and especially the reservoirs at Barn Elms and Walthamstow. So
arked has this been on a few occasions that over half the entire tufted duck population
' the Area has been at Barn Elms. The abundance of this species on the lakes in the Lon-
on parks may also be due in part to the shallowness of the water, and much remains to
: done in the study of the feeding habits of the flocks that occur on the deeper reservoirs.

Our knowledge of the origin and movements of London tufted ducks arises from
nging done at Molesey reservoirs and in St. James's Park. Birds ringed in the park in
inter have been recovered between spring and autumn in Sweden and European Russia
hree each), Finland (two) and Siberia and Novaya Zemlya (one each). One from
lolesey has been recovered in Finland, while a juvenile ringed in Iceland has been
und in St. James's Park. The only remaining foreign recoveries are of a bird ringed at
lolesey in February and recovered in Pas de Calais in the following July, and another
nged in St. James's Park in September and recovered in France 16 months later.
ucks ringed in the Area and recovered in the same winter have been reported from Co.
ntrim in Ireland, Oxfordshire and the Thames estuary (two). There are several
cords of recoveries at or near the place of ringing in following winters, and a few in
her parts of the country. St. James's Park birds have also been recovered from York-
ire in May, and Hertfordshire and the Lea valley in July. There is no evidence that any
rge proportion of the winter visitors come from other parts of the British Isles.

OCHARD, *Aythya ferina* (L.). A common winter visitor in flocks that may contain
veral hundred birds and have twice exceeded a thousand. Flocks, mainly of drakes,
so occur on some reservoirs in late summer during the moult. Has bred occasionally at
few localities since 1930.

Early in the century the pochard was probably an annual visitor in small numbers to
e Thames basin, though from the few observations available it is impossible to be more
recise. Few reservoirs had then been built except for some of those in the Lea valley

and at Molesey, and the small area of suitable wintering places must have had a limit
ing effect on the total numbers. In Richmond Park pochard were said in 1905 to be
frequent and a flock of 121 was seen in February, 1906; a hundred or more were counted
at Barn Elms in November, 1909, and forty-fifty were on the Serpentine in Hyde Park
in February, 1904. Writing of the Staines district, however, in 1906 Kerr did not even
mention the pochard, the first of the large reservoirs having only been built in 1902. The
only larger flock recorded before the gap in observations after 1914 was one of 200 or
more at Stoke Newington reservoirs in February of that year.

By 1929 the largest flock seen in the Lea valley was still only 110, and writing six
years later of Middlesex Glegg quoted the highest numbers recorded for various localities
showing a maximum of 300 at Staines in November, 1932. There is a certain amount of
evidence, however, that pochard were increasing as winter visitors in the middle
twenties. From being an occasional visitor in small numbers to Inner London they
became regular in winter on the Round Pond about 1924, and a year or two later
a flock of 49 was seen on the Thames at Chelsea. In the Lea valley higher numbers
were recorded in 1926 and 1929 (about 300 on March 2nd), and there was an unusually
large flock of 500 or more at Barn Elms on December 3rd, 1925. The normal winter
maximum at this locality remained, however, at between two and three hundred until
1933.

Between 1933 and 1939 there was an increase at several of the reservoirs, notably in
three winters at Barn Elms, culminating in a flock of 500–550 on January 7th, 1939, and
at Hampton and Ruislip. Reviewing the status of the pochard in the *London Naturalist*
for 1935, Homes considered that there must have been well over a thousand in the Area
at the end of that year. For comparison, a monthly census in the winter of 1938–39
showed a maximum of 852 for all the major waters of the Area, but the count dates
straddled the peak period at the turn of the year when the largest flock was at Barn Elms.

Since the war, flocks have contained over a thousand birds in two winters—in 1946–
47 when there were 1160 pochard at Barn Elms on December 24th and 1500–2000 at
Molesey in early March, and in 1947–48 when a flock that stayed at Staines for some
weeks contained 1267 birds on January 17th. In the first of these winters the weather
was exceptionally severe and most waters were frozen in February and March, but the
winter of 1947–48 was a mild one. Flocks of over 500 have been reported since the war
at the Brent and Walthamstow reservoirs, and on other occasions at Barn Elms and
Staines. Pochard tend to be fickle in their choice of locality, so it is important to study as
wide an area as possible. The monthly census in every winter from late 1947 covering all
the larger waters within twenty miles of London has shown that the highest population on
census dates has varied in six winters from 786 to 1600, but reached a peak of 2689 in the
winter of 1947–48. An average winter maximum is a little over a thousand, as it probably
was also just before the war. Undoubtedly the pochard has increased as a winter visitor
since the early thirties, but not within the last fifteen years except in the one winter
1947–48.

The extent to which pochard movements are governed by the need for a safe moul
ing area, by weather or by shortage of food, offers plenty of scope for research. In April
and May pochard are almost entirely absent from the Area, but in some years a few
re-appear as early as June. Numbers increase in July, and in 1936 there were over two
hundred at Staines by the 19th of this month. The increase usually continues in August
and at Barn Elms there have been over 150 and at Staines over 400 about the end of the
month. Numbers fall rapidly in September and subsequent movements are more
erratic. Despite the flock of 800 at Staines mentioned above, large numbers early in
October are exceptional, but towards the end of the month or in early November flocks
of several hundred appear, and there were over a thousand pochard in the Area on No

ember 12th, 1950. The very large numbers that have been seen on occasion do not usually arrive before the second half of December, and where these are associated with severe weather their stay may be short if conditions improve. In the winter of 1946–47, however, when there were at least a thousand pochard gathered at Barn Elms before the end of December, the weather remained extremely severe and E. G. Pedler remarked that about a week before the water froze most of the diving ducks massed together on one of the four reservoirs, presumably because of the higher temperature of the water as this was the last of the four to freeze. Very large numbers were subsequently seen on the Molesey reservoirs, and when these also froze they moved to the adjoining waters of the Thames. Under more normal conditions a pronounced drop in numbers takes place by the middle of February, and usually by early March only two or three hundred remain.

So little is known of the pochard's food in the Area that it is difficult to draw any conclusions from their habitat preference. Except when abnormally large flocks are present, they seem to prefer the smaller sheets of water of up to twenty acres or so with depths of 10–20 feet, but in contrast with this a huge flock remained at Staines for many weeks in early 1948 although the average depth of the water is considerably greater, being normally about 29 feet in one reservoir and 39 feet in the other. Flocks, which may reach one or two hundred or more, also occur quite frequently at some of the bigger gravel pits, and smaller numbers are often seen on the smaller lakes in the Area. In Inner London, where pochard now come regularly in winter not only to the Round Pond, but also to St. James's Park and sometimes to Battersea Park, there is no question that bread, provided by the public, forms one of the chief items of their diet.

A notable feature of the gatherings of pochard is the high excess of males, which is particularly marked in autumn and in some of the sudden winter influxes. For example, in January, 1948, 2071 birds sexed out of a total of 2721 counted showed a proportion of males to females of a little over 4:1, yet the ratio in the largest flock of 1267 birds was over 13:1. This very high proportion is normal in the autumn flocks, but in winters when conditions are relatively mild and there has been no marked influx, the sex ratio in the monthly counts may never be as high as 2:1 though almost invariably males will easily exceed the number of females.

Pochard were first found breeding in 1927, when a pair nested on dry ground at Barn Elms. In the next few years nesting was recorded at several localities:— Barn Elms, 1929 and 1931 (possibly 1930); Beddington, 1931–33; Richmond Park, 1930–32; and in Middlesex at Gunnersbury Park in 1931 and in Osterley Park in 1931–32 and several subsequent years. There have been single records from Essex (Sewardstone, 1945) and Hertfordshire: one pair bred at Old Parkbury in 1947, and there and at Cheshunt (4 pairs in 1953) pochard have spent the summer without being proved to breed. Nesting occurs regularly in St. James's Park, where pinioned drakes have bred with unpinioned ducks. It is impossible to say to what extent this source contributed to the rather sudden commencement of breeding elsewhere, but it does not necessarily follow that it was the cause, as the pochard has markedly increased and spread as a breeding species throughout the British Isles (Alexander and Lack, 1944). In 1953 two pairs of unpinioned birds bred for the first time in Regent's Park, and there were four, and possibly six, broods in 1954. In that year they also bred for the first time in Battersea Park.

FERRUGINOUS DUCK, *Aythya nyroca* (Güldenstädt).

Past records of this species have always been open to the suspicion that the birds had escaped from captivity, and it was not felt that they could be attributed with confidence to wild birds. As some of the earlier records suffer from a lack of detail or are from observers with no experience of the species at the time, they are not reproduced here. In the last few years, however, ferruginous ducks have appeared more frequently in other parts of the country (cf. *B.B.*, 44:352–4) and there seems no reason why some of those seen in our Area should not have been wild ones.

For historical record it may be useful to mention that a pinioned pair, which did not breed, were introduced into St. James's Park in 1912. Three birds were presented in 1930 and in 1932 a pair reared young which were not pinioned and eventually disappeared. A brood of seven young was reared in 1938, and a pair at Barn Elms, seen by Dr. Carmichael Low on July 17th, probably came from the park. An adult drake was seen at the same place by E. G. Pedler on January 12th and 29th, 1947.

A tendency of this species to occur more frequently in recent years in eastern England suggests that birds may be coming from the Continent, and there were records near London in all the years 1951–53. Two drakes were observed on artificial waters on the Dartford and Stone marshes in early 1951, and a single drake, which was first noticed in Gatton Park on December 30th, was seen either there or at Godstone until March 10th, 1952. Up to three appeared in Osterley Park and Southall in October of the same year, and a pair frequented Old Parkbury gravel pit towards the end of April, 1953 (cf. *London Bird Reports* for those years).

GOLDENEYE, *Bucephala clangula* (L.). Regular winter visitor to a few of the reservoirs since the early twenties but never more than about fifty at a time in the whole Area.

The early history of the goldeneye in the London Area is a tantalising one. Before the construction of the large reservoirs it was almost certainly a great rarity, but on December 29th, 1906, Kerr found "quite a number" at Staines and thought it could be said to be a regular winter visitor, though he did not give any further details. It obviously only reflects a lack of observation that there should be no subsequent records until the winter of 1921-22 when twenty-five birds were seen. Before that winter the only other records are of single birds at Elstree in 1908, Richmond Park, 1904 and 1906, the Thames at Kew, 1917, and at Putney, 1920, and of a party of four at Fetcham in 1917.

With the increased attention paid to the reservoirs in the early twenties the goldeneye proved to be of annual occurrence at Staines, at least from the winter of 1923–24, and at Barn Elms from 1925 onwards. Though it has been reported also in very small numbers from the Lea valley reservoirs since 1928 (maximum of 15 in February and March, 1954) and occasionally elsewhere, the goldeneye has never become very regular in its visits except to the reservoirs at Barnes, Molesey and Staines.

In the absence prior to 1947 of any synchronised counts in all its main haunts, the relative numbers from year to year can best be assessed by a comparison of the flocks recorded annually at Staines. Thus, in the five winters 1929–30 to 1933–34 inclusive, the average maximum was 40, but in the following five winters it was only 27. In more recent years the largest numbers at Staines have varied from 13 to 54 in different winters, so that on balance there has been little change. The only previous counts of fifty or more had been made at the same place on February 28th and December 25th, 1931. In Surrey the largest flock was one of 33 at Molesey on January 13th, 1934, and at the Barnes group of reservoirs numbers have never quite reached double figures. Exceptionally, over twenty were seen on the Thames at Hammersmith in the severe winter of 1946–47.

In 1935 Glegg wrote that in Middlesex goldeneye were first seen in the second fortnight of October and that some remained well into April. Subsequent records have confirmed this as a general rule, but have advanced the date of early arrivals in some years to the first days of October and have added several occurrences in May. In 1929 two immature drakes spent the summer at Staines, where also three drakes were seen from June 18th to early July, 1938, and one from June 18th to 25th, 1939.

There is a small but definite influx in most years in late February and March, and it is often in that month that the largest flock of the winter is seen.

Adult drakes are in a pronounced minority in all gatherings of more than a few birds, but display has been noticed at the reservoirs as early as December 2nd, and once on February 24th five drakes were seen displaying to one duck.

There are only five records for Inner London, but two of the birds stayed throughout the winter.

LONG-TAILED DUCK, *Clangula hyemalis* (L.). A rare winter visitor apart from one to four birds seen in Middlesex in eight successive winters.

The long-tailed duck was first observed in the Area in 1928 when one stayed at Barn Elms reservoirs from November 13th to December 17th. A few years later came the first record for Middlesex, at Staines reservoirs on November 6th, 1932. Two were seen at intervals throughout the winter of 1932–33, and on November 18th and 20th four birds in all were present. On December 9th another was observed at Walthamstow reservoirs. This winter was the first of eight in which long-tailed ducks were seen at Staines, and it seems more than probable, in view of the rarity of the species inland, that the single bird in the winters of 1933–34 to 1936–37 inclusive must have been one of the original two that stayed through the first winter. Up to three were seen in the winter of 1937–38, and one in the two subsequent winters, the run of observations then coming to an end when the public no longer had access to the reservoirs. Arrival ranged from September 25th to November 6th, and the last date from March 21st to April 25th. The second Surrey record was on January 27th, 1938, when one was seen at the Molesey group of reservoirs where it remained until April 2nd. One, probably the same bird, was at the Island Barn reservoir on April 19th.

Remarkable though the series of visits to Staines may have been, the next records were even more surprising, single birds being seen in 1947 on the River Thames near Hammersmith, at Barn Elms and Walton reservoirs and in St. James's and Regent's Parks. From a mass of reports it is clear that the extreme dates were February 25th and July 24th, and that for part of the time at least two birds were present, of which one remained in St. James's Park from March 23rd to July 24th except for a period of a few weeks in June. The sight of this maritime species swimming on the park lake among the mallard, and greedily gobbling up bread thrown by the public, provided a unique opportunity for London bird-watchers and serves, perhaps more than any other example, to emphasise the extraordinary attraction of the London parks for unexpected species.

In the winter of 1951–52 long-tailed ducks were reported from a number of localities, including Inner London for a few days in February, but all the records could have related to only two birds. In late 1952 one was seen at King George V reservoir, only the second record for the Lea valley, and at Barn Elms. In March 1953 there was a drake at Ruxley gravel pit, and in February 1954, a duck was seen at Littleton and in the Staines area until the middle of April.

VELVET SCOTER, *Melanitta fusca* (L.). A rare visitor in ones and twos since 1927; about twenty-five seen on one date in 1948.

The first recorded occurrence in our Area was of a bird seen by D. Gunn at Barn Elms reservoir on December 3rd, 1927, and ten days later one was seen at Staines. Prior to 1947 the only other records are for the Lea valley—one on February 16th, 1929, then two until March 3rd, and one from February 20th to April 6th, 1932; Staines, a male on November 23rd, 1929, and a female on April 18th, 1937, on which date Lord Hurcomb saw a male at Barn Elms.

In 1947 three were found dead at King George V reservoir between February 8th and 20th, one having been first seen alive, and in 1948 there were remarkable numbers on October 30th, when 20 birds were seen at Staines, 3–4 at Brent reservoir, and one each at Walthamstow and Walton. A male was seen at Barn Elms on November 14th. In the winter of 1951–52 an immature stayed at Staines for over two months and one was seen at Barn Elms on February 10th. There were two at Staines on December 27th, 1953, and in 1954 single birds at Littleton and King George VI reservoirs. At Staines two males were seen in 1949 on the unusual date of July 7th.

COMMON SCOTER, *Melanitta nigra* (L.). An annual visitor since 1926, chiefly on spring migration and in mid-summer and November; seldom seen in parties of over seven.

Glegg (1935) wrote that the common scoter had been seen in Middlesex in the years 1909, 1910, 1912, 1922 and 1926–34 inclusive, and had occurred in all months of the year except January and October; April had the most records with nine, and March and November four each. There are no other records for our district before 1929, when the species was first observed in the Lea valley and on the Thames opposite Barn Elms reservoirs and Ranelagh. Subsequent records and those for Surrey confirm Glegg's analysis of the months most favoured, which up to the end of 1953 were April (31 records), November (14), March (12), and July (9), these numbers referring to the whole Area.

When Glegg wrote *A History of the Birds of Middlesex* the largest parties seen had been of 16 birds on April 3rd, 1932, and of 13 on April 25th, 1933, both at Staines. These numbers have twice been exceeded, when 17 were seen at the same reservoirs on December 9th, 1950 and 18–20 at the new King George VI reservoir on June 7th, 1953. The common scoter has been seen most often at Staines but has also occurred at Brent and Ruislip reservoirs, three times in Inner London, fourteen times in the Lea Valley, once or twice at a number of other isolated localities, and on a score or so occasions in Surrey, chiefly in the Barn Elms and Lonsdale Road district or on parts of the river. Among the more unusual places where scoters have been seen are the narrow Beverley Brook on Wimbledon Common, the river Wandle at Carshalton and the edge of a sludge bed at Beddington sewage farm: such birds are usually very tired.

EIDER, *Somateria mollissima* (L.)

A party of seven eiders was seen on the River Roding near Ilford by Colin Murray on February 21st, 1917, and there were ten at the same place on March 10th, the weather being exceptionally severe in that winter (*B.B.*, 11:234).

RED-BREASTED MERGANSER, *Mergus serrator* L. An erratic visitor in very small numbers, mainly from the end of December to the end of March.

To what extent the red-breasted merganser may be overlooked among the flocks of goosander it is impossible to say, but from the available reports its visits are very erratic, which is hardly surprising as it is a much more maritime species than the goosander in winter. It was first reported this century in Richmond Park where J. Rudge Harding (*Field*, 127:329) saw four on February 20th, 1916. Apart from one in Hyde Park on February 12th and four at Staines on February 18th, 1922, no others were seen until the winter of 1928–29 when there were reports from Barn Elms, Molesey and the Thames at Hurlingham, where R. W. Hayman (*Field*, 153:486) saw five on March 8th, 1929.

Since then, mergansers have been seen in most years at one or other of the following localities:— Brent, Ruislip, Staines and Sunbury in Middlesex, the Lea valley in Essex (three times only) and Barn Elms, Molesey and Walton-on-Thames in Surrey. Ducks were seen at Ruxley and on the Stone marshes in February, 1954. Five birds are the most recorded at any time, and a very high proportion of the records have been in the second half of the winter. There have been two other records for Inner London—one in St. James's Park on October 7th, 1933 and a drake in Battersea Park on March 29th, 1950.

GOOSANDER, *Mergus merganser* L. Status before 1924 obscure, subsequently regular winter visitor in numbers up to a few hundred, increasing considerably in exceptionally severe weather.

As with so many of the ducks the recorded history of the goosander in the London Area virtually commences at the end of the first quarter of the twentieth century. In Middlesex it had been rare when Harting wrote in 1866, and in north-east Surrey the only reports before 1924 were of one in the nineteenth century and an adult male seen from Vauxhall Bridge in 1908. It was in 1922 that reports first started with a count of at least sixty at Staines on February 18th, a remarkable number if, in fact, goosanders had not been occurring there regularly for some time. From then on they were known as annual visitors to Middlesex, and from 1924 to Surrey.

There was no general census before 1937, but their relative abundance over the years has been assessed by Homes (1949) by comparing the largest single flocks recorded in successive winters irrespective of locality. This showed that from 1922-23 to 1931-32, the largest flocks were of 60+ at Staines in February, 1922, and of 62 at Molesey in March, 1931. There was also a count of a hundred on January 12th, 1929, reported by W. Kay Robinson and W. H. Spreadbury in *Country-Side* for Spring 1929.

During the six winters from 1932-33 to 1938-39 inclusive goosanders visited the Area in rather higher numbers. Some flocks exceeded a hundred in every winter except the first of this period, during which the largest numbers recorded were 174 at Staines in December, 1933, and 184 at Molesey on December 28th, 1938. It is obvious that numbers increased markedly in spells of extreme cold, and it is probable that a truer picture of the average winter population for the whole Area was given by the census of early 1939, when 213 were counted in January, 263 in February and 215 in March. After a period of little bird observation during the war, the influence of low temperatures was again noticeable in 1945 and 1947; in the first of these years a count of 320 was made at Molesey on February 2nd, while in February 1947 at least 550 were counted at Molesey and about 600 at Littleton (these may possibly have been the same flock). Subsequently, with a succession of milder winters numbers for the whole Area have in some years failed to reach two hundred, but in 1953 and 1954 the counts in February and March again resembled closely those of early 1939. Since the exceptional events of 1947 the largest flock has been one of 175 at Molesey in March, 1954.

At Staines flocks as large as these have not appeared for many years, and the eastern of the two Walton reservoirs in the Molesey group is now pre-eminently the most favoured locality. Taking into account the preferences shown at times for the large sheets of water at Island Barn, Littleton and Staines it seems probable that the chief requirements are a big expanse of water, for shelter during the day, or a fairly big one that is little disturbed, with smaller and shallower sheets of water carrying a good supply of fish reasonably close at hand. Insufficient observations have been made on the times of day at which goosanders feed, but the evidence suggests that this is largely at night or in the early morning, and in the thirties it was a common sight to see goosanders fishing actively up to about 11 a.m. in the Pen Ponds in Richmond Park, to which they were then regular visitors. Other observations from Hampton Court and Langley Park confirm the habit of visiting smaller waters in the early morning. Fish identified in the Area as prey include roach and gudgeon.

Away from the three principal localities goosanders have been fairly regular visitors to the Lea valley reservoirs since 1924, but have declined markedly in numbers since reaching a peak in the winter of 1935-36, when 59 were counted on one occasion. Elsewhere they are more irregular except in very small numbers, and have not become frequent visitors to Inner London where Cramp and Teagle (1952) note only five occurrences.

Normally the first arrivals may be seen in the second half of October or early November, but numbers do not often reach high proportions before the middle of December and are often still increasing in January. The largest flocks are often in March, when presumably they contain a proportion of birds on passage from outside the Area. Only a few remain after the end of the month and these may stay on well into April. May records are exceptional, and in 1939 an adult male was seen at Staines in June and July. On two occasions apparently injured birds have been recorded in the summer months, and in 1936 three immature birds spent the summer on the Mount Pond on Clapham Common.

Our knowledge of the origin of the goosanders that come to London is entirely due to P. A. D. Hollom, who caught a number at the Molesey group of reservoirs. Of the eight recoveries three have been in Sweden in April, one at Archangel in the same month and one in West Finland in September. Two of the remaining three have been near the place of ringing two and three years afterwards respectively, and the last bird was found, in the winter following ringing, at Slough, eleven miles to the north-west.

SMEW, *Mergus albellus* L. An annual winter visitor since 1922 at least, previously rare vagrant. Population in mild winters one to two hundred, with larger numbers in severe weather.

In most parts of the British Isles smew are seen in such small numbers that their regularity in flocks on the London reservoirs is really remarkable. Before 1922 the only records were of single birds at Kempton Park and Ruislip in the winter of 1908–09. When they first became regular in small numbers is difficult to say, as the reservoirs at one time received little attention from ornithologists. At Barn Elms smew were first observed on February 25th and in the Lea valley on March 18th, 1922; at Staines one was seen on December 16th, 1923, while at Molesey there were "large numbers" in early 1925. Up to the end of the winter 1932–33 the flocks occurring in the Lea valley, at Barn Elms, Lonsdale Road and the Molesey reservoirs in Surrey, and at Stoke Newington in Middlesex only once exceeded thirty in number—48 being seen by Major Daukes at Barn Elms on December 6th, 1925. At the large reservoirs at Littleton and Staines numbers never exceeded ten at this period.

In the winter of 1933–34 new peaks were reached at two localities with a maximum of fifty-one at Molesey. There does not appear to have been any other marked change in numbers until the severe spell at the end of December, 1938, when a splendid gathering of 117 was seen at the Molesey reservoirs. The restrictions on access to the reservoirs during the war years have prevented any comparison with the following winters, but there was a record of 37 smew on the Thames by Chiswick Eyot in the severe weather of January, 1940. Hitherto they had been seen on the river only in very small numbers and then usually towards the end of their stay. Flocks of 70–80 were seen at the Brent reservoir in February, 1943, and of 60 or more in the Lea valley and the Barnes district. Bearing in mind the scarcity of counts at this period they suggest that the tendency first noted in 1938 for larger flocks to occur in severe weather had continued, and in the first hard winter when observation was again intensive—1946–47—new peaks were reached in the Lea valley, at Barn Elms and Molesey with flocks of 89, 78 and 125 respectively (the last was reported by Keith Shackleton in *Country Life*, 103:539). As no counts were made simultaneously at the various localities it is impossible to make an estimate of the total numbers, but from later census figures it would seem that in winters when the weather is not unduly severe the total number of smew in mid-winter ranges from one to two hundred. It is equally clear that since 1938–39 many more smew have come to the Area in hard weather.

An interesting feature of the last few years has been the scarcity of smew at the

Molesey reservoirs, formerly the most popular haunt, and an increased use of the Barnes and Brent reservoirs, where in the winter of 1950–51 there were flocks of 93 and 119 respectively. That the larger reservoirs are avoided primarily on account of their greater depth is suggested by the visit to Staines of the largest number ever recorded there when there was a considerable drop in the water level in 1946, 48 birds being present on January 23rd.

Although away from the main groups of reservoirs odd birds occur at irregular intervals on most waters of any size that are reasonably secluded, yet only in nine winters have any been seen in Inner London, all singly except for three at the end of December, 1938. The cold spell at that time, when over a hundred were seen at Molesey, was responsible for another unusual record, of twenty on a flooded pit near Dartford.

In most years the first smew are seen in the second half of November, but the majority arrive at the end of December or in early January. Whether most of them stay depends on the weather: if milder conditions follow many disappear, while on the other hand numbers increase again if there is a freeze-up. Before the middle of March most of the smew have gone, and in few years are any at all seen in April, the latest in a year when none summered being April 22nd. Very occasionally one or two 'red-headed' birds have stayed all or part of the summer, notably in 1946, 1947 and 1949, and an adult drake was at Poyle gravel pit on June 2nd, 1951.

The proportion of the sexes is very variable, but it would not be unreasonable to say that, on the average, adult drakes represent a quarter to a third of the birds seen.

SHELDUCK, *Tadorna tadorna* (L.). An annual but erratic visitor in small numbers on both migrations and in the winter months. Most frequent on reservoirs along the Thames and in recent years on the marshes beyond Rainham and Erith. Bred Thames marshes 1954.

The reservoirs in the London Area have been watched so much more intensively in the second than in the first quarter of the century that it would be unwise to draw too firm a conclusion from the greatly increased frequency of records of this species since about 1928. The fact remains that, excluding the lower reaches of the Thames, only six earlier occurrences can be traced, viz. six at Staines and one at "Clapton reservoir" in the winter of 1906–07; one found dead in December, 1914, at Godstone and a pair at the same place on December 19th, 1920; five at Ruislip on February 5th, 1925, and eight at Barn Elms on September 13th, 1926. Since 1928 some have been reported annually except in the war years when there were few chances of observation.

Most of the reports come from the reservoirs, especially those at Staines, but ones and twos have occasionally been seen on the Thames, at gravel pits and at sewage farms. Davis (1907) reported the shooting of a pair in Darenth Wood in May, 1905, which bearing in mind sites chosen nearer the estuary of the Thames suggests prospecting for a breeding site. Though it is hard to believe that shelduck have not occurred regularly in small numbers around the Dartford marshes and ponds, there is only one other on record until 1949, since when parties of up to ten have been seen on a few occasions on the Stone and Swanscombe marshes on the south side of the river. Up to eight have been present during recent years in the breeding season on the Rainham-Aveley marshes, and in 1954 a pair was seen by S. W. L. Shippey with downy young. Two pairs were still present on the Kent side in the middle of June.

Analysis of the dates of occurrences is complicated by some birds moving from one water to another within the Area, but they seem to have first appeared with almost equal frequency in the months December to May, and very seldom in June and July except on the marshes. Arrivals in August are about as frequent as in the early months of the year and decline gradually from September to November.

The largest parties on the reservoirs have been ones of 12 at Barn Elms on August 26th, 1929, and March 15th, 1954 and of 14 at Staines on September 1st, 1946, the highest numbers being most frequent in April–May and August–September, immature birds usually predominating in the latter period. On the marshes in the eastern part of the Area up to ten have been seen at a time. No large parties have yet been seen crossing the Area for the "moult migration" recently described (*Nature*, December, 1949, and *Ibis* 92:405–418).

GEESE

There are a number of published references to unidentified geese passing over the London Area, and probably many people see geese but do not think it of sufficient interest to put on record. Most of the winter records fall in the months December–February and, though some may refer to Canada geese, they appear to be mainly due to hard-weather movements of grey geese. There are a few reports of 'large' numbers, but the biggest party of which any number is given was of over 100 flying E. by N. over Kensington on March 9th, 1952; these were believed to be white-fronted geese (*L.B.R.*, 17:13), and it is of interest that the last geese left Slimbridge on the Severn about four hours previously on the same day.

GREY LAG-GOOSE, *Anser anser* (L.)

All the definite records of grey lag-geese in the Area come from Essex. Glegg (1929) writes that three grey geese were seen on the lake in South Weald Park on March 23rd 1918, two being identified as this species on April 20th, and one was seen during severe weather on the Eagle Pond, Snaresbrook, on February 7th and 8th, 1919. More recently Dr. Höhn saw two on Banbury Reservoir on February 12th, 1947 (*B.B.*, 41:87). As there are no regular wintering grounds of this species in south-east England it is not surprising that so few have been reported, and there is always the possibility that any birds seen come from the various full-winged flocks in East Anglia. Full-winged birds, obviously escapes, have been seen on the lake in Regent's Park.

WHITE-FRONTED GOOSE, *Anser albifrons* (Scopoli)

This is the grey goose most often seen in the south-east of England and the one most often identified in our Area. Prior to the forties, however, the only definite reports were as follows:— a gaggle flying over Eaton Place, near Victoria, on March 2nd, 1909 (*Field*, 113:419); a flock of about twelve, of which one was secured, that passed over Caterham on February 25th, 1927 (per C. H. Bentham *in litt.*); one shot at Langley (Bucks.) on February 16th, 1929; one on April 7th, 1930, and two on April 12th, 1939 in flight near Sevenoaks. A number of other reports of geese in flight may well concern this species, and F. J. Stubbs heard white-fronts on more than one occasion passing over Theydon Bois.

Within the last fifteen years of our period there have been rather more records. J. R. Justice tells us of a party of 53 flying south-west over Sundridge Park on January 2nd 1940, and a flock of ten was seen by G. W. Collett on Staines Moor on the 24th of that month. In the same locality about 60 flew over on December 20th, 1950, and twelve were seen by several observers a week later. Other records come from the reservoirs at Brent, Molesey and Staines, Beddington sewage farm and Staines Moor again. Small parties of up to 17 have been seen in flight over St. John's Wood, West Wickham, Berwick Pond and South Norwood lake. C. B. Ashby heard a party flying over Cheam after dark on March 15th, 1953. In 1954 D. A. Cox and R. E. Scott saw 64 over Sutton

M. D. England

Plate 23.   Bullfinches are not uncommon in the larger suburban gardens

Eric Hosking

Plate 24. Starlings roosting on Admiralty Arch

on February 1st, and N. H. Pratt saw 80–100 flying east over Ruislip on March 20th, all those calling being of this species. White-fronted geese are said to have been seen often at Wennington Marsh before the last war.

There are no reports before the second half of December, and it seems probable that, while the London Area is not in the path of the geese when they first arrive, small flocks not infrequently cross it during subsequent changes of ground. In 1954 a first-winter bird stayed at the Hampstead ponds from January 3rd to May 7th: enquiries have produced no evidence of young geese of this species being reared in captivity in this country.

BEAN GOOSE, *Anser arvensis arvensis* Brehm

A party of eight was first seen at Staines Reservoirs on February 10th, 1940, by P. W. E. Currie. By the 15th the number had increased to eleven, which were last seen on February 22nd.

PINK-FOOTED GOOSE, *Anser arvensis brachyrhynchus* Baillon

There are only eight certain reports of this species in the Area, and a few more notes in which the possibility of confusion with other species cannot be entirely eliminated. Five were seen in the Darent valley in October, 1905 (Ticehurst, 1909); in the Staines district there were five on January 18th, 1929, and six on December 3rd of the same year (Glegg, 1935); ten were observed at Beddington sewage farm on December 23rd, 1938, and three at Barn Elms a week later. A suggestion that these were tame birds seems unlikely in view of the Beddington record and the severe weather at the time. Geoffrey Dent saw two skeins of about a hundred in all flying north-east over Great Parndon on March 15th, 1941. Nine flying over Moor Mill gravel pit on November 5th, 1950, were thought to have been of this species, and in the same year one stayed on Staines Moor from December 24th to 27th.

In 1954 R. H. Ryall and J. W. Donovan identified a party of 30 or more in flight near Uxbridge on January 30th, and four were seen going south-west at St. Albans on November 11th.

BRENT GOOSE, *Branta bernicla* (L.)

Inevitably ones and twos of this species should be suspected of having escaped from captivity, and in this category are one at Barn Elms on April 11th, 1935, and two at Walthamstow Reservoirs on June 26th, 1937. It is probable, however, that the following refer to wild birds :— two on the Thames by Chiswick Eyot from February 14th–16th, 1940, eight at Island Barn reservoir on December 17th, 1938 (both these occasions being during severe weather); seven at Swanscombe marshes on October 26th and fourteen on November 4th, 1950, and five flying south at Hamper Mill on December 23rd in the same year. There are also records of one at Beddington in 1942 and two at Mill Hill in 1946.

BARNACLE GOOSE, *Branta leucopsis* (Bechstein)

Davis (1907) mentions that one was shot at Chelsfield in 1902. The only other record is of a single bird which was present at Hamper Mill in Hertfordshire from February 5th to March 26th, 1950. Subsequent enquiries by C. A. White revealed that a party of ten full-winged birds had escaped from a collection at Wormley Bury, near Broxbourne, in the winter of 1949–50, and while it is peculiar that only the one bird should have been seen it is evident that it cannot be accepted as wild.

CANADA GOOSE, *Branta canadensis* (L.). A very local breeding species, usually at lakes in private parks.

Until the publication of the *Handbook of British Birds* it was not usual to mention the Canada goose in local avifaunas, and it is consequently almost impossible to trace its early history in the London Area. All that is known before 1930 is that breeding took place at Godstone in 1905 (C. H. Bentham), a pair was seen and photographed at the Walthamstow reservoirs about 1907–08 (*Birds and their Nests and Eggs*, G. H. Vos, undated), single birds were seen or shot at Westerham in 1906, Enfield sewage farm 1923 and Godstone 1926, and four were seen in Gatton Park in 1908 or 1909.

North of the Thames, Canada geese have bred at Walthamstow in 1936 (2 pairs) and 1940, and have probably done so in many other years, while a pair recently introduced bred at Valestine Park, Ilford, in 1953. In Surrey there is considerably more information on the latter part of our period. Canada geese first appeared as residents in Gatton Park in 1929 or 1930, in which year thirty-six were seen on July 6th. Three years later there were over a hundred in July, and by 1936 upwards of 130 were noted, many flying off to breed on other waters in the district. In 1938 the agent for the estate said that eggs had been destroyed for the last three years to keep down the numbers, which had reached about 200. All the geese left in March of that year, and up to May 12th only one nest had been found. As a result of military occupation of the park during the war the geese ceased to breed and became occasional visitors only, although 60-70 were seen by H. Bentham in December, 1952, possibly wanderers from a colony in Berkshire. Nesting has also been reported once or twice from Cobham, Godstone, Oxted and Reigate Priory. At Limpsfield in 1934 they were said to be present throughout the year, and at Godstone as many as fifty-three were seen in January, 1940. That the colony at Gatton provided the reservoir of breeding population for adjacent parts of Surrey is undoubted, but as the distribution of the geese is so closely linked with the presence of lakes in private parks it is impossible to obtain a clearer estimate of their distribution.

MUTE SWAN, *Cygnus olor* (Gmelin). Resident and generally distributed on the Thames, lakes, streams and ponds; also found at some of the shallower reservoirs.

Mute swans are thought to have been indigenous in parts of the British Isles, but the history of their domestication is so long-rooted that no one can tell the origin of those that now live in a feral condition on the Thames. Ticehurst, in the *London Naturalist* for 1933, gives a full account of the history of swan ownership and lists all the known swan marks. At present the picturesque survival of swan-upping takes place on the river each July when the birds are marked for the Crown (the reigning Monarch being the Seigneur of swans) and the two Livery Companies of the City of London who have a Royalty of a game of swans on the Thames. We are grateful for permission to quote from the reports of the voyages in the records of the Dyers' Company.

During the years 1900–20 the number of swans rounded up on these voyages between Battersea and Staines bridges fluctuated between 97, including 17 cygnets, and 222 of which 63 were cygnets. Subsequently there was a more or less steady increase until 1938, when there were 418, including 60 cygnets. These figures do not reflect a natural rate of increase of the population, as it is not known how many birds may have escaped inclusion in the rounding-up nor do we know what movements may take place between the stretch counted and other parts of the river or if any artificial methods of controlling the number of eggs hatched may at times have been used. Moreover, in 1937, the number of adults exceeded the total of adults and cygnets together for the previous year, so that it is obvious that newcomers must sometimes be included.

There was a marked drop in numbers during and after the last war, but the position is a little obscured as the voyages began from Putney Bridge, leaving out the stretch from Battersea to Putney; in the last two years before the war, however, there were only 2 and 38 swans respectively on this stretch. Between Putney and Staines the numbers continued to drop until 1951, when there were only 112, but in that year 157 swans were counted between Waterloo and Putney. These birds seem to have been attracted to the river by the large amount of food provided through the Festival of Britain celebrations. In the next three years numbers on this stretch of the river remained high, and there was an enormous increase between Putney and Staines, the count reaching 479 in 1954. The increase has been exclusively of adults, and rather fewer cygnets are found now than in the thirties.

Congregations of mute swans are to be found throughout the year, especially on the Thames in central London, where fifty or more, for example, may be seen above Battersea Bridge even in April and May. These congregations grow in size as the breeding-season comes to an end, and sometimes in early July may include over a hundred birds though none of the newcomers seem to be cygnets. Similar gatherings, though not necessarily quite so large, are found elsewhere and right through the heart of London to as far east as Dartford, the birds apparently obtaining sufficient food from the refuse that finds its way into this intensely busy stretch of the Thames. On the river the flocks remain during the winter months, while over fifty swans have been counted at this season even on the Round Pond in Kensington Gardens. Similar numbers are to be found on the Pen Ponds and at other localities.

At a number of apparently suitable places away from the river swans were scarce or absent fifty years ago, but as on the Thames they have increased elsewhere during the present century, and to-day they are widely distributed throughout suitable parts of the Area. Perhaps because they were considered "domestic" rather than "wild" birds their breeding and distribution received scant attention in the early years of the century. In the 1920's we know that pairs were resident and bred fairly regularly on the Walthamstow reservoirs, Fetcham mill pond, Beddington gravel pits, in the Weybridge and Godstone districts as well as round Uxbridge, Ruislip and Sunbury and on the ponds of Epping Forest. Doubtless there were other sites, but after 1930 more localities were put on record. At this time also swans were noted at Pen Ponds in Richmond Park after a lapse of twenty or more years. The flooding of gravel pits has provided them with a number of additional sites in recent years, even in developed areas such as Barking. Mute swans also succeed in rearing families on various ponds in built-up districts including, for example, Barnes, Snaresbrook and Woolwich, and on the lakes in the central parks. They suffer much, however, from human interference.

WHOOPER SWAN, *Cygnus cygnus* (L.)

The whooper swan has been recorded twice in the London Area during our period. K. E. Hoy saw four birds on Connaught Water, Epping Forest, in the early morning of January 26th, 1941, and Drs. J. M. and J. G. Harrison saw one on a gravel pit at Riverhead on April 9th, 1944 (*S.E.B.R.*, 1944:33). It is difficult to understand why so few birds of this species should have been seen, even as stragglers.

BEWICK'S SWAN, *Cygnus bewickii* Yarrell

There were eight records of Bewick's swans during the first half-century, although for the same period Walpole-Bond in *A History of Sussex Birds* (1938) gives only one certain record, and Gillham and Homes (1950) none at all for North Kent. The numerous reservoirs and other sheets of water may be the reason for this disparity, even though they do not seem to attract the whooper swan.

The most remarkable of the occurrences was of sixteen birds which descended on Barn Elms reservoir on March 5th, 1946, and stayed two days. A party of two adults and four immature birds stayed at Ruislip reservoir from February 17th to 28th, 1944. More recently, three adults and one immature bird were seen on the Pen Ponds, Richmond Park, from December 8th to 28th, 1948. The remaining records are as follows:— one bird at Gravel Pit Pond, Wanstead, from February 5th to April 14th, 1931 (*B.B.*, 24:339); an immature bird at Staines reservoir on October 27th, 1935 (*B.B.*, 29:219); two adults at Brent reservoir on December 20th, 1947; an immature at King George VI reservoir at Staines from January 8th to 23rd, 1948; one on the Serpentine, Hyde Park, on March 6th, 1948.

In 1954 nine Bewick's swans were seen at the reservoirs at Staines in early January and one on February 7th, on which day there were also three at Littleton reservoir. Four were seen at Ruislip on the 21st and one at Barn Elms on March 26th.

BUZZARD, *Buteo buteo* (L.). Scarce but regular passage migrant and winter visitor.

The buzzard ceased to breed in the home counties at some time in the eighteenth or nineteenth centuries, and it is now recorded only some half-a-dozen times a year. It is regular in that it has appeared in all years since 1912 except five, and although its visits are usually only short there have been several occasions when one or a couple have settled down in a district for several weeks. The first birds to stay were the two which for nearly three weeks in the autumn of 1909 were seen by Miss C. M. Acland soaring over the downland country around Banstead. At Gilwell Park, which lies at the south-western extremity of Epping Forest, one stayed for ten days in March, 1924, for four weeks in February and March, 1926, and briefly in March, 1927 (Miss Hibbert Ware *et al.*, *Essex Nat.*, 21:132 and 241; 23:67). Buzzards have been seen from time to time in Epping Forest itself, particularly above the steep western escarpment of the Forest Ridge where the birds presumably find currents of uprising air in which they can soar. Another favoured locality at one period was the country around Farleigh where one was seen on numerous occasions in four successive winters of the early thirties, eventually being found shot on December 15th, 1935 (H. E. Pounds, *B.B.*, 27:26; 29:83 and 357).

A pair reported by M. D. England to have established themselves near Oxted in the breeding season of 1937 might have nested had they not been shot by keepers. In fact, no nesting in the Area has been recorded, although the nine buzzards which were released in 1939 in Witley Park near Godalming, outside our Area, formed a small Surrey breeding population which still exists.

In general, the buzzards seen around London are on passage, soaring and drifting in wide circles high in the sky above a variety of habitats, even over the built-up areas. No one can say whether buzzards seen high overhead are *buteo* or *lagopus*, but most which have come lower, and even perched on trees, have proved to belong to the present species. A northerly movement in spring extends into June, followed by autumn passage from August to October. Though seen in all other months the records have been fewer, and never more than two birds have been seen together.

ROUGH-LEGGED BUZZARD, *Buteo lagopus* (Pontoppidan)

Although some of the unidentified buzzards seen over the Area were possibly of this species, it has been only twice recorded satisfactorily. The remains of at least one of three raptores found on a keeper's gibbet near Trent Park in the autumn of 1911 were identified at the Natural History Museum as those of a rough-legged buzzard (Glegg, 1935), and Professor E. H. Warmington recognised one over ploughed fields at Mill Hill on December 14th, 1946 (*L.B.R.*, 11:17). It is difficult to accept a record in the *Bulletin of the British Ornithologists' Club* (32:179) of one at Croydon in April, 1912, as there are no detail and the observer's name is not given.

SPARROW HAWK, *Accipiter nisus* (L.). Widely distributed, nesting throughout the open country surrounding the built-up and suburban areas; in the inner districts occurs not infrequently at all seasons, but breeding exceptional.

From the early records, and from the account by Ticehurst (1909), the sparrow hawk at the opening of the century may fairly be thought of as a bird which survived in limited numbers despite active and widespread persecution. In woods where game was preserved its chances of survival were small and the possibility of nesting even smaller. In the ensuing thirty or forty years its status remained much the same, pairs breeding wherever they could escape the gun and nesting from time to time as near to the built-up areas as, for example, Beckenham, Addington, Bushy and Osterley Parks, Stanmore and the northern outskirts of Enfield. At Hayes in Kent in 1937 seventeen were shot by one keeper during the year, but here nevertheless as many as four pairs nested.

By 1940, or thereabouts, the sparrow hawk was taking advantage of a lessening intensity of game preservation and was increasing. This improvement has been maintained until the present time, and is most clearly reflected in the reports of observers who have kept close watch on the birds of their district over a long period. Such observers have in the last ten years independently reported noticeable increases from over a dozen places in Surrey and from around Sevenoaks in Kent. From the Uxbridge, Ruislip, Harefield districts of Middlesex and from Radlett in Hertfordshire have come similar reports. There are others too from Essex, from Epping Forest and the wooded country of South Weald and Warley.

This very widespread increase is likely to provide replacements for those districts where the birds are still shot, and perhaps make more regular the hitherto infrequent nesting in places within the built-up areas. Around Oxted and Limpsfield, to take an example of a country district where the sparrow hawk is much persecuted, the gun did not prevent some seven pairs from nesting in 1946 and in 1948 eighteen, of which eleven were within a four mile radius of Limpsfield. Usually one pair breeds in the village, regularly hunting over the gardens. In the famous rhododendron woods at Dulwich, which are quite surrounded by building and are five or six miles from anything approaching open country, sparrow hawks have bred several times in recent years, although usually unsuccessfully. In Richmond Park and Wimbledon Common they have taken to nesting regularly. Almost all the larger woods of suburban north Kent west of Dartford now have nesting sparrow hawks, while in Greenwich Park, which adjoins some of London's closest built-up areas, pairs have bred on several occasions since 1944. In 1950 a pair nested, but did not rear young, on Hampstead Heath where sparrow hawks were seen frequently in summer in the previous three years and intermittently since 1941–42, the end of a long period of scarcity.

In the central parks and adjoining built-up districts sparrow hawks occur at all seasons but are scarce, much scarcer than kestrels. In 1953 a deserted nest with a broken eggshell was found in Holland Park, the first breeding record for Inner London, and this one resident pair may be responsible, therefore, for most of the Inner London records in recent years. Besides frequenting the parks and the bombed sites sparrow hawks sometimes fly above the streets and may even pursue their quarry over the roof tops.

According to the *Handbook* home-bred birds are sedentary, or at least do not wander far, and certainly this has been true of the recoveries, ten in all, of birds ringed as young in Kent and Surrey. Two were next heard of two years afterwards (one in January thirteen miles east, the other in the breeding season fifteen miles south) but the rest within a year, and all except two within twenty miles of where reared. The exceptions were ringed at Limpsfield and Chertsey and recovered in the following winter 95 miles N.N.W. and 45 miles E.S.E. respectively, but even this was probably dispersal rather than migration.

KITE, *Milvus milvus* (L.)

The kite has occurred twice in the Area, both records coming from Epping Forest. On May 10th, 1948, S. Austin and W. A. Wright saw one soaring and drifting at a considerable height over the Forest (*B.B.*, 42:60). In the following year on April 23rd A. V. Tucker saw two birds together flying over Baldwin's Hill at a moderate height; one bird was quickly lost to view behind trees, but he was able to identify the other as a kite. He was of the opinion that both birds were of the same species (*B.B.*, 42:391).

WHITE-TAILED EAGLE, *Haliaetus albicilla* (L.)

The white-tailed eagle has been identified with certainty three times. On November 12th, 1906, an immature male was shot at Cheverells, near Titsey. The skin was preserved and the identification was confirmed at the British Museum (*Field*, 108:1074). Sir Christopher Tower watched one soaring over Weald Hall Park for half an hour on February 6th, 1909, and one was seen in flight over Navestock Lake by G. Dent on February 1st, 1928 (Glegg, 1929). Glegg also saw an eagle near the River Roding at Passingford Bridge on December 15th, 1929, but could not determine the species (*Essex Nat.*, 23:19).

HONEY BUZZARD, *Pernis apivorus* (L.)

The only certain record of honey buzzard is for Box Hill, just within our boundary, where B. P. Austin had an excellent view of one under favourable conditions on July 27th, 1954, with the bird only some 20 feet up at a range of 100 yards. Two were seen in Hampshire about the same time.

On September 19th, 1936, Pounds (1952) saw a bird of prey over Crab Wood, Farleigh, which was almost certainly a honey buzzard, but the identification must remain only probable in view of his own reserve.

HARRIERS, *Circus* species

Both the Montagu's and the hen harrier have occurred in the Area during the present century, although the former has only been positively identified four times. Since only observers familiar with both species can separate them with any ease it is inevitable that there should be many records under the heading of "unidentified harriers". A brief summary of these is as follows: a pair, probably Montagu's, at Ashtead, March 12th, 1922; single birds at Minden Park, March 27th, 1937; Eynsford, October 22nd, 1938; Oxshott, April 18th, Letchmore Heath, September 30th and West Molesey, October 28th, 1948; Poyle, July 24th and Staines Moor, August 25th, 1949; Iver, March 14th and Regent's Park, September 8th, 1951; a probable female Montagu's on Stanmore Common on May 23rd, 1952; a 'ringtail' on Rainham Marsh, Essex, on October 10th and another flying S.W. over Barn Elms on November 7th, 1954.

MARSH HARRIER, *Circus aeruginosus* (L.)

The only marsh harriers to have come under notice this century have been a female or immature male seen by H. W. Rudd at Epping Long Green on September 22nd, 1951, and one at Beddington sewage farm seen by W. E. Barrett on September 5th, 1954.

HEN HARRIER, *Circus cyaneus* (L.). Rare passage migrant and winter visitor.

The hen harrier has been certainly identified about twelve times in the Area, mostly in the winter months. The four occasions when the dates overlap the normal migration dates of *C. pygargus* were as follows:— One shot at Langley, Bucks., on October 23rd 1911, and examined in the hand (*Field*, 118:1234); an adult male in fine plumage seen on Mickleham Downs by P. W. E. Currie on March 28th, 1935; one watched at Swancombe Marsh on several occasions between October 22nd and 26th, 1950, by Mrs. W. Brewer and K. H. Palmer, and one on Stone Marshes on October 29th, 1953.

The records all come from open stretches of country, and only twice were the birds seen on more than one day. It is probable, therefore, that the winter occurrences are of birds moving from one feeding ground to another.

MONTAGU'S HARRIER, *Circus pygargus* (L.). Very rare passage visitor.

In late April or early May, 1929, a harrier was trapped at Black Park, near Iver, and feathers from it were submitted to F. C. R. Jourdain who identified it as a Montagu's (*B.B.*, 23:98). On April 4th, 1942, near a badger's holt in Richmond Park, D. A. Rawlence found a number of feathers which were sent for identification to the British Museum (Natural History) and found to be "those of a female or young male harrier, almost certainly Montagu's." A year later on April 16th, 1943, near Mill Hill, a pair of Montagu's harriers were seen by Professor E. H. Warmington. A juvenile was seen on Staines Moor by P. J. Hayman on August 5th, 1953.

OSPREY, *Pandion haliaetus* (L.). Rare visitor in spring and autumn.

Up to the end of 1950 the osprey had been seen only twice during this century. In 1903 one remained in Weald Hall Park from October 11th–24th (*B.B.*, 2:383), and in 1930 one was observed frequently between September 17th and November 2nd in Panshanger Park (*B.B.*, 24:193). In the years 1951–53, however, there have been several reports, referring probably to ten separate birds, six of them in spring and four in autumn. Eight have been seen in the Staines district or by the adjoining reaches of the Colne, one at Ruislip and one at Moor Mill gravel pit. The only ones which were observed more than once were both in 1952, one frequenting the Staines area from April 29th to June 1st and another being seen on August 20th and again (almost certainly the same bird) from September 11th–19th.

HOBBY, *Falco subbuteo* L. Passage migrant and rare summer resident.

When in 1937 a pair of hobbies nested in an old crow's nest on the edge of the Area they were the first, so far as is known, to have succeeded since long before the start of the century. The same tree was used again in the following year and young were reared, but before the spring of 1939 this tree was felled and although one or two hobbies were seen in this part of Surrey in succeeding summers no nests were found. In the spring of 1946 a hobby was discovered sitting on eggs in a nest built on a squirrel's drey less than a quarter of a mile from the original site, but these eggs were lost and, although the birds remained for a time in the district and a pair reappeared there the following year no further nesting has been established. Nesting in 1946 and 1948 was successful at two other Surrey localities and in both years young were seen newly on the wing in September. At another site we believe that a pair had eggs in 1946 but were robbed. Since then birds have summered several times, especially in the Staines district, and pairs have been seen in spring, but although the wonderful intricacies of their display flights have been watched no proof of their nesting has been obtained. There are recent June records for Stone Marshes and Scratch Wood.

The hobbies which have bred in the outermost parts of our Area half-a-dozen times since 1937 may fairly be thought of as outliers of the established, though small, breeding population of the wilder parts of Surrey beyond our boundary. Hobbies regularly appear on passage in small numbers throughout the Area, particularly in the Thames valley, both in spring and autumn.

FIG. 5: The nort[h]

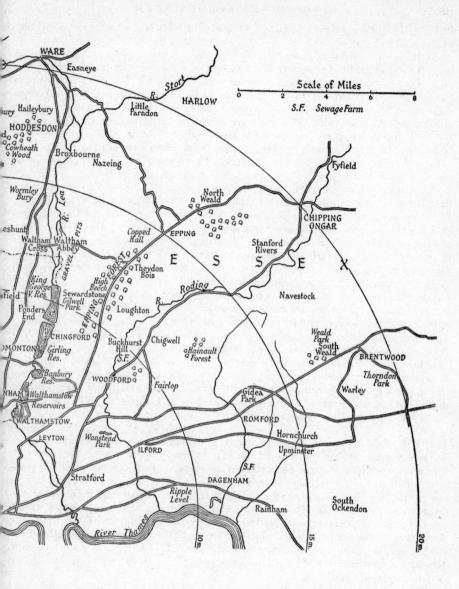

London Area

PEREGRINE, *Falco peregrinus* Tunstall. Occasional double passage migrant and winter visitor.

With close on a hundred occurrences to its credit in just over half a century the peregrine is exceptional before October but may visit us at any time during the winter and up to May, sometimes remaining for several weeks or months. In some recent winters one has been resident in that corner of Middlesex which includes the reservoirs at Staines and Staines Moor, a locality which shares with the Thames marshes between Woolwich and Northfleet the distinction of being especially to the liking of our visiting peregrines, but the chances of one being seen elsewhere are as limited now as they have been throughout the period. These records of winter residence are very recent although as far back as the winter of 1902–03 one was seen at intervals from October to February at the Elstree reservoir (E. P. Thompson in *Trans.* Herts. N.H.S., 12 (1):34–35).

Slightly more than half of the rest of the records scattered throughout the period are from the open country districts; for example, at Sevenoaks, Mickleham, Epsom Downs, Denham, or the larger parks as Richmond, Bushy, Nonsuch. Nearly half are of peregrines seen in or over the built-up areas of the centre or in the inner parks. Whether any of these were the result of confusion with kestrels no one now can tell; but enough of them are reported by experienced observers for us to be sure that travelling peregrines fly over or even come down in the innermost parts of London from time to time. In 1946 C. H. Bentham watched a peregrine soaring above the dome of St. Paul's, and Howard Lancum has described (*in litt.*) how in early March, 1931, he saw one take a pigeon there, and how during its five-day stay it was seen by a policeman to take others. The pigeons of St. Paul's were harried and fed upon by a pair in 1921 (H. J. Massingham in *Country Life*, 55:601) and other records of peregrines frequenting St. Paul's go back a hundred years or more and are quoted by Glegg (1935) and discussed by Fitter (1949).

There are records of peregrines chasing pigeons over Smithfield Market, and finding those of the Tower equally irresistible; of chasing a kestrel over Westminster; of perching on Big Ben and of flying over Lord's. Usually they have occurred in and about London singly, but sometimes there have been two and once, at Littleton in July, 1937, W. E. Glegg saw a party of four (*B.B.*, 31:297–8).

MERLIN, *Falco columbarius* L. Occasional passage migrant and winter visitor.

To the greater part of our Area the merlin is a scarce visitor which has been seen over fifty times since 1900. A large proportion of the earlier records comes from a comparatively small area of Surrey bounded by Walton, Tadworth, Banstead and Caterham. In this district, which is rich in heaths and open land, there have long been one or two resident experienced observers, and merlins have been seen in fifteen different years since 1910. The rest of the records are scattered fairly evenly over the remaining part of the Area, although in the last few years merlins have been seen with most regularity in the Staines district, including the sewage farm at Perry Oaks. There are two reports from Kensington Gardens: a male on August 24th, 1936 (*B.B.*, 30:174 and 365), and one on August 22nd, 1943 (*Field*, 25/12/43).

Merlins have been seen in all months except June, and most frequently in the period November–January. The extreme dates are July 5th and May 6th.

KESTREL, *Falco tinnunculus* L. At all seasons widely distributed; nests throughout the Area, including Inner London and the suburbs.

The kestrel is the one British falcon which has become thoroughly adapted to urban living all the year round. Its re-establishment as a breeding species in twentieth century London has upset the predictions of Hudson (1898), who believed that it was unlikely ever to return to this city which was so rapidly filling in her open spaces and expanding at the same time. Fitter (1949) and Cramp and Teagle (1952) have outlined a history of nesting successes starting with A. Holte Macpherson's record of a pair which laid eggs in a loft of St. Paul's School at Hammersmith in 1931, the first known record of breeding in the inner areas for fifty or sixty years. Evidence of nesting in towers and other high places accumulated intermittently through the thirties and forties although at first not more than one or two pairs a year were discovered. By 1946–47 it was known that kestrels were visiting shattered buildings and the forlorn towers of churches in the bomb-devastated areas near St. Paul's, and one or two pairs nested there. Of half a dozen pairs which frequented the innermost districts in the following summer some certainly bred, and by 1950 it was known that five pairs laid eggs in less than ten square miles of central London.

The sites were Bayswater, Battersea, Lambeth, Westminster and the City of London. The Bayswater pair nested in the spire of St. Matthew's church and reared two young, but the Battersea pair, which laid in an old crow's nest in the park, were robbed. At Lambeth a pair nested in a tall chimney—now demolished—of Doulton's old building, while another brought off one young from three eggs laid in the very tall Victoria Tower of the House of Lords across the river, only half a mile away. The nest site of the fifth pair was not found but probably they bred at Cripplegate, for in August two young were seen being fed on the roof of Broad Street goods station and later one frequented the bombed areas accompanied by the pair. With the exception of Battersea Park all these places have been known or suspected as breeding sites in other years, the Victoria Tower and the near-by towers of the Abbey, for example, having been frequented off and on since 1936 or earlier.

The increase which seems to have been so marked since the war cannot have been due solely to the new opportunities for nesting and feeding which were created by the bombing. The fundamental reason is more likely to be found in the surrounding country and suburbs. As open country has receded from the centre in the last fifty years, so also there has been a reduction in gamekeeping—already in a decline hastened by the two major wars. Persecution of the kestrel is still a shameful reality but, at least in the London Area, it happily no longer reaches serious proportions. A gibbet at Bayfordbury Park in June, 1944, contained the remains of eleven, and one at Hayes in 1937 exhibited about a dozen during the year. But this sort of thing has for a long time been unusual, and even as far back as 1911 nearly all the proprietors around Epping Forest, for example, had agreed to protect the kestrel. Nicholson (*How Birds Live,* 1926) has described how the confiscation of almost all weapons during the occupation of the Rhineland after the First World War soon led to a remarkable increase in the numbers of birds of prey. An untouched population of hawks in the open country made possible the penetration of Cologne itself, and much the same may be happening with the kestrel in London to-day.

Kestrels breed all though the suburbs, where they lay their eggs in hollow trees, in old crows' nests or in the towers of churches and hospitals. Very occasionally they have nested in such places as the framework of a gas-holder or the tall chimney of a power station. They nest, too, in such wholly encompassed open spaces as Dulwich Wood, Springfield Farm at Wandsworth, Ken Wood and Hampstead Heath. In the fifty square miles of suburban north-west Kent bounded by the districts of Deptford, Lewisham, Bexley and Erith their breeding strength in 1950 was assessed by J. F. Burton at about fifteen pairs. Within this area are Shooters Hill Golf Course and other wooded or partly wooded open spaces, but much of it is built over and part of it industrialised. In Richmond Park in Surrey there has been in some recent years a local concentration of as many as five or six pairs nesting in hollow oaks, although before the war breeding in the park was only once clearly proved. R. W. Hayman, in his note in *British Birds,* 42:90, attributed this increase to the exceptionally favourable conditions presented by the combination of a plentiful supply of nesting sites with a large area of wartime and post-war cultivation which provided more small mammals as food. The absence of serious persecution here as in north-west Kent is probably just as big a factor, especially as where field voles are not in sufficient supply (as in Inner London) the kestrel quickly takes to feeding regularly on small birds, in London mostly sparrows. In the outer and country districts the kestrel is a common resident, although it has been subject to local fluctuations where persecuted. It nests in a variety of situations, including some of the chalk quarries of the North Downs, but our present records scarcely permit an assessment of its numbers in open country in relation to the more closely watched built-up and suburban areas.

Seven of the eyasses ringed in Richmond Park since 1947, and two ringed at Hammersmith and Harrow, have been recovered, mostly in their first autumn or winter. From the random directions which these young had taken within thirty miles of their birth place, their movements probably represented dispersal rather than migration. Another of the Richmond eyasses, recovered in June two years later at Walton-on-Thames, may have settled nine miles from where reared. Two, nest-mates ringed in the park, were recovered after three winters: in Gloucestershire in May and at Acton in September. From these ringing returns of locally bred kestrels and from observation within the Area there is very little to suggest migration with any directional trend; but the kestrel is well known as a migrant on the north-east coast and evidently some movement does occur, for at Dulwich on March 28th, 1947, P. J. Branscombe saw ten to twenty kestrels flying south at 100 to 150 feet over a period of twenty minutes in mid-morning. They were in couples or singly, sometimes within sight of the next ahead, but why they were moving south at this season is uncertain.

RED-LEGGED PARTRIDGE, *Alectoris rufa* (L.). Resident in most suitable parts of the Area and common in many of the more rural districts north of the Thames. Generally less numerous than the common partridge, but may outnumber it locally. Absent from some parts where *Perdix* is common.

The red-legged partridge appears to be roughly maintaining the position which it held at the beginning of the century, but with some local variation. It is absent from some old haunts which have been built over, but it has increased in others. Kerr (1906) stated that it was "of the rarest occurrence only" in the Staines district, where it is now numerous and widespread, although outnumbered by the common partridge. There has certainly been a substantial increase in its numbers in the Staines and Stanwell districts in the past decade. In Hertfordshire, and in Middlesex north of Mill Hill, red-legged partridges are now common and becoming more numerous, apparently as a result of the widespread increase in corn-growing. They are also common in the Buckinghamshire sector of the Area around Iver, which is immediately north-west of one of the main Middlesex strongholds. In south-west Essex they outnumber *Perdix* by about 4:1 at Hainault, Grange Hill and in parts of the Roding valley, while in the Lea valley north of the reservoirs they are in places the more numerous species.

On the Thames marshes they are found eastwards from Erith in the south and Rainham in the north. At Stone as many as 27 were seen on manure heaps in October, 1952, and they may locally outnumber the common partridge. As long ago as 1906 the numbers at a shoot at Woolwich greatly exceeded those of *Perdix*, and though this may have been partly due to the methods used the environment is evidently a favourable one. Elsewhere south of the Thames red-legged partridges were once quite common on the lower parts of the North Downs, but are now less often reported. It is difficult to be certain how far this may be due to lack of observation, but the suburbanisation of much of the downland has almost certainly been responsible for restricting their range.

It is likely that this species is often overlooked. The red-legged partridge when approached by man seldom, if ever, adopts the technique of crouching till the last moment and then flying, as the common partridge often does. Hence unless deliberately stalked or searched for it is less likely to be seen close enough for identification. At a distance, whether on the ground or in flight, it presents very similar field-characters to the common partridge. It does not, however, raise and flick its tail when excited, as does the smaller species. When harried the coveys usually scatter. The many records of single birds may be in part due to this fact. As soon as it discovers itself out of danger a bird which finds itself alone usually advertises its presence by giving the rallying call (the well-known "Chuk, chuk, chuk, chukuk! chuker!") until it is either reunited with its fellows, or again frightened by some enemy. In most cases it is probably correct to assume that where such single birds have been noted the species is, in fact, present in the district. This is hardly likely, however, in the case of the specimen that was captured in Mortlake Road on June 23rd, 1948. Here one is inclined to suspect human transportation and subsequent escape or release. The species does, nevertheless, breed as near Inner London as Osterley Park.

The habits of this bird in our Area do not differ in any essential from those of the species elsewhere. It habitually frequents sewage farms, reservoir banks, and gravel pits, where these are surrounded by open or arable country, but its apparent preference for such places may well be due to the abundance of observers that visit them. There are records of red-legged partridges drowning in reservoirs and perishing in the viscous sewage of settling tanks. The bird's fondness for running or jumping on to any low wall, bank, or hillock, probably renders it rather liable to investigate such places, with fatal results.

PARTRIDGE, *Perdix perdix* (L.). Common resident.

Partridges have not been so commonly reared artificially as pheasants in the London Area with the result that in spite of regular shooting their numbers do not seem to have varied on such a large scale. Although they have naturally vanished from many districts which are now built over, there are still records of breeding in recent years from as near the centre as Hither Green, Dulwich and near the Brent reservoir, and in 1951 a pair spent the summer at Wormwood Scrubs; a little farther out partridges bred in the closing years of the half-century at Chingford, Mill Hill, Enfield, Chiswick, Kew, Beckenham, Woolwich Common and Shooters Hill. In the more rural parts they may be found wherever there is arable land, especially corn growing on light soil, and on grassland with a mixture of rough or waste ground with hedgerows, gorse, bushes or other cover for breeding.

In the early years of the century partridges were generally distributed in the Essex sector away from Epping Forest, were common around Willesden (Kendall) and not uncommon at Hampstead. In Essex they are considered to have gradually decreased, and on an estate where once up to 150 brace might be killed in a day Geoffrey Dent thinks that 40 brace would now be deemed a good bag. Reasons suggested for this decline include greater disturbance from people and dogs, early harvesting and early ploughing of stubbles, turning poultry on to the fields and thereby spreading disease, less grit on the roads and less roadside cover. None now breed as near in as Hampstead or Willesden, but at Mill Hill, Enfield and Hendon there are recent records and a pair was seen at Chiswick in 1947. Similarly, south of the Thames, partridges have disappeared from districts too heavily built over, as at Malden about 1936, but where sufficient open space remains they are still to be found, and golf courses and sewage farms, in particular, play a prominent part in maintaining a few pairs in districts that have been developed.

The enterprise of the partridge in occupying available territory even close to London is well illustrated by the breeding of a pair in 1947 at Dulwich, a district from which the species disappeared as long ago as 1909, while not less than seven pairs occupy Shooters Hill golf course, only some eight or nine miles from St. Paul's. In Richmond Park 165 partridges were shot in 1839, but by 1936–37, with no special preservation or shooting there were no more than five or six coveys in the whole park. Yet, in 1950, after a large part of the park had been brought under cultivation during the preceding years, 113 birds were counted on the eastern side alone. With a decline in cultivation in the years 1950–51 these numbers were almost certainly decreasing. A marked increase in the number of partridges has also been noted in the northern parts of the Area following the development of corn-growing in recent years.

In Inner London very few have been seen.

QUAIL, *Coturnix coturnix* (L.).　Scarce summer visitor; two breeding records.

Ticehurst (1909) quoting A. B. Farn, stated that a clutch of eggs was taken on Dartford Marshes about 1900. Elsewhere birds have been seen or heard occasionally during the breeding season in circumstances which suggested that they were resident, notably at Haileybury in 1901 (Wainwright, 1926), at Old Oxted on July 5th, 1909 (C. H. Bentham) and in Richmond Park during June and July, 1913 (Rudge Harding, *Field*, 122:177). In 1947 Mrs. K. M. Disney heard quail calling persistently from an area near Rickmansworth from late June until the end of August, when she saw an adult bird with five to seven young. Moreau (*B.B.*, 44:257–76) found that in that year probably at least twice as many quail visited Britain as in any other year this century.

The earliest spring record for the Area is one at Haling Down, near South Croydon, on April 17th, 1912, and during our period there are records for all months from April to November inclusive. A quail which was shot at Ponders End sewage farm on November 15th, 1923, came into the possession of the late P. J. Hanson, who made from it a skin which is now in the Society's collection.

The fact that records appear to be most numerous before 1920 may be due to the great spread of the built-up area of London, and the consequent reduction in cornland. Now that the growing of cereals has increased again as a result of the last war, and that the numbers of quail visiting this country have shown a slight upward tendency since about 1942 (Moreau, *op. cit.*) there is a possibility of the species breeding occasionally in the outer parts of our Area. Reports of odd birds have indeed been more frequent in recent years.

Two occurrences in Inner London are thought to relate to genuinely wild birds. One at Mile End on May 11th, 1915, was at a time during the first world war when quail were not being imported into this country. The second was of a bird picked up alive in the area of a house in Warwick Square, Pimlico, on September 18th, 1947. A bird found alive on the roof of the Agricultural Hall, Islington, in 1906 or 1907 was thought to have escaped from captivity.

PHEASANT, *Phasianus colchicus* L.　Common resident.

Fluctuations in the status of the pheasant are due more to human than to natural causes. Changes in the extent of artificial rearing and of shooting and the decline of gamekeeping during and after the two world wars have made it particularly difficult to give a connected account. In the more outlying parts of the Area pheasants were probably plentiful early in the century wherever they were preserved, especially in Surrey, but they were not very numerous in such widely separated districts as Richmond Park and Harrow, which suggests that within ten miles or so of London they were probably far from common even at the outset of our period—it is significant that in 1839 no fewer than 267 were shot in Richmond Park. By 1912 they were already declining on Wimbledon Common, and after the First World War they were still only stragglers to Epping Forest. At that time they were kept in semi-captivity in parts of central London and breeding occurred in Buckingham Palace Gardens, Holland Park and Kensington Gardens, accounting for records of single birds in various odd places.

The pheasant seems to have started increasing in the late twenties. A nest was found in Epping Forest in 1929, and about 1930 pheasants were said to have greatly increased in Gilwell Park, where they then nested regularly. In 1935 they were reported to have increased in Bushy Park within the last three years, and about a hundred were seen in 1936 in Kew Gardens, where they were still common in 1950. In the forties single birds were reported from Ken Wood and several built-up areas, while in Richmond Park full advantage was taken of the increase in cultivation in the Second World War and about 190 were counted one early morning in April, 1952.

Association of the pheasant with artificial control is undoubtedly responsible for many observers omitting to record the changes in its status, but it seems clear that in the absence of protection it is by no means common in the open country north of Mill Hill, and is probably most numerous in the wooded parts of Kent and Surrey. For breeding, however, it usually prefers the outskirts of woods or patches of bracken.

CRANE, *Megalornis* sp.

During a fog on the night of May 8th, 1924, Col. R. Meinertzhagen, who is familiar with several members of this genus abroad, heard a number of cranes passing over Kensington (*Field*, 179:384), and he has kindly confirmed that from their call notes he identified them definitely as *Megalornis*. The fact that there were a number of birds suggests that they could not have been "escapes", and the common crane, *Megalornis grus*, is the only likely wild representative of the genus. This species normally migrates from Spain to its northern breeding quarters without stopping, and although the birds could not be specifically identified by sight the unusual nature of the observation seems to justify its inclusion here.

In 1947 Harold Penrose saw a crane flying over London but was informed that it had escaped from the London Zoo (*Country Life*, 101:131).

WATER RAIL, *Rallus aquaticus* L. Breeding status uncertain, but it is probable that at least one pair nests in the Colne valley and others may do so occasionally elsewhere. More widespread as a winter visitor, though local.

There are few confirmed cases of breeding in the period. Davis (1904) considered the water rail to be fairly common and resident in the marshes of the Dartford district, though he knew of no nest having been found. G. W. Kerr (1906) said that in the Staines area the men cleaning out the bottoms of osier-beds had frequently brought eggs to him, but birds were rarely seen. In 1915 a possible nest was reported in the Roding valley (*Essex Nat.*, 19:90), and about 1906 a pair was present in the spring at Buckhurst Hill. A nest with one egg was found in 1935 near an old mill by the River Gade at Cassiobury Park in Hertfordshire. In 1936 it was suspected that one or more birds were present throughout the year at Chigwell sewage farm. There have been reports in recent years of a pair resident at Moor Mill, in the Colne valley, though so far no evidence of breeding has been obtained. The water rail's status on the marshes south of the Thames is uncertain, for the species has only once been seen there in the breeding season, though there are apparently suitable breeding places, such as the large reed-bed at Abbey Wood marshes.

In winter water rails are more widespread and, though no doubt often overlooked, they are reported regularly from certain areas where there is suitable cover, such as river valleys, gravel pits, sewage farms, marshes, etc. In Essex, birds have been seen or heard in most recent winters at Berwick Pond, Rainham. They have also been reported from Chigwell sewage farm (regular in the thirties), Sewardstone gravel pits, the valleys of the Lea and Roding and elsewhere. The Colne valley is a favourite winter haunt and odd birds are reported every year, from Moor Mill in the north to Staines Moor in the south, and less often from the adjoining valley of the Misbourne. A single bird was seen at the Brent reservoir in 1945 and one wintered in Bushy Park in 1935–36. In Surrey the species is most frequently reported from Fetcham Pond, Barn Elms, Godstone and Richmond Park, and used to be seen at Mitcham gravel pit and Beddington sewage farm pond before they were filled in. In 1950 one stayed for two weeks on a pond on Wandsworth Common. Water rails are seen regularly at Ruxley gravel pit and Elmers End sewage farm in Kent. In the Darent valley they have been noted on several occasions at Lullingstone and from the marshes near the mouth at Slades Green and Crayford Creek, as well as the nearby Abbey Wood marshes. Birds, injured or lost on passage, appear in various other parts of the Area from time to time and there are four records for Inner London. On the last occasion one was found at the end of October under some scrap metal on the roof of the Government Laboratory in Clements Inn Passage. There is no clear evidence of any change in numbers of this species since 1900.

SPOTTED CRAKE, *Porzana porzana* (L.). Very rare passage migrant.

All the known occurrences of this uncommon species have been in the early part of the half-century, probably owing to the fact that, while formerly it used to nest regularly in small numbers in many parts of Britain, breeding is now very exceptional (cf. Alexander and Lack, 1944).

In four of the five dated records the birds were either shot or found dead, and all these were preserved in various collections. The only one in spring was obtained at Chingford in May, 1911 and is in the possession of this Society. The other records were as follows:— one, Edmonton, October 19th, 1907; one, St. Albans, September 7th, 1910; one, Chingford, September 26th, 1914; one, identified by sight, Theydon Bois, November 19th, 1916 (*Essex Nat.*, 19:98). Davis (1907) said that several specimens had been brought to him at different times, nearly all from the neighbourhood of Sidcup.

CORNCRAKE, *Crex crex* (L.). Passage migrant in spring and summer in very limited numbers. In 1900 was still locally common as summer resident but already decreasing; probably a few pairs bred regularly north-west Middlesex up to 1926, but only certain nesting record since was at Westerham in 1941.

Norris (*B.B.*, 38:142–48) has described the decrease of the corncrake, giving the approximate period when it commenced as being Essex 1850, Middlesex 1875, Kent 1895 and Hertfordshire and Surrey 1900, but the scarcity of precise information may be partly due to the difficulty of finding nests. It is clear, however, that at the beginning of our period the decline had already begun, and Beadell, in particular, considered that on the North Downs around Warlingham it started in the years 1892–95 with the advent of the mowing-machine. In fact, although the corncrake was heard regularly, for example, at Tooting in the 1880's and was a summer resident at Streatham Common in the 1890's a scrutiny of the records for Surrey from 1900 shows that breeding was only proved in 1911–12 at Caterham (Grace Kearton, *Country Life*, 33:651) and in 1918 at Beddington. There is little doubt, however, that corncrakes still occurred in small numbers around Caterham, Godstone, Oxted and Warlingham and possibly elsewhere about that time.

In Kent, there were a few pairs breeding around Bromley in 1901 (Walpole–Bond) they were fairly common throughout the Dartford district (Davis, 1904), and were "generally distributed but nowhere plentiful" in West Kent (Macklin, in Turner 1909). In the same year Ticehurst wrote that up to seven or eight years earlier corncrakes had been found right up to the outskirts of London at West Wickham, Bromley and Lewisham, but were to be heard there no longer. A pair or two still bred in the river valleys.

North of the Thames corncrakes were still common about 1911 in south-west Essex according to Geoffrey Dent, but the only actual Essex nest to which we can find any reference was at Theydon Bois in 1917 (F. J. Stubbs *Essex Nat.*, 18:191). In Middlesex, Kendall described the corncrake as a regular visitor to the rural district around Willesden in the early years of the century and considered it fairly common in the meadowlands. It was said by Whiting to be common at Hampstead, but a decline was already being noted at Harrow and, in Hertfordshire, at Haileybury. Corncrakes were evidently still well established at Staines, as Kerr (1906) wrote that numbers varied considerably and although many nests had been destroyed by floods in one year there were more birds than usual in the next year. In Hertfordshire, arrival dates only are quoted for several years about 1905, suggesting that the bird was not a rarity, but the last nest was reported at Haileybury in 1913 and the bird was not observed at all in several districts in the following year.

After 1920 there is some suspicion of a pair having bred at the Lea valley reservoirs in 1927, and a pair was seen taking food to young at Westerham in 1941, but only in Middlesex is there any other evidence of presence throughout the breeding season. In that county the corncrake was heard regularly at Mill Hill, Northolt, and between Eastcote and Roxeth up to 1926, but thereafter only erratically, although two pairs remained throughout the summer of 1931 at East Lodge. The records suggest a possibility of occasional breeding at other times, notably at Addington and Headley in Surrey, at Westerham in Kent, near Chigwell in Essex and at Oxhey in Hertfordshire. The evidence, however, is fragmentary and undoubtedly reflects a genuine decrease before and during the twenties, even though the shortage of all ornithological information in the years immediately following the First World War probably resulted in a few pairs escaping observation at that time.

Outside the breeding season one or two corncrakes are recorded in most years on autumn passage, usually in August or September. At this season it is purely fortuitous whether their presence is noticed, and probably small numbers pass through annually. Exceptionally they are reported in winter, and there are six records for the period November to January. There are a few reports of stragglers in Inner London, including three of the winter records.

MOORHEN, *Gallinula chloropus* (L.). Common resident, breeding throughout the area on ponds, lakes, gravel pits, streams and other suitable waters. More numerous in winter.

There appears to have been no appreciable change in the breeding distribution of the moorhen in the last fifty years. By 1900 it was breeding in the central parks and had developed a tameness contrasting strongly with its wary behaviour in most rural districts. It was probably nesting in most other parks with lakes or ponds, and there are records of nests from Hampstead Heath, Springfield Park (Clapton), Walthamstow Park, Wanstead Park, Dulwich Park, Tooting Bec Common and Kew Gardens. The moorhen is still found in all these localities (despite disturbance by boating at some) as well as in several other parks close to London. In the south-east it nests on suitable waters at Woolwich, Greenwich, Lewisham and Deptford. Further out it breeds wherever there is still or slow-running water with adequate cover—on cress beds, gravel pits, sewage farms, canals, ponds, lakes, etc. It is a common resident on all fresh marshes south of the Thames. It is rarely found on the larger reservoirs, where there is no cover. Nests have been seen by the slower rivers, such as the Colne, Lea, Darent, Cray, Wandle and Mole, and on the quieter reaches of the Thames, as at Staines. In Epping Forest it is said to breed in almost every small pond and ditch.

It is not clear whether the moorhen is now more numerous as a breeding species than it was fifty years ago. Increases have been reported only from Kew Gardens and the Epping Forest area. There has been a decrease on Wimbledon Common where it nested at Queensmere and elsewhere up to 1925, but it is now only a wanderer along Beverley Brook in winter.

There has been a change in its status in winter in Central London. Hudson (1898) stated that while all moorhens formerly disappeared from London in the winter, they had become residents throughout the year in a few of the parks where there was shelter. Now there is a considerable increase in some of the parks outside the breeding season. The nesting population in St. James's Park in the summer of 1949 was not more than three or four pairs, but the numbers increased to 49 on November 6th and to 54 on December 18th. A similar increase has also been reported from elsewhere—thus moorhens are especially abundant on the marshes on the south bank of the Thames in midwinter. Birds may then be seen in unusual places, such as the one in a fountain-basin in Trafalgar Square, seen in November, 1946, by A. V. Tucker, or the ten reported by F. J. Holroyde on the Thames by Waterloo Bridge in February, 1945. Despite this considerable seasonal influx there is no real evidence of moorhens actually on migration.

COOT, *Fulica atra* L. Resident, breeding throughout the Area on most lakes, reservoirs, gravel pits and large ponds possessing suitable marginal cover. Numbers much increased in winter, when birds also occur on reservoirs and other waters devoid of cover, and occasionally on the Thames.

In the breeding season the coot is more restricted in its distribution than the moorhen. It needs a larger sheet of water (at least an acre in size and usually much more), probably because of its greater dependence on aquatic food, especially pond weeds. For a safe nesting site there must be suitably dense marginal cover or small islands. At the present time the coot nests on most waters in the Area meeting these needs—on lakes and the larger ponds (often in public parks, as at Richmond, Wanstead and St. James's Park), on many gravel pits, on reservoirs with cover (Walthamstow, Elstree, Ruislip and others) and on flooded chalk pits along the Thames marshes. It does not breed on the reservoirs with bare banks, such as Staines. Nests on rivers and streams are rare, though an adult with two small chicks seen on the slow-flowing Colne on Staines Moor by W. G. Teagle and A. J. Henty in 1950 may have come from a nest along the river as there were no suitable ponds near.

There are far more records of breeding in the Area since 1925. The increase in the number of observers is to some extent responsible for this, but it seems likely that there has been a real increase in the coot population, aided by the greater number of gravel pits with marginal vegetation now available. Coots have certainly increased in Inner London in the last fifty years. Because the wintering coots in St. James's Park would not stay to breed, eggs brought from Richmond Park were placed in moorhens' nests and pinioned birds were introduced. It was a pair of these which made the first recorded nest in the park in 1926. The colony has thrived and the pressure for nest sites is now so great that pairs have built on the open banks and in flower beds, usually with no success. In 1954 as many as 25 pairs tried to nest but only 13 young were reared. A survey in 1943—44 (*B.B.*, 40:194–98) showed that the coots held territories averaging about one acre in size, though one pair reared young with as little as half an acre. Until recently coots bred only occasionally in the other parks in Inner London, but within the last few years they have colonised Battersea and Regent's Parks.

It is clear that the numbers of coots visiting the Area outside the breeding season have increased. Kendall (1907) stated that the coot was seen only occasionally at Brent reservoir, whereas large numbers are now observed there each winter. The influx begins in some places in the last week in July and birds begin to leave about the end of February. Maximum numbers are usually found in December and January, though in some years the highest figures at certain reservoirs have been recorded from August to October. Counts made by members of the Society in the winters of 1937 and 1938 showed that the numbers on the different waters fluctuated greatly. In the census of December 17th, 1938, 1,930 coots were counted on the waters surveyed, the majority being on the reservoirs. The highest totals were 433 on Walthamstow reservoirs and 286 on Hamper Mill gravel pit, though at both Staines and King George V reservoirs flocks of over a thousand have been reported on other occasions. The species has occurred infrequently on the Thames in the winter months.

WADERS

For a variety of reasons it is extremely difficult to judge to what extent the status of the waders has changed during the half century: very few observers have left any records of visits to reservoirs and sewage farms before 1922, while the technique of field identification before the First World War was still at a stage when sight records of most of the waders inland in the London Area would have been viewed with considerable suspicion. The chance, therefore, of any but the commonest of waders being reported in the early years of the century was too small for valid comparisons to be made with more recent times, in which there has been an enormous increase in the number of observers as well as a great improvement in their optical equipment and powers of field identification.

From about 1922 visits by bird-watchers to the Staines reservoirs and the Lea valley became a little more numerous but, if we except the commoner species such as lapwing, redshank and common sandpiper, there was no appreciable increase in the records of waders until the late twenties, when the exposure of large areas of mud and shallow water at some of the reservoirs as a result of drainage showed that more birds of this type must have been passing through the Area than had been imagined. When reading the specific accounts it will be helpful to bear in mind that the periods when some of the principal reservoirs lay drained or partly drained were as follows:—

Staines reservoirs	*Autumn 1927*
Brent reservoir	*Autumn 1928*
King George V reservoir	*Autumn 1929 and 1933*

The Staines and King George V reservoirs lie in the important river valleys of the Thames and Lea respectively, but these were the first occasions when the exposure of a large extent of feeding ground came at a time when there were observers to study the results, so that the sudden increase in records of waders need occasion no surprise. The Brent reservoir, which does not lie in an important river valley, is close to Mill Hill, where at that time Harrisson (*L.N.* for 1930, p.87) records how Professor Warmington was already aware of a considerable volume of night passage of waders. It was for the Brent reservoir also, before its surroundings became urbanised, that a long and impressive list of waders was catalogued by Harting in *The Birds of Middlesex*, 1866. It seems reasonable to suppose, therefore, that wader passage through the Area in the early part of the centruy was not really so slight as the meagre records before 1927 would suggest.

At this time no sewage farms were being watched regularly, but occasional visits by P. A. D. Hollom to the farm at Brooklands produced in 1931 the second Surrey record of curlew sandpiper and notes of several other waders which had been seen very seldom in the past (*B.B.*, 28:342–3). More frequent visits in 1936 suggested that some of the species may have been of regular occurrence on passage (*ib.* 30:346–7). About the same time numbers of ringed plover and dunlin were noted at Romford sewage farm for the first time. Waders were found to be frequent visitors to the Watford farm, while in the thirties also the green sandpiper, already one of the better known waders on passage, was found to be even more regular in autumn and in winter than had been suspected.

The drainage of reservoirs, the realisation of the ornithological potentialities of sewage farms and the great increase in trained observers, which first became important in the early thirties, are together responsible for the history of many waders in our Area during the present century commencing within a few years of 1930. The fact that since 1945 many of the species concerned have proved to be regular passage migrants through the Area could be accounted for quite simply by the existence of three times as many watchers as before the war, the 'discovery' of Perry Oaks sewage farm and the unique feeding opportunities provided during the construction of the new King George VI reservoir at Staines in the late forties. Even so, the records of waders at the older concrete-banked reservoirs have also shown a marked increase, and one can only speculate to what extent these are a reflection of increased observation or a by-product of better feeding grounds in the vicinity.

Without denying the effect of more observers and better training in field identification it is still remarkable that so few waders should at one time have been recorded. It has been suggested to us that during the great increase in the population of Greater London between the wars, and before more modern methods of sewage disposal were introduced, there may have been habitually a larger expanse of mud and shallow water in the sewage settling tanks than formerly and consequently more insect food for waders. The modernisation of sewage farms was inevitably checked during the last war. There may, therefore, have been a genuine increase of waders alighting at Perry Oaks; in the late forties also a large expanse of gravel and shallow pools was available in the bed of the King George VI reservoir under construction less than two miles away. The probability of waders moving from one place to another might explain the more frequent records at the old Staines reservoirs, although previously their comparatively bare concrete banks had seldom proved attractive to waders.

There are certain reasons, therefore, for thinking it possible that the numbers of waders alighting in the Area, as distinct from passing over it at night, may have increased, and equally possible ones to account for the very small number of earlier records. In general, we feel that it must remain doubtful for the Area as a whole whether there has been any change in the volume of passage of most of the waders during this century, and for this reason *the status summary for the waders refers only to the last few years of our period unless otherwise stated.*

OYSTERCATCHER, *Haematopus ostralegus* L. Passage migrant: exceptional in winter during severe weather.

The oystercatcher has been recorded upwards of sixty times in the Area, visiting reservoirs, sewage farms and marshes during spring and autumn passage, and occasionally being driven inland in winter at times of very severe weather. It has been recorded in all months except June, but nearly one-third of all the dated records are in August.

Bucknill (1900) speaks of it as a casual visitor to Surrey, and it is a little surprising to find that there are no positive records for our Area between 1900 and 1929. From that date until 1944 it was seen about every other year, and since then there have been several records each year with a maximum of eight in 1954. The majority refer to one or two birds, the largest party being one of nine at Barn Elms on March 19th, 1953.

In Inner London, D. W. Musselwhite had the unusual experience on February 12th, 1929, during very cold weather, of seeing an oystercatcher over Broad Street, City, and in September, 1934, E. M. Nicholson saw one over Hyde Park.

LAPWING, *Vanellus vanellus* (L.). Nests on farmland, sewage farms and occasionally elsewhere, but decreasing and absent from some apparently suitable districts. For nine months of the year occurs in flocks of up to a thousand or more, commonly frequenting agricultural land, aerodromes, sewage farms, the Thames marshes and mud-flats, and inland waters; overland movements of flocks a regular feature.

"The lapwing is a bird of the soil, its regular habitats practically coinciding with those areas where the soil is accessible in large tracts either naked or under a fairly light vegetational cover." This extract from E. M. Nicholson's report on the Lapwing Habitat Enquiry of 1937 (*B.B.*, 32:170 *et seq.*) is the key to the species' distribution in the Area. Suburban housing development pushed the lapwing back from such places as the Harrow district in 1922, from fields between Greyhound Lane and Mitcham Common in 1926, from Eastcote and Rayners Lane in 1927, Perivale in 1931, New Malden in 1934, and elsewhere. The bird's persistence now within ten miles of the centre is dependent on the continuance of such refuges as Hendon Aerodrome and Beddington sewage farm, areas which although surrounded by buildings are sufficiently large and give access to the soil. Not infrequently lapwings fly over the built-up districts and the City, and may alight in the central parks or beside the Thames, but essentially they are not adaptable to urban conditions.

In the agricultural areas beyond the suburbs the lapwing remains a widespread nesting species. Here and in the river valleys, where the muddy and shingle tracts associated with sewage farms, gravel pits, and empty reservoirs are an unfailing attraction, large flocks are regular. The lapwing's status in these outer areas has been influenced by changing farming methods, the ploughing-up of pasture, and the drainage and reclamation of marginal land.

According to Nicholson (*Birds and Men*, 1951) and Spencer in *The Lapwing in Britain* (1953) there has been a general decrease of lapwings despite a lessening of persecution, a trend not obscured by a few contrary reports of recovery. The extent to which slackness in land improvement before the recent war permitted temporary increases is uncertain, but there is no doubt that drainage of farmland during and after the war years, as at Parndon and between Northwood and Harefield, caused lapwings to desert fields formerly used for nesting. The wartime extension of farmland by the ploughing-up of grass in parks and elsewhere provided fresh feeding grounds, and flocks could be seen for example on Mitcham Fair Green, Tottenham Marsh and Hampstead Heath; and in Hampton Court, Bushy and Richmond Parks. The conversion of pasture to arable in the Hendon, Mill Hill and Totteridge districts in 1942 provided a winter feeding area but nesting declined although, conversely, it was encouraged elsewhere by the incidence of ploughing.

The increase of ploughland, and particularly its doubling during the war, is an important factor in the decrease of the lapwing, which is attracted to it and is thereby subjected to such agricultural hazards as rolling and harrowing. The rapid occupation of land under wartime cultivation was seen at several places. At Harrow golf-course, for example, lapwings nested during the period when crops were grown but not subsequently (Harley, 1949). At Bushy Park three pairs nested on the ploughland in 1940, probably four pairs both here and in Hampton Court Park in 1941, and several pairs to 1949—there was one pair again in 1953. In Richmond Park lapwings had not bred since 1834 but a pair nested in 1943 when part of it was tilled, and thereafter breeding was regular until by 1950 there were five or six pairs. Large-scale cultivation in the park was abandoned after the harvest of 1951, most of the stubble fields being then left to revert to grass, and although in 1952 lapwings again nested on what remained of the arable land they failed to hatch. Nesting success was poor throughout the recolonisation, the hazards of ploughed land being shown by yearly reports of losses of eggs or chicks from nests in young wheat subjected to rolling. Human disturbance, dogs and an abundance of jackdaws and crows were additional hazards. The park was never short of potential colonists, for flocks of up to 150 were regular on the arable in winter and were still to be seen about the fields after breeding territories had been occupied.

The taking-up of territories is noticeable from March onwards and by June flocks are re-forming and may exceed a hundred. Later and in winter the flocks increase in size and one, two and even four thousand lapwings have been seen on the west Middlesex plain and elsewhere. Some of the largest companies have occurred around full moon when Spencer (loc. cit.) has shown that smaller flocks amalgamate for nocturnal feeding. Further work on this subject is at present being undertaken at Beddington sewage farm where there were about 2,000 birds at the end of 1953.

Passage movements may be obscured by the local comings and goings of feeding and roosting flocks, but genuine migration, often of birds flying very high, has repeatedly been seen and is referred to in the migration chapter. Summer immigration of Continental lapwings, mainly juveniles, into S. E. England, which may start in June according to Spencer, is illustrated by the recovery in "North London" during August of one ringed as young in Northern Bohemia in May. Conversely, a nestling ringed on the Kent marshes at Stone was recovered in *June* of the following year at Le Crotoy, Somme, France. A nestling ringed at Godalming, Surrey, was recovered 15 miles N.N.E. at Walton-on-Thames in its first February. Winter movements are frequent, the chief direction being to the south or south-west. The birds soon return again when the weather improves, so that observed flights in other directions (including north) are understandable.

RINGED PLOVER, *Charadrius hiaticula L.* Double passage migrant and winter visitor. Has bred once.

In 1901 a pair of ringed plovers nested on a sewage farm in the Lea valley near Enfield, and the hatching of their three young was recorded by R. B. Lodge (*Zool.* 59:389). Birds were seen on the farm in 1902, but apparently did not stay.

Along the Thames above Gravesend ringed plovers were mainly winter visitors in the early part of the century, when Ticehurst remarked on their excursions right up to the wharves of south-east London. The industrialised remnants of marshes and tidal fore shores which lie between Woolwich and Tilbury are still visited every year, but nearly all the modern records, including one in the docks area in 1938, refer to passage migration with a maximum of 92 at Stone Marshes in August, 1954. An exception was the record of four at Swanscombe in January, 1948, but at Romford sewage farm, in the low-lying country on the Essex side of the estuary, flocks of up to eleven, twenty-five and thirty respectively were seen in three winters between 1937 and 1940. Some of these may have remained from the flocks on autumn passage which frequented the farm at that period but some of the records suggest the arrival of winter visitors. Elsewhere in the Area solitary ringed plovers have been noticed between November and February less than a dozen times.

On spring and autumn passage they have been reported regularly since 1921 at reservoirs, gravel pits and sewage farms. Earlier than this there is little published evidence, apart from the statement by Harting (1866) that they were double passage migrants to Middlesex. The reservoirs at Staines, concrete-banked and bare though they are, have been regularly visited by ringed plovers, usually in small numbers but occasionally in parties of ten or so. When the reservoirs were drained in 1927, "two to three dozen" were recorded in May and twenty-five in August. Twenty years later the King George VI reservoir was under construction nearby and the partially flooded shingly bed was soon discovered by ringed plovers on passage. They were seen frequently from 1947 to 1949 among the pools and muddy strands, sometimes in flocks of up to twenty.

Only a mile or two to the north-east, at Perry Oaks, parties and flocks of ringed plovers have frequented the drying mud of the settling tanks every year since this farm began to be watched in the mid 1940's. They are seen from April to the middle of June and from July to October. On spring passage there have been as many as 51—in early June, 1952—while in autumn the main concentrations occur in August and September when the flocks not infrequently exceed forty with a maximum of over seventy. October movements of any size are unusual, but in 1950 fifty were seen on October 1st and at least twenty remained another week.

Ringed plover and dunlin sometimes fly up from feeding on the farm and settle on the adjoining London Airport, where in the late forties when it was still under construction the perimeter was either short grass or turned soil. On such a wide expanse of land they are easily overlooked as close observation is not possible, and their movements to and from their feeding places on the sewage beds may account for some of the widely fluctuating numbers recorded on the farm. There seems little doubt, however, that the total of birds moving through each spring and autumn is likely to exceed, and may even greatly exceed, the number in the largest flock.

Flocks of thirty or more have been seen at the King George V reservoir in Essex, and for many years ringed plover have been known as passage visitors to the reservoirs, gravel pits and sewage farms in the Lea valley. They have appeared regularly at the Brent reservoir since at least 1921 but are infrequent at Ruislip and Aldenham which also have natural banks. In the Colne valley at Langley, Hamper Mill and Watford they have been seen occasionally, and at Moor Mill gravel pit regularly in recent years. South of the Thames their visits have been to such places as the sewage farms at Beddington, Walton and Brooklands and the reservoirs at Barn Elms. For Inner London it is rather surprising that there have been only three records: on the Thames mud at Millbank in March, 1917, by the Serpentine in April, 1932 and at the Round Pond in September, 1940.

LITTLE RINGED PLOVER, *Charadrius dubius* Scopoli. First known to have nested in Area in 1944, now local summer resident and probably passage migrant.

In this century only four species, the Slavonian and black-necked grebes, the black redstart and the little ringed plover, have colonised Britain for the first time, and it is an interesting fact that the main stronghold of the last two has been in the London Area. The first record of the little ringed plover nesting in England was in 1938, at the Tring reservoirs in Hertfordshire—about twelve miles outside the boundary of the London Area Ledlie and Pedler, *B.B.,* 32:90–102). No further nest was found until 1944, when two pairs bred at Tring and E. O. Höhn found a pair with three young at a gravel pit near Ashford, in Middlesex (England *et al., ib.* 38:102–111). On August 3rd and 9th of the same year a single bird was seen at the Brent reservoir. The Ashford occurrence was the first time that little ringed plovers had been seen in the London Area since 1864, but it is possible that a pair or two may have bred unobserved at this or other gravel pits in the years 1939–1943, when conditions at Tring were unsuitable. If nesting did occur it might well have escaped notice because at that time gravel pits were not much visited—partly because of the war and partly because few of them are attractive and their ornithological possibilities had not been realised.

After 1944, a careful watch for little ringed plovers was made at many of the numerous

FIG. 6: The sou

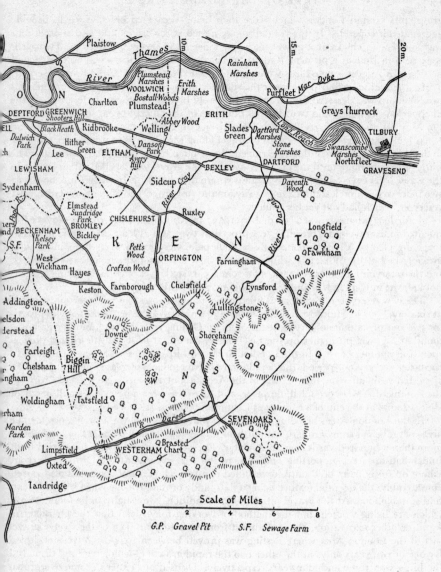

London Area

gravel pits around London which were then being excavated or enlarged to provide aggregate for concrete. In 1945 a pair again nested at the original pit and another pair was found with chicks at a gravel pit a few miles away, near Shepperton. Two birds were seen in June at a pit near Radlett, in Hertfordshire, but there was no evidence of nesting. In August, single birds were again recorded on passage at the Brent reservoir.

In 1946, at least four pairs spent the summer in the London Area. The original pit near Ashford was deserted but two pairs probably bred at another pit close by. At the Shepperton site a pair laid two clutches but none of the chicks appear to have survived. On May 5th two birds were found by the River Colne on Staines Moor. The river had recently been dredged and the heaps of gravel along the banks gave it some resemblance to the shingly rivers which the little ringed plover often frequents on the Continent. The birds were seen there until the end of May when the gravel was levelled off and a rise in the water level covered the muddy strands where they had fed. In early June, however, two pairs were found less than a mile away, on the vast gravel bed of the King George VI reservoir, which had not yet been filled.

A further extension was recorded in 1947; in Middlesex little ringed plovers frequented four gravel pits (breeding was proved at two) and at least three pairs nested at the King George VI reservoir; in Essex, four pairs were found to be breeding on the gravelly bed of the William Girling reservoir then under construction near Chingford, but the reservoir had not been visited for some years so the year in which nesting began is not known; in Kent, a pair bred at a gravel pit near St. Paul's Cray.

The new reservoir at Staines was filled in September, 1947, but birds certainly nested at six gravel pits in Middlesex and probably at a seventh. In Essex, breeding was proved for two out of six pairs observed at the William Girling reservoir and another pair was found at a gravel pit higher up the Lea Valley. In all, at least 30 little ringed plovers spent the summer of 1948 in the London Area and birds were seen at ten localities. In the latter years of our period, the population appears to have increased only slightly. In 1953, ten years after the first nesting in the Area, about 18 pairs were present. Most of the suitable sites were occupied, however, and there was even a pair on a small patch of stony ground at the end of a runway at London Airport.

In the London Area, breeding little ringed plovers have shown a preference for flat areas of gravel, or stony ground, with little or no vegetation, and the nest has rarely been more than a hundred yards from fresh water. The size of the gravel area has varied from under half an acre, supporting one pair, to the vast expanse at the Girling reservoir, where up to six pairs bred until it was filled in 1951. The area of water has also varied considerably, the essential feature being a flat, sandy or muddy edge where the birds can find suitable food. At the gravel pits, the best conditions are usually to be found at pits which are being worked, but the method of working may mean that the character of a pit, or other excavation, changes almost from year to year. Ten of the twelve gravel pits in the London Area where nesting was proved between 1944–1950 were occupied for one or two years only; at the other two the rapid growth of willow saplings displaced the birds after three and four years respectively. Disused pits either become overgrown or are filled in, but even while filling is in progress there may still be a niche for little ringed plovers—the first nest to be found in Surrey, in 1950, was on top of the clinker which was being dumped into an old pit near Richmond.

The success of little ringed plovers in the London Area is due to the large number of gravel pits, to the rapidity with which they locate another nesting site when an old one becomes unsuitable and to their astonishing disregard for human disturbance. No nesting locality in the London Area has been free from disturbance whether by workmen and excavating machines on weekdays or by anglers, small boys and ornithologists at weekends, but the most disturbed sites were probably the unfinished reservoirs at Staines and

Chingford, where, strangely, more pairs were found than elsewhere. Bulldozers, scrapers, lorries and workmen ranged over these areas and it is surprising that so many of the eggs and young survived; at Chingford, one nest was found within a foot of a vehicle track and another was located by a scraper driver who saw the sitting birds run off and stopped his machine. Fortunately, little ringed plovers will usually lay again, sometimes within a week, if the first clutch is destroyed or the chicks die. That this happened not infrequently at the reservoirs, and that it happens at many of the gravel pits, is clear from the high proportion of late clutches.

In the early years of the colonisation, the first birds were seen at the end of April, or in early May, but at the end of our period they were arriving a month earlier, at the end of March—an interesting parallel with the black redstart, which also began to return earlier once it was well established. Breeding sites are vacated in August, but birds, frequently juveniles, are seen at adjacent sewage farms and reservoirs in September and occasionally in early October. Some of these may be passage migrants from other parts of England.

KENTISH PLOVER, *Charadrius alexandrinus* L.

G. W. Kerr saw a Kentish plover at Staines reservoir on April 21st, 1915 (Hartert and Jourdain, 1920), and an adult female was seen by R. J. Raines on the gravel bed of the uncompleted King George VI reservoir, also at Staines, on September 3rd, 1947 (*B.B.*, 41:28).

GREY PLOVER, *Charadrius squatarola* (L.). Scarce visitor in spring, autumn and early winter.

Since 1930 the grey plover has been reported over forty times, divided almost equally between spring, autumn and the first half of the winter. Before that date the only record is of a party of six seen at Staines reservoirs by K. Fisher on April 9th, 1922 (*B.B.*, 16:26).

The chief month for spring passage is May, but there have been five records in April, one in March and two in June. Several reports speak of birds in full breeding plumage. The earliest date for the return passage is July 31st, 1954, when two were seen at Perry Oaks sewage farm, but the bulk of the records are spread over the months of September, October and November. There are four in December, and on New Year's Day, 1942, H. G. Alexander saw a grey plover on the Thames foreshore at Chiswick. In addition to the usual ones and twos, "trips" of four have been seen twice in November and once each in June and September.

The grey plover is a bird of the open shore or the spacious mud flat, and in the London Area it finds the nearest approach to these conditions on the borders of reservoirs and other large sheets of water, at sewage farms, gravel pits and open, marshy places such as Staines Moor and the Lea valley. In recent years it has been seen twice on the Dartford marshes.

GOLDEN PLOVER, *Charadrius apricarius* L. Regular winter visitor and passage migrant, particularly in early spring; many are only transient but some flocks spend the winter north of the Thames. Flocks of any size in the south are exceptional.

Large numbers of golden plover are to be seen annually in the London Area, partly in nomadic groups and partly in wintering flocks, which are sometimes of considerable size. There are some localities to which flocks on the move are regularly attracted, but in only a few of them do they stay more than a week or two. Elsewhere the golden plover comes usually in ones and twos and small parties, and in such numbers it may appear briefly almost anywhere on open land, and on some of the sewage farms, both in winter and on passage.

Through most of our period the main areas of attraction have been beyond the limits of intensive suburban development, and particularly in the variable belt of open country which extends north and east from the flat, low-lying plain of west Middlesex to the London corner of Essex. In a very few open spaces in the outer suburbs small flocks may still occur, as at Beddington sewage farm, where up to thirty or more have resorted periodically to the irrigated grass fields since at least 1910. Although during this time the building of houses has filled in most of the surrounding country the birds still return and in December, 1950, the flock numbered thirty-five. The growth of the suburbs inevitably excluded the golden plover from a number of former feeding grounds, but the laying out of extensive airfields, where flocks running into hundreds build up in winter, may have more than offset the restrictive effects of other types of land development.

Glegg (1930 and 1935) describes the golden plover as a decreased winter visitor, largely because Kerr said in 1906 that the species was only a straggler to Staines Moor, where twenty-five years previously it was common; but flocks exceeding a hundred have returned to these moist levels in at least four winters since 1937. Glegg knew of a flock of 120 in 1928 on the fields north of Stanwell destined to become London Airport, and of an exceptional 400–500 in the winter of 1931 near Hounslow. To-day small parties of up to ten or so can be regularly seen in various parts of the Middlesex plain, and occasionally larger numbers up to fifty or more, but we have no evidence how many may mingle with the enormous flocks of lapwings on the inaccessible parts of the airport.

Between Rickmansworth and Barnet moderate flocks have occurred since 1937 and about 200 wintered at Batchworth in 1940. A flock of 500 at Shenley in 1937 were the forerunners of a large but variable winter population which reached 600 in 1950. The main flock has of late concentrated at the aerodrome north of Radlett and this has become since 1947 one of the few sites where golden plover spend the winter. Parties which are reported at Elstree, Moor Mill, Old Parkbury, Hatfield and elsewhere may be offshoots from the main flock or wanderers which may later join it. Much hard weather movement of companies of golden plover occurs, so that the species is often noted in flight over the Area.

In the Lea valley around Haileybury, Hoddesdon, Cheshunt and Waltham Abbey flocks of a hundred or more have been known since 1906, though Lodge (1901) and others noticed a decline from the eighties. East of the Lea, Nazeingwood Common was described by M. Vaughan in 1902 as a great haunt of golden plover, and from here, from Sewardstone, from the uplands north of the Epping Forest ridge, from Stanford Rivers and the valley of the Roding, moderate to large flocks have been reported more or less regularly; some (but not all) of the largest flocks, even up to 250 and 400, occur on spring passage in March. At this season some are seen to be assuming the breeding dress of the northern form, *altifrons*. In 1930 large flocks were recorded by G. D. Cranfield at Enfield Chase at the end of March and early April. An exceptional flock of approximately a thousand was seen by M. R. Chettleburgh in December, 1950, at Fairlop aerodrome and the surrounding fields, where since 1945 flocks of up to three hundred have been present in most winters. Smaller flocks wintered at North Weald aerodrome before the war, and they may do so still.

On the Thames levels about a hundred were reported at Northfleet from December, 1948, to January, 1949, and a similar number at Rainham the following month. They are seldom found in the southern half of the Area, except at Beddington. Up to forty or fifty were seen regularly near Warlingham from 1907 to 1932 (Beadell, 1932) but the land was then developed. On passage, flocks of this size used to resort to Walton Heath from 1905 onwards, but apparently not since 1924.

DOTTEREL, *Charadrius morinellus* L.

On the evening of August 26th, 1950, four members of the London Natural History Society discovered a party of ten dotterel, with lapwings and golden plover, at London Airport. They were on a large expanse of gravel with a sparse overgrowth of grass, lying between newly constructed runways of the airport near Perry Oaks sewage farm. Three birds of the party were adults in summer plumage, six were in partial moult and one was a juvenile. On the following day the number was reduced to seven, on the 28th to five and by the 30th only one bird remained, none being seen after that date (*L.B.R.* for 1950, p.37).

TURNSTONE, *Arenaria interpres* (L.). Regular in small numbers on spring and autumn passage; occasional in winter.

In the years since the war we have become so used to a small passage of turnstones annually at our sewage farms and reservoirs that it is hard to believe that until 1931 none had been recorded for many years. Ticehurst (1909) referred to their occasional appearance as far up the Thames as Dartford, and nothing else is known of them on this part of the Thames until 1950, since when up to four have been seen on a few occasions in autumn and winter. At inland waters, on the other hand, the turnstone has been recognised with increasing frequency since 1931, when one was spotted by J. P. Hardiman and A. Holte Macpherson on August 20th at Littleton reservoir, the first inland record for the London Area for sixty-five years. Others were seen in 1933 and intermittently to 1944, from which time they have been reported regularly.

Small numbers of turnstones now appear in May and early June, and again in autumn between July and October, usually coming in ones and twos but occasionally in small parties, which do not normally stay more than a few days. Eight in spring and seven in autumn at Perry Oaks sewage farm are the most seen at any one time. Gravel workings, the grassy or marshy verges of the reservoirs at Brent and Ruislip, and even the concreted ones at Littleton, Staines and Barn Elms, have been visited. A bombed site in Inner London, at some little distance from the Thames at Chelsea and separated from it by a road busy with heavy traffic, was frequented by a crippled turnstone on January 28th, 1950, one of the very few winter occurrences.

SNIPE, *Capella gallinago* (L.). Mainly a winter visitor, often at sewage farms in flocks of a hundred or more, and exceptionally 400–500. Rare vagrant in built-up areas, including Inner London. A very few pairs breed locally on marshy land.

Writers of the late nineteenth century remarked on the number of snipe to be found in winter compared with the scarcity of nests in the breeding season, and for a long time the snipe has been fighting a constant battle with the builder and land drainage engineer. Ticehurst (1909) records that the earliest reference to breeding in Kent was at the beginning of the last century, when many nests were found in the osier ground bordering on the Surrey Canal, near what is now New Cross but was probably then a continuation of the Greenwich and Deptford marshes. At the turn of the century, however, the only evidence of breeding is of nests at Enfield sewage farm in 1901, on Dartford Marshes in 1904, at Croxley Common Moor in 1905 (the first nesting record for Hertfordshire), and near Rickmansworth in 1910. In 1913 breeding was proved in the Colne valley after a winter in which many snipe were encountered; and in the following year they again bred there, as well as at Watford and in the Lea valley. Between 1914 and 1925 pairs bred on Epsom Common, at Black Park, Langley and Limpsfield, on Itchingwood Common and in the Colne, Lea and Darent valleys. In the next twenty-five years occasional nests were found in several more areas, including Haileybury, Elstree reservoir, Romford, Harefield and the sewage farms at Beddington, Edgware and South

Harrow. Near Cobham up to half a dozen pairs nested, but after 1938 breeding ceased when the land was drained, though in subsequent years birds were heard drumming in the spring. On Staines Moor, where conditions are still suitable, a few pairs breed each year. At the present time successful nesting occurs only on some of the Thames marshes, at sewage farms and some of the least disturbed areas of marshy ground towards the perimeter of the Area.

In the late summer and early autumn numbers begin to increase. During October and early November it has frequently been noted that the birds disappear from their feeding grounds for a time, but by December the numbers increase again. At the end of the last century flocks of 400 at Mitcham and Norwood were mentioned by Bucknill (1900) and in spite of the vast expansion of building in the ensuing years, the number of snipe that have come into the Area occasionally in the colder weather has still been large. At such favourite feeding areas as Beddington, Elmers End and Watford sewage farms flocks of up to one or two hundred are normal in winter. Parties of 200 have also been recorded at Dagenham Breach in February, 1939, on Mitcham Common in the winter of 1947–48, and at Stockers Lake. On December 14th, 1945, there was an astonishing concentration of snipe on a flooded field at Watford, where 500 were counted. By December 24th this number had dropped to 100 at the onset of a sharp frost but some days later had doubled again when conditions were less severe, and from then until mid-February the flock never dropped below 130. This farm has now been closed, but in recent winters up to 400 have been seen at Beddington and there were about 600 on January 24th, 1954. Parties of fifty or more have been observed in the winter months at a number of places including Dartford, Epsom, St. Albans, Edmonton and Abridge.

There have been a few occasions when common snipe have occurred well within the built-up area, including the central parks and Kentish Town. On the Thames itself they have seldom been seen: a flock of fifty on the foreshore at Long Reach, Dartford on December 6th, 1950, was exceptional, and the only other record refers to a bird on the mud at Vauxhall.

JACK SNIPE, *Lymnocryptes minimus* (Brünnich). Winter visitor to sewage farms, reservoirs and marshy ground from mid-October to late March, occasionally April. Two summer records. Numbers usually small but frequently increase in severe weather.

The few records of jack snipe in the years around 1900 refer largely to birds shot on the marshes of Essex and Kent, and the size of some of the 'bags' suggests that the birds were occasionally present in some numbers. Ticehurst (1909) mentions a bag of sixteen on Greenhithe Marshes, and Davis (1904) describes the jack snipe as "quite common at times on Dartford Marshes, but appearance rather fitful." Up to 1920 most of the observations refer to Chingford, Edmonton, Epping, Ilford, Walthamstow, Haileybury and Thurrock, where jack snipe were sometimes encountered, while the only record for Surrey was of two birds seen between October, 1907 and January, 1908, at Gatton Park.

In more recent years regular watching at suitable places has shown jack snipe to be occasional visitors to many localities. At Beddington and Elmers End sewage farms they have been seen in most winters since 1934, with until recently a maximum of 14 at Beddington in 1951. At the beginning of a very severe spell in 1954, however, no fewer than 42 were flushed on January 31st. Observations at Chigwell, Brooklands, Hoddesdon, Langley, Harrow, Watford and Wyke sewage farms among others also emphasise the importance in our Area of this habitat. At Epsom sewage farm, where a reed-bed on soft sludge was first 'driven' in the winter of 1954–55, up to about 40 were flushed on January 23rd; in eight visits between January 16th and March 20th there were never less than about 24. The haunts of jack snipe on sewage farms are difficult to cross, and these higher numbers may only reflect a more thorough search of the suitable ground.

The marshy areas of Ruislip reservoir, Staines Moor and the Lea valley are also visited by jack snipe in small numbers in most winters, the biggest gathering being of thirteen at Hoddesdon sewage farm in the latter part of 1954. Other places visited have included a number of gravel pits, many of the Surrey commons, parts of Bushy and Richmond Parks, the old cress-beds at Leatherhead and the Thames marshes at Dartford and Stone, and, in two recent years, Hampstead Heath. On Epsom Common a jack snipe was flushed from dry bracken in October, 1937.

Vagrant jack snipe have been found either dead or injured in the heavily built-up areas on seven occasions, and only once on the Thames. While the majority of the records refer to birds seen from October to February, jack snipe in small numbers have also been noted throughout March and even into April. In the last few years there have been several records in September, from the 10th onwards. At Moor Mill W. D. Melluish noted a bird that apparently remained throughout the summer of 1948, since it was seen in April and May and on several dates subsequently, the last being August 12th. In 1949 one was seen in the same place up to July 9th.

WOODCOCK, *Scolopax rusticola* L. Few records of breeding but odd pairs may nest regularly round the fringe of the Area especially in Surrey. Regular in winter in suitable woods. Occasional as vagrant Inner London.

The status of the woodcock was reviewed in detail by Alexander (*Ibis*, volumes 87–89) who wrote of its breeding distribution in the Thames province: "On the North Downs in Kent and Surrey . . . a few pairs breed locally and irregularly . . . In Middlesex and Hertfordshire a few pairs possibly breed regularly in one or two localities, but in Essex nests are almost unknown." A probable decrease is attributed partly to the great increase in human population.

A note in the 1935 report of the Oxford Ornithological Society stated that woodcock had nested in Langley Park within the last five years. In Middlesex there have been July records from the Brent reservoir and Whitewebbs Park, and confirmation has been received that, at Ruislip, breeding was regular in Park Wood about 1880 and ceased when the undergrowth was cleared towards the end of the 19th century. Breeding has since been proved, however, in the adjacent Copse Wood. The only proof of breeding in the Hertfordshire sector concerns two nests in Cow Heath Wood in 1914, but a bird was seen at Elstree on May 16th, 1945, and one at Old Parkbury on June 10th, 1950; it seems not improbable that a few pairs may breed in private woods. In Epping Forest breeding was last recorded in 1887, and despite an occasional spring report there is no proof of subsequent nesting. Breeding has taken place, however, in Thorndon Park, near Brentwood, about 1913 (per W. A. French) and in 1940 (*fide* Canon Kuypers per Rev. L. Sargent).

South of the Thames, Walpole-Bond (1901) wrote that a pair was believed to have bred in Elmstead Wood in 1900, and A. P. Macklin is quoted (Turner, 1909) for the successful breeding of a pair in Crofton Wood "a few years back". The only definite Kent reports in recent years refer to a locality in the Darent valley, where proof was obtained in 1932, 1933 and 1944. It is perhaps significant that Ticehurst (1909) wrote of a few pairs breeding near Dartford. A pair seen over Sundridge Park on June 25th, 1946, and one over Darenth Wood on July 27th, 1949, suggest the possibility of other breeding localities. In a previous review (*L.N.* for 1934:49) only one site was given for Surrey, where nesting was proved in 1934. Recently hatched young, however, were caught near Leatherhead in 1909, and a nest was found near Limpsfield in 1935. From subsequent records it appears that breeding is regular in the last locality, and it has been proved recently at Ashtead, Leatherhead, and Westerham. In the past few years there have also been 'roding' or June records from Banstead, Cobham, Esher, Epsom, Tadworth and

Tatsfield. Nests are so seldom found except by keepers that it seems likely that many are overlooked; woodcock, in fact, probably breed regularly in small numbers along the North Downs in some of the woods on the northern slopes.

Alexander (*op. cit.*) considered that even outside the breeding season woodcock were nowhere numerous in our Area, many former haunts having suffered from encroachment by builders or from the increase in public use, as in Epping Forest. In general this is very true, though in small numbers woodcock are reported regularly from such districts as Bushy Park, Ruislip, Stanmore, Epping Forest, Hayes, the North Downs and Richmond Park, where a preference is shown for birch woods with bracken undergrowth. This list is not exhaustive and refers mainly to places open to the public. It is obvious that in some private woods birds must be equally regular, and G. K. McCulloch learnt from the lessee of the shooting in Copse Wood that in 1936 forty-one woodcock were shot over a 260-acre shoot. About 1913 or 1914 as many as seventy birds were seen in a season in Thorndon Park, Brentwood, 37–38 being shot.

Such figures suggest that woodcock are much overlooked, and the number of records from the built-up area strongly supports this contention. Birds are not infrequently seen in the Hampstead district and even in the central parks, where on two occasions birds have flown into the arms of passers-by. As would be expected these occurrences are most often at times of migration, in March and November. An interesting observation was of a party of six flying east on Stone marshes in thick fog on December 6th, 1952.

CURLEW, *Numenius arquata* (L.). A frequent passage migrant and local winter visitor.

There is no record of the curlew nesting in the London Area in the present century although a few pairs breed annually on the West Surrey heaths not far outside.

Most of the waders that migrate at night travel unheard and unseen but the wild nostalgic cry of the curlew is so distinctive and loud that it is frequently heard after dark, even over the most heavily built-up parts of the Area, and in every month of the year but most often in the spring and autumn. On the spring passage, most of the records have been in the second half of March, but the autumn movement is spread over from late June until early September. The peak of the autumn migration over London is in July and August, when more than half of all the dated records for this century have occurred.

The migration has also occasionally been seen over London at dusk and, rather more frequently, in the early hours of the morning, e.g. large numbers passed over Chelsea between 5 a.m. and 7 a.m. on July 26th, 1931, and a party of 25 was seen over Barn Elms reservoirs in the early morning of August 21st, 1936.

On both migrations, single birds or small flocks occasionally pause to rest in the London Area but, except perhaps along the Thames marshes, they rarely stay for more than a day or two. As might be expected, the most favoured places for feeding and resting are the reservoirs, sewage farms and gravel pits, especially where there is marshy ground, but curlews have occasionally been seen amongst gulls and lapwings on flooded fields and on May 1st, 1938, one was seen probing for food on a drought-hardened football field at Rickmansworth.

In the winter, curlews in very small numbers visit the foreshore and marshes on both sides of the Thames just inside the Area. Elsewhere, they are infrequently seen except during or after severe weather when their tendency to come inland may cause a sizeable influx. In the very cold first quarter of 1947, for example, nearly seventy birds were recorded from eight widely separated localities within the Area—the average for milder winters, away from the Thames marshes, is less than half-a-dozen.

There is no evidence of any change of status of the curlew in the London Area in this century: the greater number of records in recent years and our better knowledge of the bird's distribution along the lower Thames is undoubtedly due to the great increase in observers.

WHIMBREL, *Numenius phaeopus* (L.). A double passage migrant in small numbers.

The whimbrel, as might be expected, is a much less frequent visitor than the curlew. Since 1900, it has been recorded in the Area about a hundred times; the fact that well over half of these reports were after 1945 indicates that it may be a more regular passage migrant than was previously supposed. Most of the records are of birds in flight, when identification may depend on the ringing call. Occasionally, whimbrel are heard at night but there is a higher proportion of daytime records than for the curlew.

Apart from a few in April (early date, two at Mill Hill on April 9th, 1928) most of the occurrences on the spring passage have been in May, especially in the first two weeks. There are only two records for June and two in early July; the autumn records are for late July, August and early September, with the peak in the second half of August.

In London, the whimbrel has occurred as often in the autumn as on the spring migration and, as yet, there is nothing to suggest that larger numbers pass through in the spring, as they are stated to do in some other parts of the country. Many of the records refer to single birds but parties of up to half a dozen are not unusual; the largest flock, if all were whimbrel, was of 50–52 birds heard uttering the typical calls as they flew south over Colley Hill, Reigate, on August 24th, 1946.

BLACK-TAILED GODWIT, *Limosa limosa* (L.). Scarce double passage migrant, mainly in autumn.

Between 1900 and 1927 the black-tailed godwit was only twice recorded in the Area— one was shot at Edmonton sewage farm in 1911 and a party of seven was seen at Surrey Docks in 1917 (*B.B.*, 22:241). From 1927 to 1944, however, there were eight records in five different years and since then one or more black-tailed godwits have been seen in almost every year; in 1950 there were nine different birds. This corresponds well with the general increase of the species as a passage migrant in south-eastern England, an increase which has become more marked since the last war (*B.B.*, 33:98–104 and vols. 41–44).

The occurrences in spring have been from the middle of March to late May and those on the return passage from the end of June to the end of August. In 1950 one remained at Perry Oaks sewage farm from October 7th until early December, when it was found shot. The only others seen in winter were two on the Dartford and Stone marshes on December 16th, also in 1950. The largest flock was of thirteen on a flooded field at Elmers End sewage farm on March 15th, 1947. This was quite exceptional and the most at any other time were six at Perry Oaks sewage farm in August, 1952, and April, 1954.

BAR-TAILED GODWIT, *Limosa lapponica* (L.). Rare passage migrant, also three winter records.

The bar-tailed godwit has been recorded on nineteen occasions, eight times each in spring and autumn and three times in winter. The spring records fall between April 12th and May 11th, and on the return passage there has been one record each in July, August and October and five in September. In the autumn of 1916 F. J. Stubbs claimed to have heard bar-tailed godwits passing over Theydon Bois in numbers "yapping like puppy-dogs" (*Essex Nat.*, 19:90). The three winter records consist of a bird seen by J.P. Hardiman at Staines reservoirs on January 24th, 1933 (*B.B.*, 26:312), one found dead near the Pen Ponds, Richmond Park, on February 21st, 1936, and of one at Stone in February, 1954.

Most of the birds have been seen at reservoirs or sewage farms, but there were two on the Thames foreshore at West Thurrock marsh on April 12th, 1947, and one on Stone marshes in September, 1953. As the bar-tailed godwit is regular on passage and in winter on the Thames estuary, it is possible that intensive watching of the lower reaches of the river in our Area would produce more evidence of occasional visits.

GREEN SANDPIPER, *Tringa ochropus* L. Double passage migrant and winter visitor throughout the period to a very wide choice of moist habitats, but not to the waters of the built-up areas.

Long before watching at reservoirs and sewage farms received much attention this sandpiper was recognised as regular in several of our river valleys, and not unknown in many widely separated localities throughout the Area. The bird's readiness to find food and shelter along the courses of streams and canals, beside ponds and small pools, in ditches and standing water in low-lying meadows, and other watery places, brought it to the attention of the earlier generation of bird-watchers with greater frequency than waders with a more selective choice of feeding ground. During the last thirty years most of the sewage farms and reservoirs, and many of the gravel pits, have been added to the long and varied list of places visited.

The autumn passage starts in early July and for three months ones and twos and parties of up to perhaps ten or more are reported. There were eleven feeding together at Hoddesdon sewage farm on November 14th, 1954. Very occasionally they have been heard flying over during darkness or in the early morning, and two were seen flying south-west over Hyde Park by R. J. Raines at dusk on October 3rd, 1947. These are the only ones on record for Inner London, but Power (1910) noted one in Dulwich Park in September, 1900. In late autumn and early winter many of the retreats favoured by the passage migrants are deserted, and although birds may be found in perhaps as many as ten different localities in the Area in the course of a winter they tend to settle down in places which are apparently of special attraction.

Regular wintering in the Roding valley, for example, was noted by F. J. Stubbs about 1910 (*Essex Nat.*, 19:90, 99) and again for some eleven years up to 1942 by R. McKenzie Smith and others (*vide L.B.R.* for 1936:29). The valley of the Colne, especially for a few miles each side of Watford, was a favourite locality in 1906–1909, when W. Bickerton and Owen Mathews often saw them on migration and in winter, and in April, 1908, flushed ten from reeds near Bushey Lodge Farm. More recently, and especially since 1949, some marshy fields and a pool at the western edge of Watford sewage farm have been much favoured. These fields, grown with long, tussocky grass, persicaria and patches of rushes, usually held small areas of standing water and were little disturbed. Increasing pollution of the pool from a near-by works, and the closing down of the sewage farm, have now destroyed the habitat; but at its best this site could be relied upon to produce up to a dozen or so green sandpipers in every month except June, and in August, 1951, there was a maximum of 20.

From the less frequent observation of birds in most localities after the turn of the year it seems likely that some are either killed or moved on by hard weather. Others, however, persist even in very wintry conditions, particularly at cress beds and other places where a trickle of water remains unfrozen (*vide L.B.R.*, 12:44). Birds seen in March are likely to have wintered, and spring passage generally is in April and May. In the main this is an inconspicuous movement, with single birds appearing here and there throughout the Area.

WOOD SANDPIPER, *Tringa glareola* L. Regular passage migrant in small numbers, chiefly autumn, occasional in spring.

In the autumn of 1927 the reservoirs at Staines were drained and in mid-August R. W. Hayman saw two wood sandpipers there on the exposed mud. These were the first recorded in Middlesex since 1885 and the first of the century anywhere in the London

Area. Six years later Dr. G. Carmichael Low saw one on July 30th, 1933, on the R. Colne where it crosses Staines Moor. From then until 1939 four single birds in four separate years were noted—three at Brooklands sewage farm and another at Staines Moor.

When Lord Hurcomb "discovered" Perry Oaks sewage farm in 1946 he saw a wood sandpiper there on May 4th. By 1948 the farm was being extensively watched, and up to three wood sandpipers were seen almost daily from August 2nd–18th. In the succeeding autumns one, two or three were seen frequently in July, August and September. Exceptional numbers appeared in 1952 when there were up to 10 in July and 17 in August. In the same autumn one or two were seen in nine other localities, while in other post-war years they have been reported from several different sewage farms and gravel pits, and occasionally on the Stone Marshes and elsewhere.

The one locality where wood sandpipers have appeared annually, and even remained for several weeks, has been Perry Oaks, with its shallow pools and marsh-like vegetation. A similar environment at Brooklands was at one time favoured by wood sandpipers, but the marshy part of the farm has now completely disappeared.

COMMON SANDPIPER, *Tringa hypoleucos* L. Regular, widely distributed and common on passage; regular in winter in very small numbers. Has bred Hertfordshire.

The common sandpiper has been known as a double passage migrant since records have been kept, and as elsewhere it frequently occurs on passage in places where other waders are rarely seen. Some of the earliest records refer to its appearance on the Serpentine in the centre of London and it has been more or less regularly noticed in the central parks and along the Thames. Riversides and canal banks, park lakes, cress beds and ponds either open or fringed with trees are visited. The regular haunts are the sewage farms, gravel pits and reservoirs, but there is scarcely any water in the Area where the appearance of this species would occasion much surprise.

The spring passage, which mostly hurries through in the six weeks between the middle of April and the end of May, is revealed usually by single birds and small parties. At night, occasionally in spring but more often in autumn, common sandpipers are heard calling overhead both in central London and the suburbs. By day from July to September they are more or less continuously present at waters throughout the Area. The height of the movement is in August and many birds are still on the move until mid-September, the last of the passage continuing sometimes nearly to the end of October. In the autumn the numbers at particularly favourable feeding places, such as some of the reservoirs and sewage farms and the Thames saltings at Swanscombe and Northfleet, may build up to twenty or thirty or even more, but these are more likely to be scattered about the suitable feeding area than to form a flock. Nevertheless, flocks have been seen on a number of occasions.

In winter the common sandpiper was formerly almost unknown. F. W. Frohawk saw one at Wallington in February, 1914 (*Field,* 123:423) but thereafter none was seen at this season until 1928–29. Since then they have been recognised as winter visitors to the Thames and some of the reservoirs and gravel pits. Although seen in only a very few localities, and in small numbers, they are regular in that hardly a winter passes without their being noticed. In the winter of 1949–50 one to three were seen on Stone Marshes, and in the following winter up to five were present from November to March. Elsewhere numbers have been smaller, the birds usually appearing singly. Often the records are isolated and give no indication of whether the bird is settled in the locality or on the move; but in the winter of 1944–45 one apparently remained at Feltham gravel pit from December 9th to March 18th, and in the following winter from February 6th to March 23rd. At Walthamstow and elsewhere there has been similar evidence of one or a few individuals staying for at least some weeks in winter.

The alleged nesting in 1912 of a pair near Haileybury was published in the *Transactions* of the Hertfordshire N.H.S., 15 (3): 164, and the nesting of two pairs in 1913 was claimed by W. D. Wainwright (1926). Unfortunately the accounts in both are unconvincing. In 1950 two, apparently a pair, stayed all summer at Old Parkbury gravel pit, and although neither nest nor young could be found their behaviour and the utterance of alarm notes suggested that they may have bred (*vide L.B.R.*, 15:35). Similar behaviour was observed in the four years following; in 1954 adults with fledged young were seen by R. Coles and Professor E. H. Warmington at the end of June and in early July, and in 1955 the nest was found.

REDSHANK, *Tringa totanus* (L.). Summer resident, double passage migrant and winter visitor.

Redshanks breed in some of our river valleys and particularly along the Thames below Woolwich, where there are upwards of eighty pairs. Most are on the Kent side between Northfleet and Crayford, but approximately twenty pairs nest on the innermost marshes lying either side of Barking and Halfway Reaches. The flat lands of south-west Essex, extending northwards from the Thames to include the watersheds of the Beam and Ingrebourne rivers and the Mar Dyke, have not been regularly watched, but the colony of ten or fifteen pairs at East Horndon, mentioned by Glegg (1929), now seems to have disappeared. This site in some marshy fields was in regular use from at least 1908 to 1939.

In the Roding valley from Woodford Green to Navestock a few pairs bred from 1908 in riverside fields, on sewage farms and at Navestock lake. G. Dent considered that they increased to seven or eight pairs by 1937 but were subsequently reduced by drainage, and although two or three pairs were found nesting in 1942 they have not been reported since 1948. In the Lea valley two or three pairs began nesting on Nazeingwood Common in 1907 or 1908 and were regular to 1926 or later. During this period other places within a few miles of the confluence of the Lea and Stort were found to hold nesting redshanks, for example up to ten pairs near Haileybury in 1915 (F. W. Headley, *Trans.* Herts N.H.S., 16:153). Scattered pairs bred in most years to 1939 up and down the valley as far south as Walthamstow, but the same sites were not used regularly. About six pairs bred at Hoddesdon sewage farm in 1954.

In the valleys of the Colne, Gade and Brent in the north, and the Wey, Mole, Wandle and Darent in the south, the picture is much the same. The increase of breeding redshanks in England from 1865, described by Thomas (*B.B.*, 36:5 *et seq.*), was coincident with the appearance of breeding pairs in the Area in places where hitherto they were apparently unknown; so that by 1939 (Fitter, *L.B.R.* for 1939:28–9) they had nested or were nesting in all the London river valleys. In Middlesex, for example, Harting in 1866 knew them only on passage, but in the present century breeding has occurred in a number of places in the county and at Staines Moor has continued to the present time.

In general, however, the redshank has been irregular in its choice and yearly occupation of sites. Doubtless it has always been affected by drainage and ploughing and the reclaiming of marginal land. For example, a few pairs which bred between 1915 and 1920 on marshy fields at the head waters of the River Eden and the Kent Brook were lost when the land was drained about 1921. The process has been more marked during and since the war and this has certainly brought about some reduction inland. Recent examples are some pasture near Harefield, where war-time drainage prevented the continued nesting of a couple of pairs which had bred every year from 1934 to 1939, and the conversion of South Harrow sewage farm to allotments in 1942 which ended a nesting sequence extending back probably to 1921.

Against this downward trend may be set the persistence of several pairs at Beddington sewage farm (six in 1954) where conditions have remained more or less un.changed and breeding has been regular since about 1910. The new Chingford reservoir in the final years of its construction from 1946 to 1950 held up to ten pairs annually, and redshanks still breed in such inland localities as remain or become suitable.

Their return to the breeding sites may be in March, or sometimes in February, and spring passage continues until June. Most of the sewage farms and reservoirs are visited, and occasionally Inner London. The autumn movement is in advance of that of most waders, so that by the end of July nearly all the local breeding birds have gone and comparatively few redshanks are seen with the waders of many other species in August and September. A redshank recovered at Edmonton in the Lea valley on May 15th, 1954, had been ringed at Abberton reservoir, near Colchester, 40 miles N.E., on July 6th, 1950. Exceptionally, flocks of up to sixty have occurred inland in autumn, and up to a hundred on the Thames marshes in winter, but usually the numbers are very much smaller. An unknown proportion is evidently of the Iceland race *robusta*, two having been shot at Sevenoaks by Dr. J. M. Harrison on April 10th, 1943 (*S.E.B.R.*, 1943:47).

SPOTTED REDSHANK, *Tringa erythropus* (Pallas). Scarce passage migrant.

The spotted redshank was reported eleven times from 1900 to 1951, all the records, with one exception, being in August or September and all at reservoirs or sewage farms.

Single birds were seen at Staines on September 23rd, 1928 (*Field,* 152:705) and at Barn Elms on September 1st, 1938. Ten days later two were seen at the Brent reservoir. In 1945, when one of the basins at Lonsdale Road, Barnes, was drained, a spotted redshank was seen there with four black-tailed godwits, and on September 5th, 1947, there was one on the gravel bed of the new reservoir at Staines. There were four separate reports in the autumn of 1949. Single birds were seen at Walthamstow on August 6th, and a week later at Watford sewage farm, and at King George VI reservoir on September 9th. On August 14th there was a party of five at the same reservoir and later that day at Perry Oaks sewage farm. In 1951 one or two were at Perry Oaks on various dates in September.

Unusual numbers appeared in 1952, with three at Perry Oaks on August 17th and one at King George V reservoir on the 22nd. From two to five were seen at Perry Oaks on a number of occasions from September 16th to October 22nd and within this period parties of four and five were seen at the new and old Staines reservoirs. There were again several records in 1953, including two in the Lea valley, and in 1954 when one at Perry Oaks on February 7th was the first winter record.

The only spotted redshanks seen in spring have been two in summer plumage at Brooklands sewage farm on May 8th, 1937, and one at Perry Oaks on various dates from April 29th to May 5th, 1953.

LESSER YELLOWLEGS, *Tringa flavipes* (Gmelin)

In the autumn of 1953, when many American waders found their way to this country, two lesser yellowlegs appeared at Perry Oaks. One, which was first seen on August 30th, stayed until December 9th, during which time it also visited Ham Fields sewage farm and Staines Moor. The second was only seen on September 25th and 26th, but its plumage was clearly separable and it also had a different call (cf. *L.B.R.* for 1953). What was presumably the first bird was seen at Langley sewage farm on November 21st (*Middle Thames Nat.,* 6:16).

GREENSHANK, *Tringa nebularia* (Gunnerus). Regular and widely distributed double passage migrant.

Since 1925 the greenshank has been regular on passage in the valleys of the Lea, Thames and Colne, fairly regular at the Brent, and occasional elsewhere. Earlier in the century it was doubtless much overlooked, with less than half a dozen records in the first twenty-five years.

The Colne valley was not discovered as a haunt of greenshanks until 1926, when Dr. G. Carmichael Low saw two at a sewage farm near Langley (*Rep.* O.O.S., 1926:25). Besides the river and a canal the valley contains several flooded gravel pits and quiet waters, sewage farms, moist rushy levels and reservoirs. Greenshanks are likely to be found on passage anywhere along this twenty-five mile chain of waters and marsh-like sanctuaries every year, but nowhere with greater regularity than at Perry Oaks and the Staines area, where in "good" years they may be seen almost daily in autumn.

Nearly as attractive is the valley of the Lea, where greenshanks were shot in the early years of the century at Edmonton sewage farm and where in succeeding years others have been seen at the chain of reservoirs, ponds and gravel pits. Between these two main drainage systems of the northern part of the Area lie the reservoirs at Ruislip, Aldenham and Brent, three isolated lakes with natural margins. At all of these, particularly the hemmed-in Brent, the greenshank occasionally drops down to rest and feed when passing over London. The marshes and environs of the lower Thames about Dagenham and Dartford, despite industrialisation, still attract small numbers of greenshanks, and so too do the Thames-side reservoirs at Barn Elms, where they have been seen almost annually since the war. The gravel pits and reservoirs of the middle Thames, except Staines, seem to be only infrequently visited, but the small sewage farm at Brooklands used to be a favourite place before the war and greenshanks appeared there almost annually. Elsewhere south of the Thames they are only occasional.

Greenshanks are seldom in flocks, ones and twos or parties of four or five being more usual. At the Brent in 1928 eleven were seen in September and up to ten frequented the exposed mud of the King George V reservoir when it lay empty in 1933. The autumn movement starts in July, gathers momentum in August and early September, and continues only on a very small scale into October. In spring, passage takes place throughout April and the first two or three weeks of May; mid-summer and winter occurrences are rare.

KNOT, *Calidris canutus* (L.). Passage migrant and winter visitor in very small numbers.

Knots are seen in the London Area almost every year. They come in ones and twos and small parties and sometimes remain for several days. In 1954, when most were seen, there were about ten separate records, but usually there are only two or three a year. The first dated record was on September 10th, 1927, when two were seen at Staines reservoirs by J. P. Hardiman (Glegg, 1935). Ticehurst (1909) had mentioned its occurrence on the creeks of the Thames as high as Greenhithe and Dartford, but it is only recently that regular watching there has shown the knot to be still an occasional visitor to the foreshore.

Inland, it has been seen at Perry Oaks sewage farm and at five of the larger reservoirs, including those at Brent and Ruislip, which both have grassy and marshy margins, and those at Staines and in the Lea valley which have sloping concrete sides. If the water level is high these are little more than a brief attraction to waders passing over, but should the level be down there is a chance that waders, knots included, may stay for a day or two before continuing their journey. The river mud at Barnes attracted one in March, 1942, and others have been noted on the nearby reservoirs at Barn Elms.

September and October have been the chief months but knots have been seen at all seasons except mid-summer. Most have been in winter or first autumn plumage, but a few in partial and even summer dress have occurred. The largest parties have been in winter: 10 in flight at Staines reservoirs on November 16th, 1935, 9 at Barn Elms on December 22nd, 1938, and up to 10 on two recent occasions on the Thames marshes near Dartford.

PURPLE SANDPIPER, *Calidris maritima* (Brünnich)

The three records of the purple sandpiper within our period have all been in November. D. Gunn saw one on November 2nd, 1933, at Barn Elms reservoir (*B.B.*, 27: 208). At Staines reservoirs one was seen by several observers on November 29th and 30th, 1936 (*B.B.*, 30:260), and another on November 5th, 1939 (*B.B.*, 33:197).

LITTLE STINT, *Calidris minuta* (Leisler). Regular double passage migrant, mainly in autumn and usually in small numbers.

In 1903 what may have been the last little stint shot in the London Area was taken on the Thames near Dartford (Ticehurst, 1909). In the previous sixty years, when shot-gun and bird, stuffer were still in favour, sixteen, some seen but most shot, were on record from the Brent reservoir at Hendon (Glegg, 1935). If little stints visited London for the twenty-two years after 1903 they were either missed or not reported, for there is no further record until 1925, when Dr. G. Carmichael Low (*Rep.* O.O.S., 1925, p.20) saw two at a small sewage farm at Langley on September 12th.

Thereafter one or two were seen in 1929 and almost all the remaining years of the period. September and October have always been the chief months, but from 1939 onwards little stints were occasionally noticed in spring. The principal reservoirs, gravel pits at Broxbourne and Poyle, sewage farms at Brooklands, Perry Oaks and Ponders End and the slurry pool of Littlebrook Power Station, Dartford, have all been visited from time to time. During almost daily observation at Perry Oaks in the autumn of 1950 single little stints were seen on July 30th and August 16th, and there were up to five continuously for five weeks throughout September into the first week of October. The largest flock known in the London Area was seen there in the first days of October, seventeen being watched feeding and resting on the muddy strands and islets of the shallow pools; four remained until October 27th. Ten are the most seen on any subsequent occasion. The only winter record is of one seen by Mrs. W. I. Brewer and K. H. Palmer on the Dartford Marshes on December 11th and 19th, 1954.

TEMMINCK'S STINT, *Calidris temminckii* (Leisler)

The Temminck's stint has been identified four times within our period in spring and once in autumn. On May 29th, 1936, P. A. D. Hollom saw one at Brooklands sewage farm (*B.B.*, 30:347), and Professor Warmington identified another by the River Colne at Staines Moor on April 27th, 1949. One was seen at Barn Elms on May 12–13th, 1951, by B. A. Richards and Dr. A. G. G. Thompson, and another at Nazeing gravel pit on May 31st, 1953, by J. L. F. Parslow. The one in autumn was seen by several observers at Perry Oaks sewage farm on September 19th, 1954. Although the Temminck's stint is never common in this country on migration, it is more frequent in autumn than in spring, and it is surprising that regular watching in recent years, even at Perry Oaks, has only revealed the one.

BAIRD'S SANDPIPER, *Calidris bairdii* (Coues)

A Baird's sandpiper was identified at Perry Oaks sewage farm on September 17th, 1950, remaining until the 22nd. During this period it was seen by about fifty observers and exhaustive notes were taken under varying conditions, full details being published in *British Birds*, 44:252. The first occurrence of Baird's sandpiper in Middlesex, it was also the first sight record in Britain, and can doubtless be attributed to the series of strong westerly and south-westerly gales during the late summer of 1950 which produced many other unusual records, such as the appearance of Sabine's gulls and pectoral sandpipers.

PECTORAL SANDPIPER, *Calidris melanotos* (Vieillot)

The occurrence of a pectoral sandpiper at Perry Oaks sewage farm from September 16th–24th, 1950, at a time when there was a small "invasion" of this species in various parts of the country, has been fully described in *British Birds*, 44:250. Another was seen in the following year from August 31st to September 10th, and in 1954 there was one from September 13th–15th and a bird in different plumage from the 20th–21st. In 1952 one which frequented a rubbish-tip pool at Epsom from August 30th to September 8th was caught and ringed by I. C. T. Nisbet.

DUNLIN, *Calidris alpina* (L.). Double passage migrant and winter visitor; noted in all months.

The dunlin is probably the commonest and most widespread of all shore birds which visit the Area, but there was little evidence in the first quarter of the century to corroborate the statement of Harting (1866) that it was a double passage migrant in Middlesex. The few records were often separated by a lapse of years, and mainly supported by the observations of F. J. Stubbs (1910, *Essex Nat.*, 19:90) and P. W. Horn (1921) in and about the Thames estuary between Dagenham and Thurrock. There were scattered observations from 1922 of passage birds at the reservoirs at Walthamstow, Staines and Barn Elms but few were seen until 1927, when the reservoirs at Staines lay drained, with drying mud exposed, and there was an autumn flock of forty. Flocks of this size had apparently not been recorded inland in the Area before, and although from then onward dunlin were observed more frequently on passage at the reservoirs and elsewhere the flocks were still small. In 1945, however, at the same reservoirs and in similar conditions of drainage with mud exposed, a late autumn flock in October and November again exceeded forty and some of the birds remained for the winter. Unusual numbers were seen on Stone marshes in the autumn of 1953 with a peak of 73 on August 25th.

As a winter visitor the dunlin was known to R. B. Lodge (1901) at Enfield sewage farm, and to W. A. Todd (*Country-Side*, vols. 4, 6, 8), who in 1907–08 saw up to six in winter at Barn Elms and Putney. Ticehurst (1909) knew them along the coast of Kent "from the outskirts of London to the Sussex border" in autumn and winter, and Horn (1921) was able to say that at Thurrock Marsh they were regular and were especially numerous when the weather was hard. In December, 1938, the first in recent memory of a series of cold spells, up to thirty-two were seen at Barn Elms and twenty on the Thames shore opposite Chiswick. In the following winter, also severe, a very large flock of eighty-five appeared on December 9th at Romford sewage farm, a locality which at that period was being well watched. In the early months of 1947 when wintry conditions were both severe and exceptionally prolonged, and even the large reservoirs froze, nothing was seen of dunlin beyond a half-dozen at Beddington sewage farm. In 'normal winters', if such a term has any validity, dunlin in ones and twos and small parties may appear in the Area, usually briefly, but not in flocks of any size. Exceptionally, about fifty were seen on a jetty at Stone at high tide on February 12th, 1951, and 270 in the same locality on February 7th, 1954.

It is as spring and autumn passage migrants that dunlin are best known, when they visit many of the reservoirs and marshy places in the Area and particularly, of late, the sewage farm at Perry Oaks. Here they are likely to be seen in spring from late March to May or even early June, the largest flock at this season being one of 66 on May 2nd, 1953. In most autumns they are continuously present from July to October or November. In some years the main passage occurs in August and the first half of September, but in others the movement of fair numbers may continue much later in the season until well on in October. The autumn of 1948 was of this character, when flocks were held by the double attraction of the farm at Perry Oaks and the nearby bed of the King George VI reservoir, which was then under construction. Upwards of thirty were seen in July, August and September, with a maximum of seventy on the reservoir bed on September 25th. Forty or more continued until mid-October.

Small numbers of dunlin have occasionally been noted on passage and in winter resting beside the park lakes of Inner London and flying over the built-up areas at night. At Mill Hill, during the war, gunfire at a low-flying aircraft in the small hours forced a flock of dunlin almost to the roofs of the houses, their calls sounding everywhere in the moonlight (Professor E. H. Warmington, *L.B.R.* for 1943:14).

CURLEW SANDPIPER, *Calidris testacea* (Pallas). Regular autumn passage migrant in small numbers; scarce in spring.

In recent autumns it has been no unusual thing to see parties of half-a-dozen or more curlew sandpipers in south-west Middlesex, but elsewhere and in earlier years they have been infrequently noticed. The first record for fifty-four years was in 1927 when J.P. Hardiman saw two on mud at Staines Reservoirs in September (*B.B.*, 21:205), and thereafter small numbers were noticed in most years until the war, and again in 1946 and 1947. The subsequent focussing of attention on Perry Oaks and the Staines group of reservoirs, where areas of mud and shingle were exposed at the King George VI reservoir over long periods, resulted in their being reported day after day in autumn from this corner of Middlesex. By the autumn of 1950 the new reservoir had been full for several months, so that Perry Oaks, which was in a very suitable condition for waders, was the main attraction. Curlew sandpipers were seen intermittently in August and throughout September and the first half of October; for about a week in September 10–15 were regularly present and 17 were seen twice. In the next three autumns not more than five were seen at a time, but in 1954 numbers rose to 23 on August 22nd.

On the Stone marshes there was an exceptional autumn passage in 1953, lasting from August 30th to September 26th with a peak of 26 on the 14th. Elsewhere, at the reservoirs of the Lea valley, the Brent and Elstree reservoirs, Beddington, Brooklands and Ponders End sewage farms, a gravel pit at Sewardstone, and even Richmond Park, the curlew sandpiper has only appeared briefly in ones and twos, for a day or two at most and usually in autumn; the largest number together were four seen by W. G. Ellis at Brooklands on June 2nd, 1939. Three May records, all of single birds, are the only others in spring. Various stages of transitional plumage even to almost full summer dress have been noted occasionally both in spring and autumn.

SANDERLING, *Crocethia alba* (Pallas). Regular double passage migrant in small numbers.

A few sanderlings now appear on passage every year but at one time they were either very much more infrequent or, as seems more likely, they were less often spotted. Ticehurst (1909) referred to their (undated) occurrence at Gravesend, but in the present century none was certainly identified until 1928 when T. H. Harrisson saw one at Staines reservoir on September 4th and L. Parmenter found one at the Brent on September 12th. Thereafter one or two were recorded in most years up to the war and regularly from 1946.

At the old Staines reservoirs they have been seen at the water's edge on the sloping concrete banks, or searching for food along the silted cracks between the slabs with which the banks are faced. In 1947 one was present on the gravel bed of the new King George

VI reservoir at Staines, and when one of the reservoirs at Barn Elms was left drained in the spring of 1949 up to three were watched feeding there in March, April and May. Elsewhere they have been seen infrequently at the reservoirs and sewage farms in the Lea valley, at Littleton and on the Stone Marshes, but regularly at Perry Oaks sewage farm since 1948.

Sanderlings mostly appear in ones and twos, occasionally up to eight. Two unusually large flocks have been seen: one of 16 which stayed at the reservoir at Staines for a week in May, 1950, and one of 17 at Perry Oaks sewage farm on May 16th, 1953. Passage is mainly in April and May, August and September, but sanderlings have been noted in all months from January to October.

BUFF-BREASTED SANDPIPER, *Tryngites subruficollis* (Vieillot)

One was identified by L. Baker and B. A. Richards at Perry Oaks sewage farm on October 18th, 1953, and remained in the neighbourhood until November 3rd (*B.B.*, 47:310–11).

RUFF, *Philomachus pugnax* (L.).

Regular double passage migrant; usually in small numbers but occasionally in flocks up to about thirty, and exceptionally over a hundred in spring 1954.

In November, 1912, R. B. Lodge saw at Lower Edmonton sewage farm the first reeve to be recorded in the London Area for forty-one years. Two were shot at the same place in September, 1915, by W. W. Hartwell, and thereafter none was recorded until Dr. G. Carmichael Low (*Rep.* O.O.S., 1923–24, p. 54) saw three near Langley, Bucks., in September, 1924.

Since 1924 ruffs and reeves have been known as regular passage migrants. At first they were noticed only once or twice annually, usually in autumn. In the thirties and forties, however, it became apparent that the species was visiting a number of inland waters and marshy places in most of the main river valleys and even ploughed fields, besides such comparatively isolated waters as the reservoirs at Elstree, Brent and Ruislip. In the valley of the Thames the concrete-banked reservoirs at Barnes, Molesey and Littleton, and a sewage farm at Walton, were all visited at various times, as well as many places in the Colne valley from Wraysbury in the south to Old Parkbury in the north. Edmonton, Hoddesdon and Ponders End sewage farms, Cheshunt Marsh and the large reservoirs of the Lea have proved attractive, while south of the Thames ruffs and reeves have been noticed at Beddington, Brooklands and Molesey sewage farms, the one at Brooklands having been a favourite halting-place until the open tanks disappeared with war-time developments.

The attention of bird-watchers has now been switched to the farm at Perry Oaks, where every autumn since at least 1947 conditions have been such that migrant ruffs and reeves could feed and rest for days or even weeks. The coming of fresh arrivals, and the going of birds which have rested, obscure our knowledge of the length of stay of individuals, but for these last several years the passage here and at the nearby Staines reservoirs has proceeded intermittently during July and almost continuously through August and September to the first week or two of October. Until 1945 the only two records later than the end of October were both early in our period: the Edmonton bird in November, 1912, already mentioned, and one shot on ploughed land at Colnbrook on December 5th, 1925 (*Bull.* B.O.C., 46:114). The autumn numbers are usually small, and ones and twos and little parties of four or five are the rule, but in recent years up to 14 have been seen at Ponders End and Perry Oaks sewage farms. At the last of these farms there were 28 on September 20th, 1953, and 29 on September 11th, 1954. Odd birds were still about at the end of the year.

In spring, passage is usually in March, April and May, and once again until recently few birds were involved. In 1949 J. O. Owens saw 20 at Wraysbury gravel pit on March 10th (*Middle Thames Nat.*), and in 1954 there was an unprecedented influx commencing at the end of January. Between January 30th and February 7th up to three at a time were seen in seven localities. From February 21st there were slightly more, and between March 20th and 24th the flock at Perry Oaks suddenly jumped to the exceptional number of 115. From then until April 10th the nine counts made did not fall below 70 and reached a peak of 119 on April 8th. There were still as many as 80 on the 22nd after which numbers fell slowly until the last bird was seen on May 9th.

AVOCET, *Recurvirostra avosetta* L.

There have been five occurrences of the avocet in the Area. On August 10th, 1909, H. Meyrick saw one flying in a westerly direction over Hampstead, and heard it calling (*Zool.*, 67:316). One was seen at Brooklands sewage farm by P. A. D. Hollom from June 13th to 16th, 1932 (*B.B.*, 26:55). On March 28th, 1949, two were watched at close range at Mayesbrook gravel pit by H. Tarrant. In the winter of 1952–53 one frequented the slurry pools at Littlebrook Power Station and the nearby tide-line at Stone from December 22nd to January 24th. At Perry Oaks sewage farm one was seen by I. C. T. Nisbet on April 8th, 1954.

BLACK-WINGED STILT, *Himantopus himantopus* (L.)

Two black-winged stilts were seen at close range on the muddy foreshore at Brent reservoir in September, 1918, by J. C. M. Nichols, and referred to in his *Shooting Ways and Shooting Days* (1941). The reservoir at that time was empty except for the main channel, and had attracted many waders. Details of these birds have been kindly supplied by Mr. Nichols and published in *British Birds*, 43:344.

GREY PHALAROPE, *Phalaropus fulicarius* (L.). Rare visitor in autumn and winter.

From time to time grey phalaropes visit the Area in ones and twos on autumn passage and there are about eighteen records since 1900, covering the period from mid-August to mid-December, but mostly in September. They have not been seen in spring.

Grey phalaropes are sometimes driven inland in numbers if strong westerly gales should occur during their passage off the western sea-board of Europe. For instance, one seen at Staines reservoir on August 19th, 1930, appeared "during a fierce westerly gale", and in September, 1950, in similar circumstances, two were seen at the Brent reservoir from September 8th to 14th, and one at King George VI reservoir, Staines, from September 18th to 24th. Full details of the 1950 invasion and the weather conditions which produced it can be read in *British Birds*, 44:245–256.

The major reservoirs have accounted for most of the records, Staines and Barn Elms having provided fourteen between them. From 1928 to 1935 inclusive grey phalaropes were seen every year except 1929, and they also appeared annually from 1950 to 1953. On September 2nd, 1951, a phalarope, which was probably of this species, was seen on the Thames near Tower Bridge.

RED-NECKED PHALAROPE, *Phalaropus lobatus* (L.)

On August 1st and 2nd, 1949, a red-necked phalarope was seen at King George VI reservoir, Staines, by several observers. It allowed approach to within a few feet and very detailed notes were taken of its plumage by C. A. White. It had a noticeably slender, tapering bill. This was the first certain record of this species for the county of Middlesex. However, Glegg (1935) refers to a phalarope seen by himself and others at Staines reservoir on September 28th, 1930, which he considered to be a red-necked, but as the identification was disputed by other observers he quoted the record only in square brackets.

STONE CURLEW, *Burhinus oedicnemus* (L.).   Rare migrant, mainly on spring passage.

On rare occasions stone curlews halt in the London Area on passage, and away from the North Downs have been met with seventeen times in all, twelve in spring, once in July, and four times in autumn. All were alone except for a party of three seen by J. R. Crawford at Drayton on October 4th, 1929 (Glegg, 1935). In addition, experienced ornithologists have, on five occasions in March and three in April, identified their call notes as birds passed over at night, and three times when this has happened stone curlews have been seen on about the same date. They have usually selected places free from cover, such as farmland, a sewage works, old allotments or open spaces like Richmond Park (four times), Hainault Forest, Wimbledon Common and Chingford Plain.

On the North Downs between Woldingham, Tatsfield and Chelsham birds are reported to have been heard on a number of occasions in spring according to M. D. England, but there is no suggestion of breeding although the undulating downland, partly cultivated and partly dotted with scrub, would appear to be quite a suitable habitat if less disturbed.

Of the stone curlews seen in spring eight were in April, three in March and one in May. On the return passage two were in October and one each in July, August and November. The August bird was picked up in a children's sand-pit at Kilburn Grange Park.

PRATINCOLE, *Glareola* sp.

A pratincole was seen at Barn Elms reservoirs on September 8th, 1948, by Mrs. R. Brown, and again on September 11th by H. A. Baylis and A. Williams. The observers were unable to state with certainty the colour of the axillaries and under-wing coverts, the only distinguishing characteristic between *G. pratincola* and *G. nordmanni*, and therefore the actual species remained in doubt although it was certainly one or the other. It was considered to be a bird of the year and fuller details appear in *British Birds,* 42:221.

ARCTIC SKUA, *Stercorarius parasiticus* (L.).   Rare passage migrant; one winter record.

Arctic skuas are essentially maritime birds outside the breeding season, and only eleven have been reported in our Area. Of five in spring between April 24th and May 28th the first was one flying low over Hyde Park on May 16th, 1916 (*Field*, 27.5.16). The second was seen by T. L. Bartlett over South Harrow on May 21st, 1943. In 1946 there were two, one at Stockers Lake with black terns on May 11th (A. C. Frost, *Trans.* Herts. N.H.S., 23(3):98) and the other seen at the Lea valley reservoirs on May 28th by H. B. Fossey and W. A. Wright. A bird of the dark phase was identified by H. A. Craw and C. Hughes at Staines reservoirs on April 24th, 1948.

Of the five in autumn one was seen by F. Baden-Powell at Wimbledon on August 28th, 1922, and later by D. Seth-Smith on September 8th (*Field*, 140:387 and 476). A second was seen in St. James's Park by G. Hopkins on September 18th, 1935, and a third by W. A. Wright at King George V reservoir on August 21st and 28th, 1938 (*B.B.*, 32: 198). C. A. White and W. N. Mitchell had close views on October 9th, 1949, of an immature bird at Staines reservoirs, where it stayed for five days at least. An adult was identified by H. P. Medhurst at Barn Elms on September 9th, 1954.

The single winter record is of one, reported by E. C. Stuart-Baker, which frequented the Surrey Docks during December, 1920, and was seen there again in the following month (*B.B.*, 22:24).

GREAT SKUA, *Stercorarius skua* (Brünnich)

The great skua has been seen four times in the London Area, once in each of the months January, February, April and July. According to *The Handbook* very few winter off the east coast and in the English Channel, and most spring passage takes place direct from the Atlantic to northern breeding quarters, so that its rarity in winter, and inland at all, is not surprising.

Two were seen by P. F. Bunyard harrying black-headed gulls at Waterloo Bridge on April 14th, 1915 (*Bull*. B.O.C., 51:104). On July 19th, 1928, Professor E. H. Warmington saw one, which he thought was an immature bird, chasing a carrion crow at Mill Hill. One remained at Staines reservoir from February 14th to 22nd, 1931 (*Bull* B.O.C., 51:74) and another was seen by Mrs. M. E. Price flying over Kingsbury on January 15th, 1942 (*L.B.R.*, 10:21).

POMATORHINE SKUA, *Stercorarius pomarinus* (Temminck)

A dark phase bird which was found by Mr. and Mrs. W. C. Doughty at Banbury reservoir on November 28th, 1954, remained until December 4th when it flew away strongly. It had fed mainly on dead birds during its stay.

LONG-TAILED SKUA, *Stercorarius longicaudus* Vieillot

On the extreme fringe of our Area, at Easneye, near Ware, Herts., a female long-tailed skua was found dead in September, 1937, and identified at the British Museum (Natural History) (*Field*, 4.12.37).

GREATER BLACK-BACKED GULL, *Larus marinus* L. Mainly an autumn and winter visitor, in some numbers at suitable localities. A few occur in other months.

The greater black-backed gull was the last of the five common species of gull to take advantage of the plentiful food afforded by rubbish dumps, sewage farms and tidal mud in the Area, and of the safe roosting places provided by reservoirs. Up to 1921 there are only six records, all of individual birds, though it was probably more plentiful in the Thames estuary, which was then little watched. From 1922 onwards it was seen every year, though still in ones and twos, except when H. A. F. MacGrath observed seven adults at Westminster in April, 1924, after a southerly gale. From the winter of 1929–30 onwards it became a regular winter visitor, especially to the Thames and nearby reservoirs, though it was still sufficiently rare in 1935 for W. E. Glegg to list every occurrence in his *Birds of Middlesex*. In the last ten years it has steadily extended its winter range in the Area, while its numbers have increased remarkably.

The first flock of more than 10 birds together above Greenwich was recorded in 1931; of more than 20 in 1941 and of more than 30 in 1947. During the day they are dispersed along the whole of the river below Richmond, but some measure of their numbers may be gauged from the presence of flocks of over 200 at Hampton reservoirs where they collect before the final flight to their roosting places. The chief of these is at Walton reservoirs where, in recent years, certainly over 300 and possibly as many as 500 forgather. On the eastern side of the Area they fly down river to roost on the North Kent marshes or the open river.

Along the river greater black-backed gulls are most numerous near rubbish dumps or refuse barges, or resting on stretches of gravel which are undisturbed and on boats anchored in midstream (Cramp and Teagle, 1955). They rarely rest on buildings, except at Billingsgate fish-market, where they join the smaller gulls in the struggle for offal. In counts of twenty miles of the Thames between Barnes and Woolwich, made from a launch, 164 adult greater black-backed gulls were seen on January 29th, 1950, and 113 on January 28th, 1951; if immatures had been included, these totals would probably have been increased by about a third. The species has been a regular visitor to Barn Elms since 1926 and to most other large reservoirs since 1930. It occurs at some sewage farms, such as Beddington (first seen in 1947) and Epsom. The Thames, however, remains its main haunt. In many rural areas it is rare or absent, for unlike other gulls it does not usually feed or rest on agricultural land, and, even in the Colne valley, it occurs rather infrequently and in small numbers.

The greater black-backed gull may now be seen in the Area at all times of the year, although it is still uncommon from May to mid-July. By late July it is sometimes surprisingly numerous; for example, J. R. Crawford counted 26 on July 23rd, 1947, between Gravesend and Dartford and in 1949 Lloyd Mills saw 25 on Dukes Meadows, Chiswick on July 17th. Over 80% of the birds in 1949 were adults, presumably those which had failed to breed, or perhaps almost indistinguishable fourth-year birds. In general, however, the numbers build up slowly through the autumn months, reaching a maximum in December and January.

An adult, ringed at Littleton reservoir in February, 1935, was recovered at Gravesend in November, 1940.

LESSER BLACK-BACKED GULL, *Larus fuscus* L. Numerous in late summer and autumn, much less so in spring. Has recently increased considerably in winter, and a few are seen in early summer.

Until 1925 there were fewer than thirty definite records of the lesser black-backed gull, presumably the British form (*L.f. graellsii*), in the Area. These all refer to odd birds or small parties, which were seen in almost every month, including December to February. Curiously enough, in view of the present status of the species, most of the records refer to spring passage, thus agreeing with the experience of H. G. Attlee who, between 1900 and 1927, found it most frequent in the latter half of April, moving north-west, and only occasional in autumn. The increase began in the late summer of 1925, when up to 12 were seen at Barn Elms. Smaller numbers were present there in 1926, but in 1927 the invasion became really marked, beginning on June 10th and lasting until late September. It reached a maximum on August 29th, when J. P. Hardiman counted 57 by the reservoirs and more than a hundred on the Thames nearby. This autumn invasion has continued annually since, the numbers steadily rising and the feeding range of the birds gradually extending.

Throughout the thirties Barn Elms and the adjacent stretches of the river continued to be a favourite haunt of the species, with peak autumn numbers ranging from 120 to 277. In 1931 Rowberry (*L.N.* for 1933) discovered large numbers at Wyke sewage farm in the Lower Brent valley, recording up to 400 in the two succeeding autumns. Birds were seen also at Staines and Littleton reservoirs in this period, but rarely in any numbers elsewhere. W. E. Glegg (1934) described it as a rare visitor to the Lea valley reservoirs, and the first large invasion occurred there in the autumn of 1938. At Brent reservoir there are no records of large numbers until 1940. In 1937 an extension of feeding range was noted when big flocks were seen on several occasions on sports fields and golf links at Wimbledon, and in the last ten years these gulls have become even less restricted to the Thames. Flocks of twenty or more birds have been reported from other reservoirs; from filter-beds, such as Leyton Marsh and Hampton; from airfields at Heathrow and Hornchurch; from Chiswick and Richmond Parks; from sewage farms, such as Perry Oaks, Beddington and Watford, and from playing fields in many parts of the Area.

Large flocks occur usually in the late summer and autumn. Although the species has become both more regular and numerous on spring passage in the last twenty-five years flocks of more than twenty at this season are uncommon, the record of 200 seen at Barn Elms by J. McHoul on April 6th, 1949, being most unusual. It is perhaps significant that Barnes (*B.B.*, 46:238–252) has shown that there is often a difference between the routes used on spring and autumn passage. The spring passage continues from March until May, with a few non-breeding birds still present when the return movement begins towards the end of June.

Regular counts at Barn Elms by many observers show that the date of the peak of the autumn migration varies considerably from year to year. In fifteen years for which sufficient counts are available, the date on which the largest flock has been noted has varied between July 22nd and October 25th. August is the most usual month (in seven years), followed by September (four years). At Staines in 1952 there was a peak of about 520 on July 22nd.

A similar variation was found in counts of two stretches of the Thames in Inner London made in 1951–53 by Cramp and Teagle (1955). There, for six months of the year, from early April until early October, the lesser black-backed gull was found to be *the* gull of the river, outnumbering all other species.

Since 1929–30 a few of these gulls have wintered in the Area. Their numbers ranged from one to six up to 1943 (Fitter, *B.B.*, 36:163–4), and since then have tended to increase, especially in the last year or two. In the winter of 1954–55 about 100 were seen at Springwell gravel pit in early November and up to 50 frequented a rubbish-dump at Shepperton, while at Beddington they first appeared in numbers in December when there were 25–40 daily and 81 on the 12th; they steadily increased until by March 5th there were no less than 119 (cf. *B.B.*, 48:370).

In 1931 Harrisson noted that, in the Harrow district, the passage of lesser black-backed gulls was confined to the extreme east of the area, and Rowberry in 1933 (*loc. cit.*) confirmed this movement along the lower Brent valley. He believed that this was then the only regular passage route in the Area, although the gulls moved eastwards and westwards along the Thames for feeding and roosting. His observations at Purfleet had failed to detect any movement up the Thames, and he argued that the gulls flew inland from the area of the Wash and passed over East Anglia to cross London by the Brent valley. In 1934, however, E. M. Nicholson reported a conspicuous passage up the Thames past Westminster for a week after July 29th, reaching at least one a minute on August 3rd. The growth in autumn numbers in recent years has meant that roosting and feeding movements have made it more difficult to distinguish true passage, and definite records are few. J. A. G. Barnes (*loc. cit.*) believes that generally migration takes place over a wide front, with visible concentration in a few places. From observations in the last ten years it seems that the Thames and Brent valleys are still important routes, although small numbers of birds seen migrating in many parts of the Area suggest that some movement takes place on a broad front. Further research on this point is needed.

A lesser black-backed gull ringed as a nestling at Walney Island, Lancs. in June, 1933, was recovered at Littleton in January, 1935.

The Scandinavian form (*L.f. fuscus*) was first recognised in the Area in 1929, and, except for 1931, has been reported each year since. They are usually seen between August and March, and less frequently in April and July. There are no May records, and only one for June—two seen by Dr. G. Carmichael Low at Hammersmith on June 30th 1941. They occur most frequently along the Thames and the reservoirs, but have been noted occasionally at sewage farms, parks and fields away from the river.

HERRING GULL, *Larus argentatus* Pontoppidan. Winter visitor, often in large numbers at suitable feeding places. A few occur in other months.

In the early years of the century small numbers of herring gulls were reported fairly regularly, not only from the Thames estuary and the docks, but also from further inland. Kendall (1907) described them as of not uncommon occurrence in the Willesden area in the winter months, mostly immature birds consorting with the black-headed gulls. Stubbs (*L.N.*, 1916) said that they were regular visitors, mainly to the docks and St. James's Park—the presence of pinioned herring gulls in this park in the early years of the century no doubt helped to attract wild birds. For the next few years the position appears to have changed little, odd birds being seen from time to time along the river, in the parks and over reservoirs, but in February, 1924, A. Holte Macpherson reported a big flock at Staines reservoir, and in December, 1925, there were over thirty. In December, 1929, L. Parmenter saw about forty at Barn Elms and from then on there was a rapid increase in numbers. Thus in 1931 at least 100 were seen flying to roost over Barnes; in February, 1932, more than 200 were counted at Staines; in October, 1935, about 700 were seen at the same reservoirs where, in January 1936, the first gathering of more than a thousand birds was reported. At the same time they began to spread over the Area discovering new feeding grounds, especially sewage farms. Thus they were first seen at the one at Beddington in 1930, and at those at Epsom and Watford in 1933.

Herring gulls are now widespread in considerable numbers in the winter months wherever there is food for scavenging. In a recent survey of gull roosts it was found that about 10,000 were roosting at Littleton, Staines and William Girling reservoirs, 90% of them being at the two former (Homes, 1955). During the day they may be seen along the Thames (where 691 were counted in the twenty miles between Barnes and Woolwich on January 29th, 1950), feeding along the tideline or scrambling for scraps in the rubbish barges. Large flocks of several hundreds occur at many sewage farms, reservoirs and refuse dumps. They have spread to agricultural land, playing fields and some of the outer parks. G. K. McCulloch (1939) has described how the herring gulls in two areas in the Colne valley fed on fields or at a sewage farm, making use of nearby gravel pits for washing and resting. The birds from these two nearby areas did not appear to mix to any extent, although both groups flew to reservoirs at Staines for roosting. In Inner London herring gulls are still mainly confined to the river, and to the parks where the numbers are usually small. They rarely perch on buildings and do not join the black-headed gulls in taking food from them, although in the cold spell of 1947 they were seen landing awkwardly to feed in small backyards at Wanstead and Goodmayes.

Herring gulls usually arrive in September (occasionally in August), staying until late March or April. In inland areas small numbers are not infrequently reported from May to July, usually passing over, but I. C. T. Nisbet found evidence of larger numbers in some parts of Middlesex in the summer of 1952. They are probably more common at that time lower down the river, and in 1947 J. R. Crawford counted 48 between Gravesend and Dartford on July 23rd and 47 between Erith and Woolwich on July 30th.

The ringing of herring gulls at Littleton and Molesey reservoirs has thrown some light on the origin of these winter visitors. The returns suggest that the majority come from Scandinavia, for the only two recoveries of these gulls in the breeding season were both in Norway, while two birds ringed as juveniles in Denmark were found in Middlesex in later winters. One ringed at Littleton and found in Brechin, Angus, on August 15th, and another from Molesey recovered at Grays, Essex, on July 25th, may have been on return passage or of British origin. The other six recoveries of gulls ringed at the reservoirs have all been in the winter months and from eastern England.

COMMON GULL, *Larus canus* L. Common winter visitor and passage migrant; occasional in summer.

In the low-lying parts of the London Area the common gull has always been much less numerous than the black-headed gull, although on grassland, including playing fields and the downs, it is often the commoner bird. It is almost impossible to trace its spread in the Area, owing to the unreliability of the few observations that were made at the beginning of the century, even Hudson apparently finding it hard to distinguish black-headed and common gulls in winter. His statement in 1906 that this species was abundant on the Thames at Kew in winter must therefore be treated with reserve in the absence of supporting evidence.

Typical of the bird's status at that time are Davis's statement in 1904 that it was fairly common on the Thames at Dartford, especially in winter; Kerr's in 1906 that a few spent the winter on Staines reservoirs, and Todd's in 1909 that it was becoming a much more numerous visitor to the Thames at Putney, being quite common early in that year. Away from the river, it was as late as 1926 when Howard Bentham saw the bird for the first time in the Tadworth-Epsom Downs district, showing that like the black-headed gull this species was slow to spread over the high ground south of the Thames. Two years later Macpherson stated that there had lately been a striking increase in its numbers in Inner London, especially in cold weather.

At present our common gulls seem to have two distinct habitats. On the one hand, along the Thames and by other fresh waters, a few will often hang around at the back of screaming flocks of black-headed gulls, which are being fed with scraps, and chase the successful ones skua-fashion instead of competing directly for food themselves. The other main type of habitat and behaviour is represented by large one-species flocks of 50 or even 2–300 gulls frequenting grassland, including playing fields, and other farmland. Thus, according to Professor E. H. Warmington, the common gull is the normal winter gull on playing fields in the Mill Hill–Colindale district, and as long ago as 1909 Bentham remarked that in the Waddon–Beddington district it tended to avoid the sewage farm, preferring the downs, farmland and playing-fields. This habitat-preference is also typical in many parts of the Cotswolds and Chilterns, where the common gull is the commonest of its kind and the black-headed is almost unknown.

Most of the London common gulls arrive in October, but they are quite numerous by the end of July on the river below Woolwich and there have been at least four London recoveries in September of birds ringed in Denmark. The recoveries of ringed birds suggest that all the common gulls wintering in London come from the Baltic. There are no records suggesting that birds breeding in the north and west of the British Isles ever winter in the London Area, and, of course, the common gull does not breed in Central Europe. There have been six recoveries of Danish birds, four each from Germany and Sweden, two from Finland and one each from Norway and the Isle of Bornholm.

It is difficult to say when the wintering birds leave, as there is a pronounced increase in the proportion of common gulls to other species in late winter and early spring. In recent years numbers roosting at the reservoirs in mid-winter have been estimated at 10–15,000, but on March 5th, 1940, Hollom considered that probably nearly half of about 37,000 gulls at Littleton alone belonged to this species (*Handbook*, V:51).

GLAUCOUS GULL, *Larus hyperboreus* Gunnerus. Formerly very rare, but one or two seen in most recent winters.

In the winter of 1941–42 two glaucous gulls and three birds considered at the time to be Iceland gulls were seen in the London Area. The appearance of five such gulls in a single winter, when hitherto they had been very rare, coincided with an increase in Shetland and an unusual number of records of glaucous gulls on the east coast of Great Britain. Since then some have been seen on London waters almost every year.

Previously, the only known occurrences of the glaucous gull were of one in St. James's Park, seen by C. Borrer on March 20th, 1915 (*B.B.*, 8:269) and an immature at Staines reservoirs from February 9th–14th, 1934 (Glegg, 1935). In addition there are records of Iceland gulls, a species not previously recorded in the Area, in the spring of 1939 and the following winter. For reasons which are explained under Iceland gull it is no impossible that these and other 'Iceland gull' records may refer to glaucous.

The present status of the glaucous gull as a fairly regular though very scarce visitor to the London Area dates, then, from as recently as the winter of 1941–42 (*vide L.B.R.* for 1942, p.21). Either one or two undisputed glaucous, which typically are large enough to make identification fairly straightforward, have been seen in most subsequent winters. If records are included of white-primaried gulls which were either briefly seen or small enough to lead to possible confusion with Iceland gulls, the total is doubled and no winter has passed without at least one having been present.

Some were adults, but most have been in varying stages of immature plumage. In some winters the birds have settled down for several weeks, especially on the reservoirs at Lonsdale Road and Barn Elms and the adjacent stretch of the Thames, where refuse barges have been particularly attractive to them as to large numbers of other gulls. Other reservoirs, certain gravel pits and sewage farms, and even the Inner London parks and Thames, have been frequented. An immature glaucous was watched by J. F Burton on Swanscombe marshes for two hours on the unusual date of July 30th, 1950 (*L.B.R.*, 15:41), but all others have been between November and March, except for an immature bird at Barn Elms on April 3rd and at Waterloo Bridge on April 5th, 1954

ICELAND GULL, *Larus glaucoides* Meyer. Very rare winter visitor.

In the spring of 1939 and the following winter birds which were considered to be Iceland gulls were seen by reliable and experienced observers and ranked as the first records for Surrey, Middlesex and the London Area (*B.B.*, 33:28, 281; *L.B.R.* for 1939 and 1940). Three were reported in the winter of 1941–2 including an adult which stayed for sixteen days on the Round Pond in Kensington Gardens and was considered by E. M. Nicholson to belong to this species on account of its brick-red orbital ring. Others were reported subsequently, but at about this period it came to be realised that the identification of the Iceland gull was more difficult than had been made clear by the *Handbook*. It was shown by G. T. Kay in 1947 (*B.B.*, 40:369) that the projection of closed wings beyond the tail was not diagnostic of the Iceland gull as had been thought, and that identification must be based on the relative size of head and bill and other fine points of detail. Aided by this information and by the showing of some of Mr. Kay's films of both species, bird-watchers in London have been in a stronger position of late to judge whether gulls which are not so large as to be obviously glaucous are in fact Iceland or small examples of the glaucous, a species which apparently varies considerably in size

Since 1947 reports of gulls believed to be Iceland have been limited to three: one at Hammersmith in January, 1948; one at Epsom sewage farm in January, 1949; one at Barn Elms in March, 1949. The detailed field notes taken of these suggest that they were probably Iceland, but the distinctions are so very fine that southern observers, who perforce see very few of these gulls, are inevitably at a disadvantage and some slight element of doubt remains.

LITTLE GULL, *Larus minutus* Pallas. Scarce visitor from late summer to early winter very rare on passage in spring.

There are upwards of fifty reliable records of the little gull in the Area, all of them since 1927, and all except two at the reservoirs. Nearly a half have been in September and October, a third from November to January, three in August and one in July, while the only three spring records have all been in early May. Most of the late summer and early autumn birds are immature, the earliest being a second-year bird at Barn Elms on July 21st, 1947. The earliest adult was seen at King George VI reservoir on August 9th 1953. The largest party on record is one of five seen by W. E. Glegg at Littleton reservoir with seven black terns on May 6th, 1936; the other May records are of a first-year bird at Barn Elms from May 6th–10th, 1947, and two adults and an immature at Staines on May 8th, 1954—an adult was seen at Perry Oaks on May 9th and 16th. There are two records for Inner London, one in Regent's Park on January 17th, 1936, and the other on the Thames at Westminster on October 1st, 1945.

BLACK-HEADED GULL, *Larus ridibundus* L. Present throughout the year, chiefly as a common and often abundant winter visitor; not infrequent in summer and perhaps also a passage migrant. One breeding colony established in the early forties.

In 1900 the black-headed gull had only recently become a regular winter visitor to the Thames in London. It appears always to have been present along the estuarine part of the river, and probably also in the docks (though here there is an almost total lack of observations), but from the winter of 1880–81 it began to visit the Inner London reaches of the Thames with some regularity. Stimulated by a series of hard winters, increasing numbers appeared, and the extremely severe weather of the early part of 1895 established the bird as a regular visitor to Inner London in some numbers.

By 1900 the black-headed gull was also resorting to the central parks. Further out, however, it was still something of a nine-days wonder, though some began to be seen regularly over Tooting from 1895 and over Brixton from 1898. During the last decade of the century it was largely confined to the main river valleys of the Area, notably the Thames, Lea, Colne and Brent. In February, 1901, large numbers appeared on flooded fields at Enfield; as early as 1902 black-headed gulls were believed to have wintered at Watford sewage farm; in 1903 large flocks were frequenting the Thames and near-by fields at Twickenham; three years later it was the most abundant gull along the Thames at Kew and a frequent visitor to the lakes and ponds in Kew Gardens; in the same year, 1906, it was the most numerous gull on Staines reservoirs and could often be seen following the plough in that district; and in the Woolwich area in 1909 it sometimes fed on arable with rooks.

Away from the river valleys, however, it was slow to spread in some districts, especially in the south. At Coulsdon it appears not to have been seen, at any rate regularly, before the winter of 1925–26, and between Sutton and Banstead it is said to have first appeared in 1929. In the Warlingham and Chelsham district also 1929 marked the beginning of the regular invasion of black-headed gulls each winter, though from about 1922 onwards odd birds had appeared for a day or so from time to time.

Now, the black-headed gull is one of the most ubiquitous birds in the Area in winter, not only on the estuary and by fresh water, but on arable land, sewage farms and all kinds of built-up ground. The habit of frequenting buildings for food offered by kindly bird-lovers dates from at least 1917, when Bertram Lloyd saw about a hundred hovering round an open window of the Hotel Cecil, from which a man was throwing bread. The habit became much more widespread in the inter-war years, and especially, despite the regulations of the Ministry of Food, during the 1939–45 war. It was then also, as a result perhaps of the three severe winters from 1939–40 to 1941–42, that these gulls began to patrol the whole built-up zone of London. Now in winter it is hardly possible to look up in any London street for five minutes or so without seeing a black-headed gull cruising over, while in some districts they also come down for food in suburban gardens.

The regularity with which black-headed gulls frequent the same part of London was first demonstrated by T. L. Bartlett, who has ringed several hundreds at their park or riverside feeding-stations. Over thirty have been re-caught in the same locality, ten of them more than once, and so far none of those feeding in St. James's Park or along the embankment have been found to interchange. Recoveries have ranged from the same winter to twelve winters after the original capture, and two birds have been caught in the same place in three different winters. The value of this work in tracing life histories is well illustrated by one bird which was caught in St. James's Park in February, 1939, again in February, 1945 and was then recovered three years later in June in the Kattegat. Two birds have been recovered when at least 13 years old.

The long lines of gulls flying to their roosts on winter evenings have become one of the most familiar sights of London, and in two recent years the number roosting on the reservoirs in mid-winter has been estimated at 85–100,000. These roosts are discussed more fully on pages 47-49.

Before the 1914–18 war the black-headed gull was exclusively a winter visitor, arriving in September or October and departing again in March or April, though in 1909 individuals were seen at both Kew and Richmond as early as the first week in August, and the first arrival in St. James's Park in the autumn of 1908 was on August 19th. Just when non-breeding birds began to stay the summer is not clear, but as far back as 1921 it is recorded that many gulls were still on the water at Barn Elms on May 4th, and one was seen at Staines reservoirs as late as June 22nd, 1913. By 1928 Macpherson was able to say that some immature birds frequented the Thames every summer. Since the establishment of the gullery at Perry Oaks adult gulls in breeding plumage and juveniles in their first plumage have, not surprisingly, become much commoner in the Area in summer.

The discovery of the gullery at Perry Oaks sewage farm, on the edge of London Airport, by Lord Hurcomb in May, 1946, was one of the most interesting events in London ornithology. The colony, which owes its survival and protection against egg-thieves to its situation in a bed of sewage sludge, is believed to have been founded in 1941 or 1942. From 50–60 nests in 1946 the colony expanded rapidly to about 300 nests in 1947, remained at roughly the same size for the next two years and has subsequently fluctuated between about 150 and 250 nests. In some years, however, hatching and fledging success is very low.

There have been a great many ringing recoveries of black-headed gulls relating to the London Area, and it is apparent that the winter population is drawn mainly from birds breeding around the Baltic, especially in Denmark and Sweden. There are also one or two recoveries from central Europe, a bird ringed near Lake Zürich in June, 1928, having been found at Woodford Bridge in the following February; several others have been ringed in Bohemia and Silesia. The only definite indication that birds from British breeding colonies spend the winter around London comes from the recovery in 1952 of a young one ringed in Midlothian, and very few London-ringed black-headed gulls have been recovered in the British Isles in summer. It is not possible to say if one ringed in Westminster in January, 1953, and found dead at Gravesend on April 24th, 1954, was on its way back to the Continent or was one of the east coast breeding population.

SABINE'S GULL, *Xema sabini* (Sabine)

In September, 1950, following a period of westerly gales in the Atlantic, Sabine's gulls were seen in several parts of the country, and in our own Area an adult was first observed at Staines reservoir on September 11th, being followed by an immature bird on the 18th. They were indifferent to spectators and constantly hawked up and down the eastern fringe of the reservoir, where they remained until the 27th (*B.B.*, 44:254).

KITTIWAKE, *Rissa tridactyla* (L.). Known nowadays in the London Area chiefly as a scarce winter visitor, although occasionally it occurs on passage.

In contrast to its present-day status is Bucknill's account, published in 1900, describing it as "of regular occurrence" on the Thames in winter and being seen or shot on some of the waters of Surrey "more or less frequently", though admittedly only as a straggler.

One further quotation from the same source and a summing-up by Fitter (1949) leave us with the impression that, at least for a certain period at the end of the nineteenth and the beginning of the twentieth century, the numbers of kittiwakes visiting London reached an inexplicable maximum: " . . . the Thames is really the only Surrey locality which it can be said to visit in abundance annually and, until recently, it seems to have been regarded even there as decidedly uncommon." To what extent Bucknill was justified in using the words "in abundance" is impossible to say in the absence of further information. But he was not alone in recording higher numbers of kittiwakes than we see nowadays, for Ticehurst (1909) reported that in autumn and spring "many" used to come up the Thames as far as Dartford, which is certainly not the case to-day.

Although during the second quarter of this century the number of observers in the Area was growing, the records of kittiwakes have shown no tendency until 1954 to keep pace with this increasing intensity of observation. Instead, they were steady during that period at up to four or five a year in the years when the species was known to occur, and in nine years out of the twenty-five there were no records at all. Evidence before 1926 is only fragmentary. In 1954 kittiwakes were seen in eight months of the year, but never more than three at a time except in December, when during a heavy westward movement of gulls throughout the 24th H. P. Medhurst counted 13 adults and two immatures between 13.30 and 14.50 hours. On the following morning the movement continued and five adults were seen in a period of thirteen minutes.

Distribution, as one would expect, is almost confined to the Thames and the reservoirs, although there are five records of kittiwakes visiting inland ponds in the Area and one of a bird picked up dying in a park at Southgate in February, 1950. Almost a third of the records refer to dead or oiled birds, and probably most kittiwakes seen inland are victims of some unfavourable circumstance.

BLACK TERN, *Chlidonias niger* (L.). Spring and autumn passage migrant to larger gravel pits and similar waters. Exceptionally large passage in spring in several recent years, especially 1950.

Up to 1925 there are only some ten records of the black tern in the Area, seven of these being in spring and the largest party one of ten at Batchworth on July 16th, 1915 (*Trans. Herts. N.H.S.*, 16(3):153). The last of the ten records, in 1923, was the first one at a reservoir although in the ensuing twenty-five years it was at the larger reservoirs in the Thames and Lea valleys that most black terns were seen.

From 1926 onwards, if we exclude the war years, black terns were observed annually in autumn, and in only three years were none seen in spring. Up to 1939 the largest party in spring consisted of eight birds at Mitcham on April 26th, 1937, while in autumn 10–21 were seen on three occasions during this period at Staines reservoirs in late August or early September. Elsewhere, they were seen in six years at Barn Elms with a maximum of twelve and at ten other localities including reservoirs, gravel pits and a sewage farm: in Inner London one was observed in Hyde Park on May 27th, 1935, and there has only been one subsequent record.

Since 1946 inclusive there have been several years when spring passage has been exceptional and three when slightly larger numbers than usual were seen in autumn. In 1946 black terns were seen at gravel pits and reservoirs throughout the northern part of the Area or near the Thames. Extreme dates were April 30th and May 26th, with a peak in the second week in May when twenty or more were at Stockers Lake and up to 43 at Staines during a very strong north-east wind. Two years later there was again an unusual number, the largest flocks being about 30 at Barn Elms and 39 at Springwell Lake on May 21st and 25 or more at Staines on the following day. The highest numbers seen in autumn in these four years, 1946–49, were 18 at Barn Elms and 27 at Staines. Apart from an August party of twelve, up to five was the most seen on any occasion in autumn

From a series of reviews in *British Birds* by Hinde and others it appears that the unusual numbers inland in spring generally occur when easterly or north-easterly wind off the seaboard of France follow an increase of temperature in France or Spain during the period of migration. The most exceptional passage in the London Area was in 1950 (cf. *B.B.*, 44:170–73) when 153 birds were recorded at nine localities on May 14th including a party of 47 at Staines. On the 16th there were 121 at Staines alone, and the next day up to 63 at King George V reservoir in the Lea valley and up to 109 at Staines. Barn Elms had 40 on the 18th and Ruxley gravel pit in Kent had about 20 on the 21st. In the autumn there were 27 at Staines on October 1st and 14 on the 7th. In 1954, when the spring passage in the British Isles as a whole was even greater (*B.B.*, 48:148–169) black terns were seen at eight localities between May 9th and 10th, with over 70 birds on the second date. In the autumn up to 46 were seen in the Lea valley and up to 21 at Staines during August.

It is still uncertain by what route black terns reach the London reservoirs in spring. Although Hollom (*B.B.*, 32:76) suggested, in view of the number of records for Berkshire and Oxfordshire, that some of the birds probably worked their way up the Thames— and certainly the largest number of birds are seen at Barn Elms and Staines—there is no evidence of birds following the estuary above Dartford and it seems unlikely that along the river they would always fly high enough to escape observation. Moreover, in May 1948, black terns were seen to leave Staines and Tring reservoirs, in Hertfordshire, in a north-easterly direction, while in May, 1949, they were seen arriving at Tring from the south-west. Evidence from other localities confirms that the main direction of the movement at this season is between north and east. In autumn it seems probable that black terns usually enter the Area from the north-west, and many observations in the Midlands show that an inland passage of terns is quite regular in spring and autumn. Some black terns, however, do follow the Thames in autumn as far as Dartford where, for example 17 were flying west at low tide on August 17th, 1952. None have been seen above this point, and it may well be that they return with the tide (cf. Gillham and Homes 1950).

In spring the largest numbers are usually seen about the middle of May, the earliest of the few April records being of six birds at Mitcham on April 11th, 1914 (*Ibis*, 1914 533). Birds seen in early June probably represent late spring passage, and there are four notes for the second half of June and one for July 3rd. Black terns appear on return migration later in July, but few are seen in the Area in autumn until towards the end of August, and from then they may occur at any time up to early October; there is one record in the second half of October and three in November, the latest being on the 19th.

COMMON TERN, *Sterna hirundo* L. Spring and autumn passage migrant, chiefly to reservoirs and lakes in Thames, Lea and Colne valleys. Parties seldom contain over fifty birds, but exceptionally large numbers seen in Staines district in autumns 1949 and 1950, and spring 1952.

Common and arctic terns are not usually seen well enough at the large reservoirs to be separated with certainty, and for this reason the whole of this account refers to the two species jointly unless one or other is specified. It was not until 1924 that 'common terns' were first recorded in the Area with any regularity, and the only one among this handful of earlier observations referring to more than two birds was a note by A. Holte Macpherson of about twenty terns, believed to be *hirundo*, flying east over the Serpentine on May 12th, 1906 (*B.B.*, 22:242). Hudson, however, wrote in 1906 that common terns were not infrequently seen along the Thames at Kew, while Ticehurst (1909) said that stragglers ascended the river in spring, and that during August and September the species "commonly makes its way up the Thames as far as tidal water extends". Glegg (1929) was also of the opinion that there was a passage up the Thames in autumn.

There is no indication of the evidence on which Ticehurst based his statement and Glegg was apparently giving a personal opinion. Careful study of tern movements in the Thames estuary has shown that the majority of the birds travelling up the river in autumn turn back again before reaching Gravesend, but in recent years westward movements have occasionally been noticed as far up river as the Dartford marshes, where on September 5th, 1953, F. J. Holroyde saw several parties totalling about 139 birds. In five years' watching, however, J. F. Burton saw none above Dartford. Reasons have already been given under black tern why it seems more likely that terns reach the London Area overland rather than by following the Thames. In support of this is the relative frequency of occurrence of common or arctic terns in October, whereas in the estuary Gillham and Homes (1950) knew of only three records in that month.

Two of the earliest reports when observations became more numerous are among the most unusual. On March 9th, 1924, an exceptionally early date, Miss Hibbert-Ware saw a party of nine common terns at Walthamstow reservoirs (*Essex Nat.*, 21:132), while on December 16th, 1925, E.C. Stuart-Baker had close views of two common terns on the ground at Tooting Bec Common. On the following day he saw a party of about twelve terns, believed to be the same species, flying high over West Norwood (*B.B.*, 19:256); The only other winter record is of one common tern at Walthamstow on December 9th, 1932 (*B.B.*, 26:258).

Common and arctic terns are usually more numerous in autumn than in spring, when passage normally takes place between the last week of April and early June. Apart from an exceptional flock of 304 at Staines reservoirs on April 28th, 1952, the largest spring party consisted of 26 birds at Barn Elms on April 26th, 1947, at a time when there was an unusually strong inland passage of common and arctic terns, following persistent south-westerly winds. A large proportion, however, of the birds seen at this time were identified as arctic terns. There was also a party of 27 at King George V reservoir on April 25th, 1954.

Occasionally common or arctic terns are seen in late June or July, but they do not appear with any regularity until August, and almost all parties of ten or over have been in the period August 15th to September 15th; the chief exceptions have been 21 on August 1st, 1927, and 30 or more on October 4th, 1930. Records in October are by no means unusual and there have been some annually since 1946, the latest being on October 30th.

The vast majority of tern records come from the reservoirs, but there are scattered observations from many of the smaller waters. Parties of over twenty are unusual and in four years only have over fifty been seen at a time. In 1949, at King George VI reservoir, Staines, about twenty at 11 a.m. on September 4th were joined by fresh arrivals from the north until by 12.30 p.m. there were 114 on the water, but half an hour later only twenty remained. In the following year 226 were counted at the same place on August 21st and two days later there were up to 500 at the adjacent Staines reservoirs—only twenty remained next day. The large flock in the spring of 1952 has already been mentioned, and less striking numbers were seen in the autumns of 1953 and 1954.

Common terns have been seen several times in Inner London, usually singly.

ARCTIC TERN, *Sterna macrura* Naumann. Passage migrant identified more in autumn than in spring but exact status obscure owing to uncertainties of identification.

Most records of common or arctic terns at the reservoirs are not separated by those observers who are aware of the difficulties of identification, and the present discussion is confined to the relatively few definite records of this species reported in four springs and ten autumns between 1926 and 1953. Undoubtedly, however, many of the common, arctic terns reported belong to the present species, and all records attributed to one or other of them are discussed under common tern. The only occasions when more than four arctic terns have been reported at a time were in 1931, when a party of 15 was seen at Walthamstow reservoirs on August 22nd by R.W. Pethen, and in 1947, when there was an exceptional spring passage of arctic and common terns throughout south-east England. On April 26th there was a party of 26 terns at Barn Elms of which several were definitely this species, which appeared to predominate in this particular movement. From four to six were seen on the same day at Walthamstow reservoirs and there was one on May 3rd at Perry Oaks sewage farm. None have been identified with certainty later than October 10th.

ROSEATE TERN, *Sterna dougallii* Montagu

A roseate tern was seen by W. H. Dady and D. A. Preston at Perry Oaks sewage farm on May 16th, 1953, and full details appeared in the *London Bird Report* for that year.

On April 28th, 1921, J. Rudge Harding saw four terns at Barn Elms reservoirs, one of which had a rich pink colour on the breast. As no other details of identification are available there is inevitably an element of doubt about the observation (*Country-Side*, June, 1921).

LITTLE TERN, *Sterna albifrons* Pallas. Occasional spring and autumn passage migrant chiefly to reservoirs in Thames valley but also rarely to a number of other reservoirs ponds, gravel pits and sewage farms.

Ticehurst stated in 1909 that the little tern moved as far up the Thames on autumn migration as Dartford, but we have no other evidence of this and recent observation suggest that very few of the many terns which frequent the Thames estuary below Gravesend in autumn come so far up the river. The only two dated records of little terns before 1925 are of one at Putney on August 11th, 1911 (*Country-Side*, 2:237) and another at Highgate Ponds on April 30th, 1913 (*Zool.*, 72:239).

More frequent watching has shown the little tern to be an irregular visitor on spring and autumn passage, but there are still years when none are seen. Of a little over fifty records about half have been at Barn Elms or Staines reservoirs, five only in the Lea valley and the remainder at a variety of other reservoirs, ponds, gravel pits and sewage farms. The only one in Inner London was a bird seen on the Round Pond in September, 1932 (*Field*, 161:56). Most little terns are seen singly, and the largest party has been one of eleven at Staines on September 3rd, 1954.

The nineteen records in spring have been between April 21st and May 25th, half of them in the first ten days of May. In autumn rather over half have been in the period September 9th–22nd with extreme dates on August 4th and October 22nd.

There is no indication of the routes followed by little terns in reaching or leaving the Area, and the only one seen on the Thames was flying down river between Brentford and Hammersmith on May 2nd, 1946.

SANDWICH TERN, *Sterna sandvicensis* Latham. Occasional spring and autumn passage migrant to larger reservoirs and gravel pits.

When Ticehurst stated in 1909 that young Sandwich terns were occasionally seen on the Thames in autumn he was probably referring to the part of the estuary well beyond our boundary. The only two records in the Area for the first twenty-five years of this century are both anonymous and should, therefore, be treated with reserve; one bird was seen in Hyde Park on September 2nd, 1908 (P.J.M., *Country-Side*, 7:220) and one over the Lea valley on May 3rd, 1913 (*Bull.* B.O.C., 34:184). The next reported occurrence was on August 28th, 1926, when A. Holte Macpherson saw two at Barn Elms. The first certain record for Middlesex (*B.B.*, 25:134) was of a single bird at Littleton reservoir five years later.

Since 1931, however, Sandwich terns have been noted almost every year, but only on three occasions have the numbers reached double figures: Dr. Carmichael Low saw 25 at Barn Elms on September 19th, 1947, and 20 on the following May 21st, while P. F. Yeo watched about 20 at Staines reservoirs on September 12th, 1950. In view of the scarcity of any tern records from the Thames above Dartford, compared with the number at the reservoirs, C. W. G. Paulson's observation of three Sandwich terns over the river at Limehouse on September 11th, 1937, is particularly interesting. In addition to the Hyde Park record already mentioned there has been one other occurrence in Inner London, at the Round Pond in September, 1937 (*Field*, 170:888).

The spring records fall between April 25th and May 28th, while from then to the last third of August Sandwich terns have been seen only seven times, including early parties at Staines on July 3rd, 1950, and July 4th, 1952. Between August 20th and October 10th they have been seen on some forty occasions, and exceptionally there was one at Staines on October 19th and November 4th, 1934.

RAZORBILL, *Alca torda* L. Rare and accidental visitor.

In common with other auks razorbills reach the London Area on rare occasions. During the middle thirties there was a period of five years, from 1934 to 1938 inclusive, when they were seen every year, but there have been only five other records since 1900.

Most of the reports have been in October and November, and the three occasions when parties of razorbills have been seen in the Area have all been at that time. On November 20th, 1911, after a fortnight of storms, A. K. Collett saw five on the Thames near Blackfriars Bridge (*B.B.*, 22:244). A party of sixteen was observed on Littleton reservoir on October 22nd, 1934. Four days later they were all dead and on examination were found to be infested by a fluke (*Cotylarus platycephalus*) (*B.B.*, 28:188 and 245). W. A. Wright found four razorbills at Walthamstow reservoirs on October 5th, 1948, and on the same day W. G. Teagle saw seven near Lambeth Bridge. That evening C. H. F. Parsons, in poor light, saw an undoubted auk near Hammersmith Bridge, and the next day an immature razorbill appeared on the Round Pond, Kensington Gardens, and remained there until October 18th.

Of the remaining nine records two perhaps deserve special mention. A bird which was first seen on Walthamstow reservoirs on November 11th, 1934, remained there until May 4th, 1935, when it was found dead. While watching the Boat Race at Mortlake on April 6th, 1935, Professor Warmington saw a razorbill swimming rapidly upstream with one motor-boat ahead of it and another astern.

LITTLE AUK, *Plautus alle* (L.). Accidental visitor.

Little auks have reached the London Area on about twelve occasions, usually after periods of persistent gales. A fair proportion of them have succeeded in reaching one or other of the reservoirs, but, like other storm-driven birds, some inevitably got stranded in incongruous situations. Two were found at Cudham in 1905 (Davis, 1907).

In February 1912, which was one of the well-known "wreck" years, a little auk walked in at the door of a doctor's surgery in Finsbury Park (*B.B.*, 6:164). 1910 was another "wreck" year, and two birds were seen in the Area.

One was taken alive on November 21st, and another was seen on November 28th at Rickmansworth (*Trans.* Herts N.H.S., 14(4):283).

Little auks were seen in five of the winters from 1927–28 to 1934–35:— at Staines in the latter months of 1928, 1929, 1932 and 1934; at Dartford on December 13th, 1927; at the Round Pond on December 31st, 1929, when there were also two at Staines, and at Molesey on the following day. In February, 1950, the remains of one were found on the bed of the King George VI reservoir at Staines. All the records are for the months of October to February inclusive.

GUILLEMOT, *Uria aalge* (Pontoppidan)

Guillemots have reached the Area four times during our period. All were probably victims of storms at sea, although positive evidence of such severe weather is given in only one of the reports. An exhausted bird, found at Winchmore Hill by O. G. Pike on November 22nd, 1911, died soon afterwards (*B.B.*, 5:230). P. H. T. Hartley saw two on the Thames above London Bridge on November 7th, 1930 (*B.B.*, 24:197). One, which was found at Bunhill Fields, E.C., on December 15th, 1933, and died later, proved to be a female of the Northern race, *U.a.aalge* (*B.B.*, 27:263). In the same winter, on January 14th, 1934, one was discovered in a garden at Limpsfield after a night of severe storms (*S.E.B.R.*, 1934:80).

PUFFIN, *Fratercula arctica* (L.). Scarce vagrant.

Despite their maritime habitat some twenty-nine puffins have been found in the Area during the present century. Of the twenty-three which were still alive only seven were found in or near water, showing clearly that most were storm-driven and weakened. The great majority were found in the last three months of the year.

Davis (1907) states that "in most years" specimens were brought to him, but no numbers are mentioned, and it is Middlesex and Surrey which have the most published records. Easneye in the Hertfordshire sector and Banstead in Surrey have had two records each at an interval of ten and twenty-five years respectively. There have been three records in Inner London, including a bird which was found slightly oiled outside the Savoy Hotel. Other puffins have crashed through the roof of a glasshouse or have been found walking in one of the streets of a country town.

PALLAS'S SANDGROUSE, *Syrrhaptes paradoxus* (Pallas)

In Volume 1 of *British Birds* W. Wells-Bladen wrote that he saw a Pallas's sandgrouse flying over Hendon on September 23rd, 1907, but in subsequent publications this observation is omitted, presumably on account of the lack of detail. A considerable invasion of these birds occurred in May, 1908, in various parts of Britain including the Home Counties and on September 1st one was shot at South Ockendon, Essex (*Field*, 12.9.08 and *B.B.*, 2:208).

STOCK DOVE, *Columba oenas* L. A common but somewhat local resident.

The stock dove in summer is found most frequently in parkland and open woodland, where nesting holes are available in mature trees, less often in thick woodland, such as Epping Forest, where feeding grounds are restricted. It is the common breeding pigeon on the Thames marshes between Woolwich and Northfleet, as it is on the marshes further along the estuary, where it breeds in isolated cattle sheds and in the quarries fringing the marsh. In this open territory birds are easily noticed, but elsewhere they are not conspicuous when nesting and their presence is advertised chiefly by their note.

In winter, stock doves assemble in small flocks, often in company with woodpigeons, and resort mainly to arable land on which gatherings of up to three hundred have been seen. Besides stubble and ploughed land, derelict ground at the site of a new reservoir under construction and the marshes along the Thames below Woolwich are among the places where flocks of over a hundred have been noticed. The grain formerly put down for deer in Richmond Park was always attractive. There is no evidence of the origin of the larger flocks, but one of over 300 was seen flying north-east in the Chingford district on November 27th, 1949. Flocks of several hundreds at Sevenoaks in late March and April, 1943, reported by J. G. Harrison (*S.E.B.R.*, 1943, p.46) were thought to be on migration.

Large flocks are sometimes seen in the nesting season, such as 100–150 in young wheat on the Dartford marshes in May, 1951, and about 200 at Perry Oaks sewage farm at the end of May and in early June, 1953. There is evidence that summer gatherings are attracted from a wide radius to some especially desirable source of food.

Nesting has been reported from holes in trees, the tops of pollard willows and cracks and sheltered ledges in chalk quarries. More unusual sites have been in the base of an empty heron's nest in Richmond Park (*Birds in London,* 1947:25), and inside a boat house on Navestock Park Lake in 1906 and 1909 (Glegg, 1929).

In the parks of Inner London there is little information for the earlier years of our period, although a pair nested regularly in an elm in Hyde Park some years before 1927 (Holte Macpherson, *B.B.*, 22:240). Stock doves were nesting in the grounds of Holland House in 1927, and were not infrequently observed in Kensington Gardens. Since 1934 reports have been more frequent, and nesting in Kensington Gardens has probably been regular to the present time: as many as 25 were counted on March 28th, 1951, and in 1954 there were seven pairs within a 200–300 yard radius of the Round Pond. In recent years stock doves have spread and in 1952 nesting was reported for the first time in Battersea and Regent's Parks, while birds were also seen in the breeding season in Green and Holland Parks. D. Goodwin, in 1950, watched large numbers displaying and seeking nesting sites in Kensington Gardens in late winter and early spring, from 7 a.m. to about 10 a.m., and noted that they very seldom settled on the ground. When they alighted they were extremely nervous, and he believed that they were feeding outside the park.

In the inner suburbs the bird is somewhat irregularly, but in Greenwich Park it has probably nested in several years, and there were at least three pairs in 1950. In the late autumn, at this period, small flocks with larger numbers of woodpigeons visited this park to feed on acorns. About the same distance north of St. Paul's stock doves are seen throughout the breeding season on Hampstead Heath and presumably nest there.

FERAL PIGEON, *Columba livia* Gmelin. Extremely numerous in Inner London, less so in the peripheral areas, but colonies are present in most towns and suburbs where old buildings, church towers, bridges or other suitable breeding sites coincide with possibilities for obtaining food.

In Inner London the pigeon is found almost everywhere. Its numbers are greatest in areas where much food can be obtained, such as Trafalgar Square, the parks, and the docks where grain is unloaded and spilt. Almost every square or open space, however, provides a feeding ground for some pigeons, and smaller numbers, which probably total many hundreds, if not thousands, forage in the gutters of the quieter streets for their living. In general little distance separates the places where pigeons feed and roost, but a short watch at almost any large colony will show that some birds are coming in from a considerably greater distance than the majority, and the distances travelled for food and the extent to which individuals shift their feeding grounds would be an interesting study. The birds that forage in the parks all roost and nest on buildings outside, although they perch quite freely on trees during the day, as they do in some of the squares. This habit is sometimes spoken of as if it were something entirely foreign to the bird's nature, but it is not confined to London specimens. In some places pure-bred wild rock doves settle on trees, and have even bred in them, which the London pigeons have never yet done so far as is known.

For a nesting site the pigeon prefers a hole, cavity or well-sheltered ledge, preferably in semi-darkness. It will, however, nest (often unsuccessfully) on quite exposed ledges if orced to do so by lack of more suitable sites. Other things being equal there seems to be a definite bias in favour of sites that are either high up or over water. Birds may roost at or near their nest-sites or some little distance away, high sheltered ledges being preferred, but many birds choose very exposed situations, particularly in the suburbs. Most of London's suburbs are inhabited by pigeons, the main colony being usually based on some church or other building that offers suitable and safe nesting or roosting sites. At Richmond a colony inhabits the bridge over the Thames, and at Twickenham twenty or more birds roost nightly on an exposed ledge of a building near the station.

Feral domestic pigeons have been a feature of London's bird-life at least as far back as the 14th century and there is a very full discussion of the varied population of this species by Goodwin in *The Avicultural Magazine*, vol. 60, pp. 190–213. From mediaeval times onwards pigeons were kept in dovecotes, being left free to find their own food in the fields, and their young, or most of them, were taken for human food. Naturally many strayed and took up other quarters, and such birds were the forerunners of our feral pigeons in London and elsewhere. Even to-day lost or strayed domestic pigeons are continually joining the London birds. Of these only nondescript birds and racing homers (commonly miscalled carriers) normally survive long enough to affect the stock by interbreeding, since the highly artificial "fancy" breeds soon succumb when cast on their own resources.

There is no evidence for the suggestion that feral pigeons in London have reverted, or are reverting, to the type of the wild rock pigeon from which all the domestic breeds have been evolved, although the old-fashioned dovecote pigeon closely resembled the wild bird in form and colour, as do a few of the London pigeons to-day. There is a continual infusion of lost racing homers, and most of our birds are intermediate in type between the rock and the homing pigeons, or more closely approximate to the latter, which tend to be larger with proportionately thicker bill, larger cere and usually more bare whitish skin around the eyes.

The London pigeons are condemned as a nuisance by many council officials, the chief complaints against them being that they foul buildings and gutters with their nests and droppings, and that they damage buildings by eating the mortar. It is perfectly true that pigeons when breeding will eat quantities of mortar, since they need lime which is not otherwise easily obtainable in London, but their bills are not strong enough to start the damage by pecking, and the removal of mortar by pigeons is a sign that it was already crumbling and in need of repair. Large numbers of pigeons are trapped and shot by officially accredited pigeon-killers, but as the numbers are primarily controlled by food supply the periodical pogroms have no lasting effect, and only result in more food and suitable nesting sites being available for younger birds, which soon restore the level of the population.

The feeding grounds of London pigeons are the parks, the squares, the river mud at low tide and, to a lesser extent, the streets, the banks of reservoirs and bombed sites. In most of these places the birds feed largely on bread or other human food that has either been thrown to waste or else deliberately given to them. Although by nature feeders on seeds and (to a lesser extent) molluscs picked up on the ground, the London birds have learnt through necessity to devour almost anything edible and most of them will freely eat even apple, meat or chocolate. However, they much prefer grain or pulse if they can get it, and in some areas feed much on waste seeds found on the ground after the hay has been cut. At Barn Elms they habitually forage on the reservoir banks when the grass has been cut, and in Richmond flocks feed on the stubbles in the park. Among other natural foods eaten by London birds are broken or half-rotted acorns (for they cannot or will not swallow them whole like the woodpigeon), and the spangle galls from fallen oak leaves.

The extent to which London's pigeons are directly dependent on man was made evident in the last war, when their numbers declined greatly through lack of food, and persecution. They began to increase again after the war, and the increase seems to have been accelerated after the abolition of bread rationing, when the population soon returned to approximately the level of 1939. The great decrease in horse traffic must have deprived of a ready source of food the many pigeons that at one time fed largely on the grain spilled daily from the horses' nosebags, but there is no evidence to what extent this affected their numbers. It has been suggested that the vast numbers of pigeons present in London is proof that other birds do not compete with them. Observation in any park where sparrows, ducks or gulls are present will, however, soon show that these birds do compete with the pigeon for food, particularly in hard weather in winter, when the gull and duck population is at a maximum, and fewer people bother to bring food for the birds. There is every reason to suppose that could ducks, gulls and sparrows be wiped out there would be a corresponding increase in the pigeon population, provided, of course, that the same amount of food was distributed.

While there is no doubt that food supply is the basic factor limiting the numbers of London pigeons, it is possible that lack of suitable nesting places may locally be a factor. Certainly in South Kensington some potential breeding pairs are unable to find suitable nest-sites, and the extent to which blitzed buildings throughout London have been used for nesting suggests that a similar housing shortage may exist elsewhere.

Apart from man the London pigeon has few enemies. Carrion crows and the larger gulls are sometimes seen eating dead young pigeons on the Thames mud at low tide. In most cases these are doubtless birds which have fallen from their nests under bridges and drowned, though in some cases their consumers may have killed them. Possibly jays, jackdaws and crows may rob their nests on occasion, but the only definite evidence concerns a party of jackdaws in 1916 (Fitter, 1949, p.52).

WOODPIGEON, *Columba palumbus* L. Common resident, breeding throughout the Area.

By 1900 the woodpigeon, one of the wariest birds in rural areas, had successfully colonised central London. Fitter (1949) has described in detail how, from a few pairs breeding in Kensington Gardens and other parks, the woodpigeon began to increase rapidly after 1883, spreading to squares and gardens and even to isolated trees in the built-up areas, until by the nineties it was one of the commonest of London breeding birds. Its history in the suburbs is less clear. In the north an increase seems to have taken place during the same period, but in some southern suburbs the growth in population occurred rather later. Thus Power (1910) said that a great increase had occurred in Brixton, Dulwich and Herne Hill only in the last ten years, while at Lee it was still increasing rapidly in 1904. Walter Johnson described it as "peculiarly rare" on Wimbledon Common as late as 1912. In the rural districts it was a common resident until the early forties, when the organised shooting campaign caused a striking reduction in its numbers in all parts of the London Area. After the war woodpigeons began to increase again, slowly at first but more rapidly in recent years, and in most places they have now regained their former strength.

The tameness of the woodpigeon in Central London has long excited comment. Without this tolerance of man it would never have become one of the dominant birds of the inner zone, but it is hard to say why this normally shy species should have changed its behaviour so markedly and so suddenly towards the end of the last century. The woodpigeon had become tame in Paris and Berlin long before it did so in London, yet even at the present time it has not established itself in most other British cities. It has been suggested by Miriam Rothschild (*Ibis.*, 91:108–110 & 356–8) that the woodpigeons breeding in the parks of large towns may be compared to island populations exhibiting a striking degree of genetic tameness in sharp contrast to the main population of woodpigeons breeding in the surrounding countryside. Yet the woodpigeons of central London are not sharply cut off from the country birds but are connected to them by the suburban breeding stocks, which exhibit varying degrees of tameness. Thus in Deptford, Lewisham and Greenwich the woodpigeons will feed in the street with the feral pigeons, yet in other suburbs, though willing to breed near man, they retain much more of their normal wariness. Again, in the late autumn the great majority of the woodpigeons leave central London and are not seen again until they return to take up their breeding territories in December and January. Flocks are seen in the autumn every year at Richmond Park, Bushy Park, Ken Wood, some sewage farms and on the fields in rural areas, feeding on acorns and grain, and it seems probable that some of these birds are from the central areas, mixing with the country stock and adapting themselves to a different pattern of behaviour. In September, 1951, there were up to 2,000 in Richmond Park and R. W. Hayman identified about 95 per cent of them as birds of the year. When the numbers in Inner London were seriously reduced by shooting during the war the survivors became much more wary, and it is only gradually that the former tameness has returned as the numbers have increased again.

In London the woodpigeon perches readily on buildings and often uses them for singing and display. The habit of nesting on buildings has been noted in Inner London since the 1890's but has never become widespread. Nests on buildings may be commoner, however, than records show. They have most frequently been found in Westminster and four of the ten cases reported in 1954 were in this area. In 1953 one pair built a nest entirely of wire netting, on the fire-escape of London Transport Headquarters, and in 1954 a pair reared young *inside* an occupied Kensington flat, on the bathroom window-sill. Other nests have been found on station girders, scaffolding, ledges, pipes, and in window-boxes. Unlike the feral pigeon, woodpigeons do not roost on buildings but resort to the communal roosts in trees which have been described in a separate chapter.

Flocks of woodpigeons have often been recorded passing over the Area, mostly between late October and early December. These flocks have been seen moving in two main directions (between north and north-east and between west and south-west) and on occasion parties following these two lines have been seen crossing in flight. These observations may correspond with the movements which have been observed in recent years over the coasts of East Anglia and Sussex. More rarely numbers have been seen flying over in late December, January and February.

TURTLE DOVE, *Streptopelia turtur* (L.). Summer resident, common in suitable rural areas, scarce in built-up areas except on migration.

The turtle dove frequents open country with tall hedges or scattered bushes, and open woodlands, plantations and large gardens. It is scarcer in thickly wooded districts. The great majority of nests are built in hawthorns or blackthorns, but small trees may be chosen, particularly where there is cover of twigs or even ivy. Birds are more frequently heard than seen while nesting, and are usually in pairs, although even at this time several may collect on an attractive feeding ground. Occasionally the flocks may be large, such as one of fifty seen in a strawberry field at St. Mary Cray on May 30th, 1948. Sewage farms are especially favoured, and smaller parties seem to be particularly fond of the cinder heaps of the filter media at Perry Oaks. As they are also frequently seen on the cinder tracks of market gardens around Feltham, it looks as though blown seeds may be easy to find in such places.

Writing of the Parndon district in 1941, G. Dent refers to the bird as abundant generally, but formerly local, having shown an enormous increase. In the Harrow district an increase over the period 1925–30 was chronicled by T. H. Harrisson (*L.N.*, 1930:114), and Professor Warmington speaks of the bird as slowly increasing in recent years in the Edgware, Mill Hill and Finchley area. In some other localities a decrease has been noted, but it is usually stated that numbers arriving from year to year do not vary to any extent.

Birds normally arrive during the first fortnight of May and depart towards the end of August and into early September, extreme dates being April 16th, 1946, and October 10th, 1946. On completion of nesting in late July many of them forsake their usual haunts, and when in flocks are difficult to distinguish from birds on passage. Thus, while no migration has been recorded actually in progress, parties of up to fifty birds have been seen on telegraph wires, on the beds of reservoirs under construction, on corn stooks and at sewage farms. Some feeding on the foreshore at Barnes, within the built-up area, on September 14th, 1941, were more obviously on migration.

In Inner London stragglers are noted almost every year in Regent's Park, Kensington Gardens, squares and private gardens, usually on spring or autumn migration. They are shy and, as they have little opportunity to feed undisturbed on the ground, rarely stay for more than a day.

A nestling ringed at Stone, Kent, in June, 1953, was found in the Gironde, France, on May 11th, 1954.

CUCKOO, *Cuculus canorus* L. Common and generally distributed summer resident in the rural or semi-rural areas, but in the suburbs, the built-up districts and the parks of Inner London known chiefly as a regular double passage migrant.

Fifty years ago the status of the cuckoo was much the same as it is to-day, but its distribution as a breeder has not unnaturally been affected by the growth of building. To take one simple example, as comparatively recently as 1938 a pair of reed warblers reared a young cuckoo in their nest among the willow-herb at the edge of a disused gravel pit at Mitcham. Now willow-herb, gravel pit and reed warbler colony have all gone and in their place stands a group of factories. The expansion of the suburbs to fifteen miles or so from the centre has not, however, created an area wholly unacceptable to a cuckoo looking for somewhere to lay. In parts of the middle and outer suburbs the process of urbanisation has doubtless had the same result as the building of the factories at Mitcham, but open spaces remain and here the cuckoo still finds a hedge sparrow, robin, pied wagtail or other small bird to foster its young.

The normal inner limit of suburban breeding now is nine or ten miles from the centre, and so it has been, broadly speaking, throughout the period. For the very innermost records of breeding we must go back to the first ten years: to 1900 when a pair of sedge warblers reared a cuckoo among the osiers of Chiswick Eyot, to 1905 when a pair of robins fostered one in a garden off the Marylebone Road, and to 1909 when a robin was seen feeding a young cuckoo in the grounds of the Zoo in Regent's Park (Glegg 1935). The small birds of Hampstead Heath and nearby gardens, which are nearer to the centre even than Chiswick Eyot, have had to put up with the cuckoo as a breeding species at intervals during the last three decades at least, and doubtless before. Other fosterers have raised cuckoos at Dulwich in 1935, at Beulah Hill in 1931, in the grounds of the Crystal Palace in 1918, and in a garden of Exford Road, near Lee, in 1950.

All these records, however, are out of the ordinary. The cuckoo has never, at least never in our period, been anything but an exceptional breeder anywhere within the built-up districts, even the open spaces which have survived so long and now, presumably, will be perpetuated. Fitter (1945) has suggested that the cuckoo's inability to adapt itself to suburban living is a result of its being unable to find sufficient fosterers. In the countryside, however, the hedge sparrow and robin are among the more frequent of its foster-parents, and both are common suburban nesters, so that one might, if fosterers were the only limiting factor, expect the suburban nesting of the cuckoo to be rather less rare than it is. The absence in the suburbs of the super-abundance of potential fosterers which obtains in the open country may be an important reason, but it may equally be that suburban conditions are unfavourable to attempts by the hen cuckoo to keep a close watch on the nests of possible victims and to attempts by observers to keep a close watch on birds living in private gardens.

Cuckoos do in fact spend the summer in the built-up areas from time to time without our knowing anything of their breeding success. For example, the bubbling note was heard from one of a pair in the grounds of Holland House in the spring of 1921, and a young bird appeared there in July. There are many other summer records throughout the period, among the most recent being that of a pair which summered on and around Streatham Common in 1949, though no young were seen. The following year a young bird on the wing was encountered there on June 26th, a date early enough for it to have been locally reared. Every late summer and autumn a movement of juvenile cuckoos is detected in the suburbs and the parks, even the parks and small private gardens of the centre.

At this season the furry caterpillars of the vapourer moth (*Orgyia antiqua*) swarm among the plane trees of the London parks, and the full-fed larvae of the buff-tip (*Phalera bucephala*) are a common enough sight on suburban fences and pavements under trees. The only records of cuckoos taking such caterpillars are those of F. D. Power (1910) at Brixton and H. Browning in 1909 at Forest Gate (*Country-Side*, 9:228). More recently the practice was suspected in 1932 by C. S. Bayne. In autumn, as in spring, the cuckoo is on record for almost all of the London parks, most parts of the suburbs, and even, very occasionally, the plane trees of Berkeley Square or such innermost sanctuaries as Neville's Court in Fetter Lane and the gardens of Gray's Inn.

Beyond the built-up districts the status of the cuckoo as a familiar and generally distributed summer resident calls for no comment. It fosters its offspring on a variety of small birds, including even garden warblers and bullfinches, but, at least in the London Area, its chief victim is the hedge sparrow. Of the 132 young cuckoos of which we have records, 38 per cent. were battened on hedge sparrows. Second in importance as fosterers are robins, which reared 13 per cent., followed by reed warblers, pied wagtails and whitethroats, in that order. Twenty other species, including woodlarks and blackcaps, are on record as having reared London cuckoos, but none of these accounted for more than four young cuckoos out of the 132, or about three per cent.

In the thirty years 1921–50 inclusive both the mean and median of the first dates when the cuckoo was reported in our Area was April 10th, its appearance being remarkably regular as the mean variation over this period was under three days.

BARN OWL, *Tyto alba* (Scopoli). A local resident; nowhere common, and absent from the more heavily built-up districts.

In the early part of the century, barn owls were evenly distributed in the rural areas around London. They were not abundant (senseless persecution by gamekeepers saw to that) but locally they were fairly common. In Kent, for example, Ticehurst said that no locality was without a pair or two and Bucknill described them as common residents in the rural districts of Surrey. In the second and third decades, however, the population of barn owls decreased and the species was reported as absent or rare from many places where formerly it was common. G. Dent attributed the decrease in south-west Essex to competition from the little owl, which was spreading enormously at this period, and he stated in 1939 that the barn owl had vanished from many immemorial nesting trees which had been occupied by little owls. Nevertheless, in Kent, one of the places where little owls were first introduced, the barn owl appears to have held its own. The decline can be attributed with more certainty to the destruction of habitats brought about by the growth of London; another factor, mentioned by Fitter (1945), was the wiring up of many church towers and belfries against jackdaws.

The present status of the barn owl in the London Area is a little uncertain: the fact that birds have been seen more frequently in the breeding season in the last decade is probably a reflection of the greater number of observers. Actual breeding records are still scarce, but as the nests must often be sited on private property it is perhaps not surprising that they are seldom found.

Although the barn owl has occurred occasionally in Inner London—it has even been seen in flight over the Strand—it has never, as a breeding species, penetrated so far towards the centre as the tawny owl. R. B. Lodge (1901), relates that a pair built in the eaves of an unoccupied house in a side street of Enfield in 1901 and P. J. Hanson found birds nesting in similar sites in Enfield in 1907 and Winchmore Hill in 1908. The only other record of this unusual choice was in 1923 when a pair reared two broods in the roof of a house on Clapton Common. Nests have occasionally been found in hollow trees in suburban gardens and at least once in a cemetery; an unusual site was among bales of hay in Hampton Court Park, where four young were found by workmen in 1948.

There appears to be a small influx of barn owls to the Area in the winter, especially to the marshes bordering the Thames, but there is no evidence to show their origin. The dark-breasted barn owl (*Tyto a. guttata*) has never been identified in the Area.

[SCOPS OWL, *Otus scops* (L)]

Davis (1907) refers to a scops owl which was shot at Chelsfield in 1904 and preserved by W. Blackwell. In view of the absence of identification details, and as the little owl was then still a rare bird, having been introduced into Kent with success only in 1896, the possibility of confusion between the two species must not be overlooked.

[HAWK-OWL, *Surnia ulula* (L.)]

The record of an owl which was seen by W. Kay Robinson and R. W. Heenan at West Molesey reservoir on December 27th, 1926, and described by them as "without any doubt one of the forms of *Surnia ulula*", was treated by the editors of *British Birds* as a probable (*B.B.*, 20:226).

LITTLE OWL, *Athene noctua* (Scopoli). Common resident, except in built-up areas.

The major introductions of little owls into Britain were made by E. G. B. Meade-Waldo near Edenbridge, Kent, in 1874, 1896 and 1900 and by Lord Lilford at Oundle, Northants, some years previous to 1889. Birds from both these centres spread rapidly into the London Area. In the south, little owls were well established at Westerham and Sevenoaks by 1900. One was shot as a rarity at Knockholt in 1901 and one at Farningham in 1905. But even before this, little owls appear to have penetrated down the valley of the Darent as far as Dartford and from there east to Swanscombe, where, according to Ticehurst, one was seen in the winter of 1883–84. There are insufficient data to analyse in detail the directions of the further spread, but by 1910 the little owl was reported to be established at Bromley, Hayes and Keston in Kent and in Surrey, along the North Downs, at Oxted, the Godstone valley, Warlingham and Chipstead.

North of the Thames, the southward spread from Lord Lilford's introduction at Oundle was no less rapid. The first report of nesting in Hertfordshire was in 1897 at Easneye near Ware, less than half a mile outside the London Area; at the time it was considered necessary to keep the locality a secret! (*Trans.* Herts. N.H.S., 22:193). In the following year, little owls were shot at Heronsgate and West Hyde and seen at Moor Park. A pair nested at Gerrards Cross, in Buckinghamshire, in 1900 (*Selborne Mag.*, 123:12) and one was trapped at Watford in 1901. By 1907 the little owl was considered to be well established as a breeding species in Hertfordshire. In Middlesex, one was shot at Hampstead in 1909 and a pair nested in an orchard near Enfield in 1912. In Essex, the picture is complicated by a subsidiary introduction at Loughton in 1905 when ten were liberated by C. H. Roper; as a result of this, or as a further extension of Lord Lilford's introduction, birds were seen at Chingford in 1913 and at Woodford Green and Brentwood, where two pairs nested, in 1914.

Between 1910 and 1930, the little owl continued to increase and spread with great rapidity; by the 1920's it had become numerous in most parts of the Area. By about 1930, the population appears to have reached its maximum and in the next few years there were reports of decreases from several districts: i.e., Sevenoaks, Hampton Court and Bushy Park, many places in Hertfordshire, and Gilwell Park in Essex. Although the Little Owl Food Enquiry of 1936–37 had shown that their diet is predominantly mammals and insects, nearly every gamekeeper's hand was against them and persecution probably played a part in the temporary decline. After the last war, with fewer gamekeepers, the little owl appeared to be holding its own and in some parts it was even described as increasing, especially on farm land.

Numerically, the little owl is probably more common in the Area than the tawny, but it is certainly less widespread. It shuns the heavily built-up areas and has not yet bred in Inner London; single birds occasionally penetrate to the central parks and the bombed sites, especially in the autumn and winter. The nearest nesting site to the centre appears to be Dulwich Wood. In the rural areas, the little owl is scarce or absent in expanses of dense woodland, such as Epping Forest, and prefers parkland and open country with hollow timber; of seven nesting sites found by K. R. Chandler in the Limpsfield district, five were in trees away from woods and two in woods but only about twenty yards from the edge.

The most common nesting site is a hole in a tree but nesting has also been recorded in rabbit burrows, in disused quarries, in the roof of a shed and on the roof girders of a store at Beckton Gas Works.

TAWNY OWL, *Strix aluco* L. Resident and widely distributed.

In the early 1900s, surprising as it may now seem, the tawny owl was much less common than the barn owl. Even so, it was less scarce than it had been 20 or 30 years previously. Bucknill, writing in 1900, described it as a "fairly common" resident in the rural parts of Surrey, but he said that it was somewhat less common near the Metropolis. In the next ten years the tawny owl evidently began to increase and Dixon (1909) said that although it was rarer than the barn owl within the Metropolitan limits its "melancholy, deep and far sounding cry" was very familiar in the wooded districts of suburban London. Apart from a pair in Kensington Gardens, first recorded by W. H. Hudson in 1898, its inner limits at this time appear to have been (to quote Dixon again) Dulwich, Wimbledon, Richmond, Bushy Park, Kew, Osterley, Hampstead, Epping and Wanstead. Ticehurst, writing of the same period, added Beckenham, Bromley and Lee in Kent.

During the next two decades, the tawny owl steadily increased in the London Area, as it did in other parts of the country, probably as a result of the decrease in gamekeepers or perhaps of the more enlightened attitude of their masters. Although the spread of London must have deprived it of some nesting sites, sufficient old trees were left in parks, large gardens and cemeteries for the tawny owl to be recorded as common in all but the most heavily built-up districts. It is possible that its far-sounding hoot made it appear more numerous than it was in reality, but there is no doubt that by the 1930's it was firmly established and widely distributed. Now its status is much the same except in a few districts where there has been extensive tree-felling.

In Inner London, Cramp and Teagle (1952) said that although definite breeding records are few it probably nests in most years in the grounds of Holland House, Kensington Gardens, Hyde Park, Regent's Park and Battersea Park. It is also heard, especially outside the breeding season, in many of the London squares and large gardens.

Provided they can find a secluded hollow in which to nest, tawny owls appear to have a remarkable tolerance for man, and even perch in trees overlooking busy streets; in 1947 one was watched pursuing a heron along the east side of Long Water. Suburban fences are not infrequently used as observation posts and on one occasion a bird sat on a goal-post cross-bar near Acton Town Station. The tawny owl remained in London during the air raids of the Second World War, and was frequently heard hooting in the noisiest periods.

The tawny owl appears to be almost sedentary in London, as elsewhere. Two nestlings ringed at Banstead in May, 1910, were both found two years later, one in January at Coulsdon (2½ miles away) and the other in April at Carshalton (3 miles away). Nevertheless, the number of birds heard outside the breeding season, and at places where they are unlikely to nest, suggests that there may be a dispersal movement if only for short distances.

LONG-EARED OWL, *Asio otus* (L.). Occasional passage migrant or winter visitor; may still breed sparsely south of the Thames.

In the early part of the century long-eared owls were not uncommon in the pinewoods and plantations of Surrey and West Kent, and in the first decade nests were found at such places as Esher, Dorking, Titsey and West Wickham. Nearer to London long-eared owls appear to have inhabited the Isabella plantation in Richmond Park, and Collenette (1937) notes that they were included, without comment, for 1925–27 in Rudge Harding's lists of birds nesting in the Park. The only definite recent breeding records south of the Thames are from Dartford Heath, where F. Howard Lancum saw a nest in 1929, and Coulsdon, where H. Bentham records that a pair reared young in 1934. Harrison (1942) stated that they could be met with in the woods of the Darent valley, around Shoreham and Preston Hill, and it is possible that a few pairs still survive here and elsewhere very locally along the North Downs.

North of the Thames, where there are few pines, long-eared owls have always been scarce, and are only known to have nested once—at Bushey Heath, where T. B. Andrews found a nest in a fir tree in 1925. A pair may have nested at the same place in 1928 and perhaps at Mill Hill in 1929, where a pair was seen by E. H. Warmington throughout the spring and summer.

Since the last war, only a very few long-eared owls have been recorded. There was one at Perry Oaks sewage farm on November 16th, 1947, and again on January 25th, 1948, and it seems likely that they may have been immigrants from outside the Area. One was heard at Bentley Priory, Stanmore, on February 14th, 1954, and there was also one at Stanmore on April 23rd, 1949. At Walton Heath one was seen on March 18th, 1954, while at Orpington E. H. Gillham heard them often during a cold spell in early 1954, and saw two in a spinney on August 15th. These last few records suggest that a few pairs may still be breeding in the Area.

SHORT-EARED OWL, *Asio flammeus* (Pontoppidan). ·Occasional winter visitor to marshes, sewage farms, heaths and rough grassland.

Ticehurst records two 'irruptions', linked with an abundance of field-voles, in North Kent in 1903 and 1906; in December, 1906, thirteen were flushed within a few yards from under a blackthorn hedge on Woolwich Marsh. But apart from these two years, the short-eared owl was a very rare straggler to the Area in the early part of the century and was recorded on only four occasions in the thirty years after 1906. Latterly, however, it has become a more regular visitor and one or more has been seen in nearly every winter since 1936, with peaks in 1938–39 (nine), 1946–47 (ten), 1950–51 (seven), 1952–53 (up to eight) and 1954–55. Most of the occurrences have been between October and March, but one was seen at Watford sewage farm on August 2nd–3rd, 1951, one near Iver Heath on September 4th, 1939, two at Watford sewage farm on May 7th, 1948 and one at Aldenham Wood on May 30th, 1952.

Sometimes birds have stayed in one locality for several months; three out of five first seen on February 12th, 1939, on Walton Heath were still there on March 25th; at Beddington sewage farm, one to four were recorded between December 26th, 1946 and March 30th, 1947. Recently they have wintered regularly at Beddington and on the adjacent Mitcham Common, up to three being seen in the winters of 1952–53 and 1954–55 from late October or early November until about the middle of March. At Walton gravel pit a single bird was seen on many dates between December 28th, 1946, and March 23rd, 1947, and was found shot on March 29th.

In two of the peak winters, 1938–39 and 1946–47, the larger numbers are probably correlated with exceptionally severe weather; in the latter winter short-eared owls were also unusually numerous on the marshes of the Thames estuary. There is no evidence of vole plagues in these two years; eighteen pellets found on Walton Heath in 1939 contained remains of small birds but none of mammals. In late 1954, however, voles and birds of prey were plentiful on the east coast, and in December short-eared owls appeared on the Dartford marshes, where there were as many as six at the end of the month.

On three occasions in October and one in early November, single short-eared owls have been seen flying, evidently on migration, in a westerly direction. One over a derelict gun-site on Hampstead Heath extension on November 3rd, 1951, is the nearest to the centre of London.

NIGHTJAR, *Caprimulgus europaeus* L. Local and decreasing summer resident.

At the beginning of the century the nightjar was tolerably common in all suitable parts of the Area and it was reported as breeding as close to the centre as Wembley, Highgate, Hampstead and Winchmore Hill in the north and Eltham, Bromley, Shirley, Wimbledon Common, Richmond Park and Kew Gardens in the south. Even so, it was already described as decreasing and its status in the Area at that time can be summed up in the words Bucknill (1900) used for Surrey:— "although perhaps much less abundant in most districts at the present day than formerly, owing to the increase of building and the consequent diminution of open spaces, it is still plentiful in almost any locality where it is able to obtain its requisite food . . . ". Such localities were most frequent on the heaths and commons and in the open woodlands of Kent and Surrey, but nightjars were by no means uncommon north of the Thames, except in Essex, where there were few suitable sites outside Epping Forest and its environs.

As the century progressed, and London spread, the nightjar was pushed further out and became progressively less abundant. By the end of the First World War all the closer-in sites north of the Thames mentioned above had been abandoned; in the south, the nightjar no longer nested on Wimbledon Common or in Kew Gardens, and in Richmond Park it was considerably less numerous than formerly.

At the beginning of the Second World War, the only places from which the "churring" of the nightjar was consistently reported were Ruislip, Cuffley Great Wood and Epping Forest in the north and Walton Heath and Epsom, Shirley and Hayes Common in the south. In Richmond Park, it was described by Collenette (1937) as a scarce summer visitor, and no nest had been found there since 1930.

Disturbance by military training and manoeuvres and more intensive cultivation during the war hastened the decline, and in 1945 Epping Forest and Limpsfield and Far-leigh Commons were the only places where nesting was recorded, but as this was one of the war years other sites were almost certainly missed. In one or more of the ensuing years, however, nightjars have been present in the breeding season near Black Park and at Bricketwood and Chorleywood Commons, King's Langley, near Rickmansworth, Ruislip and Stanmore and in Epping Forest in the north, and at nearly twenty localities in the Kent and Surrey parts of the Area. It is difficult to say whether this apparent increase was genuine or a reflection of the new interest in bird-watching. Some of the "new" localities are almost certainly old ones which had escaped observation in the immediate past. This seems especially likely for such sites as Darenth Wood; nightjars were recorded there early in the century but there is a gap in the records, probably caused by lack of observation, until 1947 when D. F. Owen found a nest. In 1949, the same observer, with J. F. Burton, located no less than ten breeding pairs, four to five of which were double-brooded. On the other hand, Richmond Park has always been well watched and the birds which nested there in 1950 were almost certainly the first night-jars to do so for twenty years. Unfortunately, the nest, and its surroundings, were destroyed by a bulldozer before the young had hatched.

Although the earliest record for the British Isles (Gilwell Park, April 2nd, 1926) comes from within the London Area, the first birds do not normally arrive until the second week of May. In the late summer, nightjars are occasionally seen in August and early September; the latest date is of one seen at Stanmore on September 19th, 1939. They are occasionally seen away from their breeding haunts at the beginning or end of the season, but there is no evidence of their origin. In Inner London, the nightjar has occurred only four times on passage, all prior to 1928.

SWIFT, *Apus apus* (L.). Common summer resident, occurring in all built-up parts of the Area, except the centre. Widespread on migration.

Close to central London in the early years of the century the swift occurred at Tooting Graveney in fair numbers, with three or four pairs around the church and others elsewhere. At Enfield it nested in London Road in 1900 (Lodge, 1901) and L. J. Tremayne found a nest in the thatch of a barn there in 1909. Birds were found occupying old house martins' nests at Shooter's Hill in 1904 and bred in large numbers in Stone-bridge Park and neighbourhood (Kendall, 1907). F. D. Power said that it nested at Crystal Palace in 1909, and summing up its status in that year Charles Dixon wrote that swifts bred regularly in the "more rural suburbs", such as Willesden, Kilburn, Putney, Tooting, Woolwich and Enfield, but although he had seen birds closer to the centre he had no knowledge of breeding there.

From this it would seem that the inner breeding limit of the swift has not varied greatly in the last fifty years. At present swifts nest in small numbers on the edge of the Inner London area, at Kilburn, St. John's Wood and perhaps elsewhere. In June and July, 1928, Dr. Stuart Smith watched three pairs feeding young in nests under the eaves of the General Post Office in the heart of the City. This appears to be the only City breeding record since the days of Gilbert White. Just outside the boundary of Inner London it is known to breed at Cricklewood, Brondesbury, Hampstead, Finchley and Highgate. Two pairs nested at Islington in 1937 and 1938. There is less information about the north-eastern suburbs, but at Tottenham at least two pairs bred at West Green in 1942, and further out, at Wood Green, there were two or three pairs in 1949. Still less is known about the position in the East End, but Sir Philip Manson-Bahr reported that eight birds he saw flying around 'blitzed' houses in Canning Town in 1946, as if nesting, were the first noticed there for forty years. South of the Thames there were small colonies in 1950 at Blackheath, Kidbrooke and Lee Green, and swifts still breed at Shooters Hill and Eltham. At Dulwich H. E. Pounds stated they have bred in small numbers on old houses from 1916 until 1941 at least. In 1949 H. G. Attlee noted a few pairs in the breeding season at Wandsworth, Tooting Common and Streatham Common, and in 1952 there was a small colony at Clapham Common. Fairly large colonies are still to be found at Putney, Barnes and Hammersmith.

This gives an idea of the present inner limit of the breeding zone of the swift, so far as it is known. Further out it is found in all built-up parts of the area, from suburbs to villages, though its distribution is patchy, with much of the population concentrated in large colonies. This was shown by the census carried out by the London Natural History Society in 1949 (Cramp, 1950). Four sample areas (representing as far as possible the inner zone, the inner and outer suburbs and the outskirts, and totalling about 24 square miles) were chosen in the western sector of the area. No nests were found in the inner zone, although birds (probably nesting just outside it) fed regularly over some of the park lakes. The highest density (about 24 definite nests per 1,000 acres, and nearly 40 if probable nests are included) was found in the inner suburbs, with the nests concentrated in four main groups. In the outer suburbs the density fell to nearly half this, and although the nests were more spread out the great majority were in three large groups. In the outskirts the density was about 13 nests per 1,000 acres, with nearly all the nests in two colonies at West Drayton and Dawley, whilst several of the villages were devoid of nests. More census work is required before firm conclusions can be drawn, but it seems that, though lack of suitable buildings for nesting may cause the absence of the swift in some parts, food is the main factor affecting density, and the swift tends to be most numerous in areas near water with their richer supply of flying insects. Swifts are often very faithful to particular nesting sites—thus one house at Mill Hill has been used by birds for twenty-seven years, and some old cottages at Belmont since 1914. In several areas observers believe that the swift has increased in numbers, although information is too scanty to decide whether there has been any general change in the period.

The earliest arrival date for the area is April 11th, in 1935, but the median date of first arrival over the twenty-seven years up to 1950 was April 23rd. Movement usually continues throughout May, and sometimes later. H. J. Burkill saw up to a thousand swifts at Fetcham on May 28th, 1938, and smaller numbers up to June 1st, while in 1939 E. W. Pearce reported thousands over Hampton reservoir on June 14th–16th. These gatherings however, may represent concentration due to adverse weather conditions rather than late migration. The return passage normally begins about the middle of July and is mostly over by the middle of August, although smaller numbers may be seen much later, the last swifts being usually reported in early September. There are, however, six October records, the latest being of a single bird seen by L. J. Winter-Joyner at Ealing on October 31st, 1912 (B.B., 4:255).

KINGFISHER, *Alcedo atthis* (L.). Resident; widespread along rivers and streams.
    The kingfisher is a bird whose status cannot be judged by the number of times its nest has been located and put on record. There are palpably many more pairs of breeding kingfishers in the Area than the surprisingly small number of definite breeding records would suggest. It is in fact to be found during the breeding season on all the larger rivers, on many of the brooks and streams and on some of the larger artificial

waters which have suitable banks. In certain waterless areas, notably the North Downs, it is virtually unknown. The population of the kingfisher is liable to substantial fluctuations, mainly due to hard winters, so that statements about increase or decrease in any one district need to be treated with caution. Since 1900, however, it does seem to have retreated somewhat from the outer suburbs. Thus at the beginning of the century a pair bred under one of the bridges over the Ravensbourne in the recreation ground at Lewisham, and Ticehurst (1909) states that it bred sparingly but regularly on the banks of this and other streams and at ponds in Lee, Bromley, Blackheath and Lewisham. According to C. A. White there were half-a-dozen breeding pairs along the canal at Southall during 1920–24. At the beginning of the century too it must have bred regularly in the Hampstead and Highgate district, and was still doing so in 1932–33, though not apparently since. In all these three districts there seem to have been definite contractions of range. Elsewhere in the suburban zone, kingfishers are liable to breed sporadically. Thus they nested at Barn Elms about 1924, near the Isleworth Gate of Kew Gardens in 1936, and at Ranelagh in 1946. In 1951 a nest was found on the heronry island at Walthamstow reservoirs. Occasionally a pair will nest a hundred yards or more from water, usually in a sand or gravel-pit when no suitable bank is available by the nearest water; they did this regularly at Bushy Park for many years, and in the sand-pit in Ken Wood near the Spaniards Inn in 1932–33 and probably earlier.

Out of the breeding season the kingfisher is much more widespread, and may turn up on any piece of water containing fish, from the suburban goldfish pond to the lakes in the central parks, where indeed they are seen fairly regularly. There appears to be a definite movement away from the breeding territories. Before the Wild Birds Protection Acts put a stop to the evil practice, kingfishers were often netted for their plumage, and in August, 1911, no fewer than 22 were caught in this way on a short stretch of the Ching Brook at Woodford, all flying downstream. Many find their way right down to the Thames marshes in Essex and Kent, where they are common in autumn until Christmas, but much less so afterwards, when they evidently start their journey back to their breeding territories, which are often reoccupied in February. In the London parks, and places like Richmond Park where they are often seen but do not breed, their visits do not seem to be any less frequent in the second half of the winter. Some of the birds seen in the Area in autumn are evidently passage migrants from higher up the Thames valley, for one ringed at Wokingham in Berkshire in July, 1927, was recovered at Barking Marsh in August, 1928, while another ringed at Eton in July, 1924, turned up at Staines the following November.

HOOPOE, *Upupa epops* L. Recorded about thirty-six times, March to November, mostly in spring and early summer.

There is no evidence to suggest that the hoopoe has ever attempted to breed, although eight of the occurrences are in June and July. In 1949 reports were received from local residents that four had been seen in various gardens in the Oxted area in April, and that two had remained for several weeks; the remains of a hoopoe which had apparently been killed by a sparrowhawk were found in the district on July 27th.

Over half the records have been since 1945, some from as near the centre as Hampstead Heath and Lewisham, and others from suburban gardens. In 1954 one remained in the neighbourhood of Perry Oaks sewage farm for about three weeks in August, and another was seen near Epping by Mrs. C. G. Ehrenborg on the exceptionally late date of November 26th.

GREEN WOODPECKER, *Picus viridis* L. Resident, common and well distributed in rural districts and outer suburbs. Probably increasing in inner suburbs and has bred in inner London.

At the beginning of the century the green woodpecker was common enough in the rural parts of Essex, Kent and Surrey (and probably also in other rural parts of the Area), but seems to have been distinctly scarcer in both the inner and the outer suburban districts than it is now, both absolutely and relatively to other woodpeckers. Whereas it was generally regarded as the commonest woodpecker in the country districts, in the suburbs it was considered less common than the lesser spotted (the greater spotted was then much scarcer than to-day). Its subsequent local fluctuations have been sometimes attributed to competition from starlings for nesting-holes, but it seems probable that Ticehurst (1909) is right in saying that "although there is no doubt that green woodpeckers suffer a good deal of persecution from starlings", it is doubtful if "in districts where suitable trees are abundant the attacks of starlings have any more effect than to postpone the woodpeckers' nesting operations for a week or two". Fitter (1949) has suggested that a contributory factor in the general increase of woodpeckers in London has been the ageing of large numbers of trees, planted in parks and gardens in the 19th century, to the point at which they become rotten enough for woodpeckers to excavate nesting-holes and find food in them.

At the present day the green woodpecker is found in woods and all kinds of well-timbered country, such as parks, golf courses and large gardens. It is fairly common in the outer suburbs, where birds may often be seen feeding on lawns in quite well built-up districts. There is some suggestion that they may have become increasingly tolerant of London conditions within our period, and it may be that their greater addiction than the other woodpeckers to ground feeding has also assisted their colonisation. In the inner suburbs they are probably increasing and are often seen where there are large open spaces, such as Greenwich Park, Dulwich Woods, Wandsworth Common, Kew Gardens and Hampstead Heath, at all of which green woodpeckers have certainly or probably bred in the last few years. In Inner London they have recently been reported from Bayswater, Kensington Gardens, Notting Hill, Regent's Park and St. James's Park, while in Holland Park a pair bred in 1952, 1953 and possibly 1954.

GREATER SPOTTED WOODPECKER, *Dendrocopos major* (L.). Resident, common and widespread in wooded and suburban districts.

Throughout most of the 19th century the greater spotted woodpecker was regarded as a great rarity, and only towards the nineties did it begin to increase in the London Area. By the first decade of the twentieth century it was already locally common in a few places, such as Epping Forest and the Kentish sector, but over most of Surrey (except the portion right up against the Kentish border) it was notably scarce where it is now so common. During the 1920's the greater spotted became widespread all over the Area in suitably wooded places, and eventually outnumbered all other woodpeckers in the suburban districts. Indeed, along with other typical woodland species, such as robin, hedge sparrow, blackbird and blue tit, the greater spotted woodpecker has now become virtually a regular inhabitant of many suburban gardens, in some of which it is a frequent visitor to the bird table, even taking bread. It is this liking for quite small gardens, its abundance in birch woods and its relative shunning of hedgerow timber in open farming districts that chiefly distinguish it from the green woodpecker.

The general reasons for the increase of woodpeckers in the London Area have been discussed under the green woodpecker, but it must be remarked here that starlings compete for nest sites even more fiercely with this species than with the green, yet it has been even more successful in colonising the Area. Bucknill (1900) suggests another possible reason for the increase of woodpeckers generally—the passing of the fashion for keeping cases of stuffed woodpeckers in the parlours of inns and private houses. Victorian gamekeepers seem to have had an antipathy to this species which can be explained only by the good prices they must have received from taxidermists.

One consequence of the greater spotted woodpecker's liking for gardens has been its colonisation of Inner London, where, out of the breeding season, it is now liable to turn up almost anywhere. From at least 1922 onwards one, and later more pairs, have bred in the grounds of Holland House, and in 1940 this small colony had spread into Kensington Gardens, where a pair now breeds almost annually. Pairs have also bred, probably bred, or attempted to breed in recent years in Hyde Park, Regent's and Battersea Parks, St. John's Wood, Campden Hill and Ranelagh. In the large open spaces a little further out, where the green woodpecker breeds, the greater spotted is just as common as its relative if not commoner.

LESSER SPOTTED WOODPECKER, *Dendrocopos minor* (L.). Resident but local, in suitable localities throughout the Area.

At the beginning of the century the lesser spotted woodpecker was generally regarded as commoner than the greater spotted and usually as commoner than the green; now it is universally assessed as the least common of the three. Yet there is every reason to suppose that it is the other two which have changed their status, while the lesser spotted remained static. It is, however, an exceptionally difficult bird to make valid generalisations about, for its nest is much less often recorded than the nest of the two others, in relation to the total number of sight records. The verdict of R. W. Robbins in his chapter on the birds of the Oxted district in 1932 holds good almost throughout the Area:- "present but seldom seen".

The habitat of the lesser spotted woodpecker does not appear to differ materially from that of the greater spotted, and the chief difference between the two is that the lesser spotted does not venture right into London as a breeding species, but remains in the suburbs at approximately the same ring of large open spaces as the green woodpecker. However, the bird has so often been seen in some part of Kensington in April and May that it is hard to resist the conclusion that in some years at least it has bred on Campden Hill or in the grounds of Holland House. In the Central Parks it is an occasional visitor, and this evidence of some kind of local migration or post-breeding wandering throws some doubt on the advisability of accepting records of the presence of the bird elsewhere as constituting evidence of its probable breeding in such districts. It is resident, and presumably breeds, on Hampstead Heath.

WRYNECK, *Jynx torquilla* L. Decreasing summer resident and passage migrant.

Every April, May and June reports of wrynecks come in from various parts of our Area, mostly south of the Thames, but they do not exceed twenty a year. In parts of Kent outside our boundary the bird is as numerous as anywhere in Britain, but around London the records are usually of isolated pairs or individuals. However, the wryneck in the breeding season is so secretive that proof of nesting is most likely to be obtained when a pair settles in an observer's home district, which probably accounts for the preponderance of breeding records in the outer suburbs, when there are so few from the rural areas. Most of the nests reported are in garden nest boxes, where they could hardly be overlooked. But as not all owners of nest boxes are recording ornithologists it is likely that the actual breeding strength of the wryneck, low as it is, is not quite as low as the records suggest.

Of late, not more than half-a-dozen nesting pairs a year have been recorded, constant difficulties being the self-effacement of the birds when breeding and the exclusion of bird-watchers from practically all gardens but their own. Considering how much of the London Area is taken up with suburban gardens, which collectively form an area more impenetrable and closely out of bounds than the most rigid of game preserves, this factor may be important, especially so in the case of a small breeding population. A wryneck heard calling soon after its arrival could be easily overlooked later if it settled down unobtrusively to nest, perhaps not until late in June, a few gardens away.

Nevertheless, the decline of the wryneck is a reality and cannot be gainsaid. Bucknill in 1900 described it as quite a common bird in the rural districts of Surrey, frequently to be heard in spring even close to London. It nested on Hampstead Heath to 1908, with some regularity at Harrow until 1909, in the Willesden area to 1910, and around Enfield to 1912. Ticehurst said that it was plentiful and generally distributed throughout Kent at that time. In what are now the inner suburban districts of Sydenham, Dulwich, Tooting and Wimbledon the wryneck was said by Charles Dixon in 1909 to breed regularly, a surprising statement but one which is given some support by their having been seen, if not actually recorded as nesting, at Mitcham regularly to 1905. They nested at Morden in 1910, at Upper Norwood and Croydon in 1913 and 1914, and in a box at Orpington for three consecutive years to 1915.

By 1929 Glegg was recording the decrease of the wryneck in Essex, including Epping Forest and its surroundings, although a pair bred at Loughton in 1927 (and perhaps in 1949). Of Middlesex in 1935 Glegg said that it had decreased to such an extent that it could no longer be described as a regular summer resident. In parts of north Middlesex and south Hertfordshire where formerly it nested the wryneck was not known to breed after about 1926, although it bred intermittently around Northwood and Ruislip until ten years later.

It has been most faithful to a few localities in Surrey, but it has not been found breeding at its former sites around Chelsham and Warlingham since 1932, and Epsom and Ashtead since 1936. Up to ten pairs a year bred with great regularity about Godstone, Limpsfield and Oxted, one particular nesting box site being annually in use for seventeen years. By the late forties only one or two pairs persisted, and none have been known to nest there since 1949. Even at Tadworth and the adjoining heathland, where Howard Bentham used to know of up to six pairs, none were proved to breed in 1954. In and about large gardens at Chipstead L. I. Carrington has found a nesting pair fairly regularly since 1943.

The wryneck is at present a very scarce and erratic breeder in such North Downs localities as Purley, Coulsdon, Chipstead and Tadworth, with occasionally a pair or two about Leatherhead and Ewell in Surrey, and Orpington, Bexleyheath and Long-field in Kent. The Limpsfield area, despite continued watching by M. D. England and others, is conspicuously absent from this list at present. North of the Thames the wryneck has almost vanished as a known breeding species; pairs nested at Park Street in 1950 and 1951, and at Osterley Park probably in 1952.

Some of the isolated spring records certainly refer to birds on passage. In 1946 M. D. England reported an intermittent movement at Limpsfield from the end of March to early May, up to four being seen in the garden at once. A bird could be heard approaching from the east and later becoming fainter as it moved westward along the foot of the North Downs (*L.B.R.*, 11:15). Single birds seen twice in open spaces of Inner London similarly have been passage migrants.

A wryneck ringed as an adult at Limpsfield in June, 1920, was recovered there almost exactly a year later.

CRESTED LARK, *Galerida cristata* (L.)

On March 8th, 1947, at the end of a long spell of very cold weather, Miss M. Curtis saw two crested larks on the foreshore of the Thames between Chiswick Eyot and Hammersmith Bridge (*B.B.*, 41:345).

WOODLARK, *Lullula arborea* (L.). Local resident, once rare, has increased since the last war.

It is pleasant to be able to record for the London Area that a bird has increased, instead of the usual account of regression with the spread of the Metropolis. Everyone likes the woodlark and its success in recent years must delight all those who, like the writer, rank its song among the loveliest of all.

In 1950, approximately 45 pairs or presumed pairs of woodlarks were counted in the London Area and with well over 300 observers it is likely that this total was very close to the actual population. It is more difficult to assess the status of the bird at the beginning of the period. North of the Thames it appears to have been almost unknown: in Essex, the only sight record prior to 1945 was as long before as 1905; in Hertfordshire, a pair bred in 1915 at Symonds Hyde Great Wood (through which our boundary passes) but thereafter there are no records until the 1920's; in Middlesex, if one discounts the dubious and unsubstantiated statement by J. E. Whiting in *The Hampstead Annual* for 1900 that "it breeds on the Heath and elsewhere", no woodlark was identified before 1924. Persecution by bird-catchers was often put forward as the reason for the extreme scarcity of woodlarks but it seems doubtful if they were ever common north of the Thames. In Surrey and Kent, where much of the soil is lighter and there are more heaths and commons, woodlarks appear to have been relatively abundant in the middle of the 19th century but by 1900 they were rare and extremely local. In Surrey, birds were seen occasionally in Richmond Park and on Wimbledon Common; Bucknill's account (*Zool.*, 59:251) of three nests found by the Epsom College N.H.S. about 1901 is not regarded as satisfactory by Howard Bentham, who probably knows as much about the woodlark in its Surrey haunts as anyone. In Kent, Ticehurst (1909) said that there were a few small colonies of woodlarks in the neighbourhood of Westerham and Sevenoaks and that they still bred near Orpington.

The status of woodlarks in the Area remained unchanged until the mid-1920's when, for no very obvious reason, they began to increase. Between 1923 and 1938 it was usually possible to find a pair or two nesting at several localities along the North Downs, and at a locality in north-east Surrey in 1925 at least eight pairs reared young in this district. Breeding was proved on Wimbledon Common in 1925 and 1926, and in Richmond Park a maximum of 2-3 pairs nested annually between 1926 and 1935. North of the Thames, a pair bred on Stanmore Common in most years between 1924 and 1928 (E. H. Warmington *in litt.*) and adjacent to the Common in 1929. Just before the Second World War the small breeding stock of woodlarks declined rapidly. It is doubtful if any nested in Richmond Park in 1936 and by 1939 they had disappeared from the Park altogether. On the North Downs, they were much scarcer than usual in 1938 and none nested on Box Hill, which had been one of the strongholds. In the following year the only record for the whole of the Area was of a bird singing at one of the Surrey localities on March 22nd. This rapid decrease may well have been accelerated by the very severe cold spell of December, 1938, although it evidently started before then; the probability of a quick recovery was prejudiced by a succession of severe winters.

Thereafter, no woodlarks were seen or heard in the Area in the breeding season until 1944, when a pair bred at Shoreham and birds were seen in Richmond Park, on Reigate Heath and Bookham Common and at Otford. In 1945, a pair probably bred in Hainault Forest, providing the first sight record for the Essex part of the Area since 1905 and only the second breeding record for the whole county since the mid-19th century. In Surrey, two nests were found on the North Downs and birds were reported in the breeding season from nearly a dozen localities.

The continued spread of the woodlark in the last five years of the half century is detailed in the *London Bird Reports* for 1946–50. By 1950 there were about 45 pairs in all, reports of nesting or singing birds coming from six localities in Essex, four each in Hertfordshire and Middlesex, three in Kent and thirteen in Surrey; the Surrey localities included Richmond Park (four to five pairs present), Wimbledon Common (five pairs present) and Putney Heath, only six and a half miles from St. Paul's Cathedral, where a nest was found fifteen yards from the main road. The nature of the spread and the fact that a similar increase was reported from other parts of southern England, makes it clear that it was more than a reflection of the parallel increase in observers. But the cause of the increase remains a mystery. In subsequent years fewer pairs were reported but it is doubtful if there was any real decrease.

It seems likely that the breeding woodlarks are resident in the Area. Small flocks (twice of 20 or over) have occasionally been seen feeding on stubble land, but they are rarely far from a known breeding place and may represent a dispersal of the local population rather than the presence of immigrants.

Woodlarks have been seen twice in Inner London: in Regent's Park on January 17th 1937, and in Cripplegate on July 28th, 1953.

SKYLARK, *Alauda arvensis* L. Summer resident, also passage migrant and winter visitor.

Like other ground-nesters, the skylark has suffered severely from the growth of London and especially from the disturbance caused by the increasing public use of open spaces. At the beginning of the century it had long since ceased to nest in the central parks but a few pairs could still be found as close to the centre as Streatham Common and Hackney Marshes. Power, writing in 1909, said that skylarks were then breeding in Dulwich Meadows, and Johnson (1930) records that they were still resident even on Clapham, Tooting and Wandsworth Commons and on Peckham Rye. Now, however, Wimbledon Common is the nearest locality to London from which nesting is regularly reported, although six pairs were found at Wormwood Scrubs in 1950 and breeding was proved in 1951. From 1946–52 one pair bred on a derelict gun-site on Hampstead Heath extension. In the rural districts the skylark is still widely distributed and tolerably common on agricultural land, open commons and rough grassland. Like other species, skylarks took advantage of the rough ground during the construction of the new reservoirs at Staines and Chingford; at this time little ringed plovers were also nesting there and confusion was often caused by the perfect imitation which the larks gave of the "pee-u" note.

In winter the skylark is much more widespread and congregates in flocks on sewage farms, stubble fields and other open spaces. Skylarks are often seen passing over in the autumn; the distinctive flight makes the migrating flocks conspicuous and the movement over London frequently continues for most of the day, unlike that of other diurnal migrants. The passage begins towards the end of September and continues through October, with the peak about the middle of the month. The majority of the recorded movements are in a westerly direction and are evidently a continuation of the vast immigrations from the Continent which take place on the East Coast and up the Thames Estuary. There is no evidence that any of these flocks remain in the Area and the origin of the wintering birds is uncertain.

Further large movements sometimes take place just before or during exceptionally hard weather. For example, on December 22nd, 1938, following a day of 16 hours' snowfall, many thousands of skylarks were flying west over London all day, mostly in flocks of about fifty at a height of 100–150 feet. For several days after they were reported in many snow-clad squares and streets in central London. In the suburbs, hungry birds fed at bird-tables and on patches from which the snow had been swept; the food taken included bread, cake, seed, meal and currants. At Beddington sewage farm the skylarks were estimated in thousands, and hundreds died of cold and starvation. At Loughton some 250 took refuge on allotments, eating cabbage leaves and roosting under the cabbages at night.

Under more normal conditions, in winter and early spring, skylarks sometimes alight to feed on open stretches of grass in the central London parks. Very occasionally they have been heard singing there, and once even over the bombed area in Cripplegate.

SWALLOW, *Hirundo rustica* L. Summer resident, common in most rural areas, but local in the outer suburbs and rare or absent as breeding birds elsewhere. Widespread on migration.

Although in some parts of its range the swallow breeds in towns, in Britain it is largely a country bird, being found especially around farms, which provide abundant food and open sheds for nesting. By 1900 the swallow was no longer breeding regularly in Inner London, though a pair bred in a deer-shed at the Zoo in 1907 and 1908. It was still, however, found in some numbers in many of the suburbs. Kendall (1907), for example, wrote that it was common in Willesden and nested in Neasden and Wembley. It was breeding in Hampstead in 1909 and commonly at Finchley in 1911. Lodge (1901) said that it nested in every cowshed and barn around Enfield and under all the New River bridges, and Dixon (1909) reported it as breeding at Hornsey, Wood Green, Wanstead and Stratford. At Greenwich Park swallows nested annually in the old barn and deer-sheds (Webster, 1902). In the south it was to be found breeding as near to the centre as Dulwich, Clapham Park and Streatham, while in the west it nested from Barnes, Chiswick and Acton westwards.

The growth of London has pushed the breeding zone of the swallow steadily outwards. A few pairs still breed each year in the school farm buildings at Harrow, and it nests sparingly at Harrow Weald and Mill Hill. There has been a steady decline in the Epping area, and no nests have been seen at Walthamstow reservoirs since 1929. The last nest in Greenwich Park was found in 1928, but a few pairs still breed along the marshes south of the Thames from Plumstead downstream. In the south-eastern suburbs, where J. W. Tutt (Turner, 1909), reported that swallows bred freely throughout, the species has now almost vanished.

In 1941 M. Milne-Watson saw a pair making repeated visits to a bombed building in Westminster, and in 1952 a pair bred in the deer-shed at Golders Hill Park; otherwise, it is in the south of London that swallows have bred nearest to the centre in recent years. A pair with young were seen at a football ground at Camberwell in 1945, and a pair nested under the roof of the station at West Dulwich in 1928. T. H. L. Mills saw birds nesting in a low building behind Norbury police station in 1947 and 1948. The swallow does not seem to have bred at Wimbledon since 1938 nor at Putney Heath since 1932, but in 1947 a pair nested in a barn near the Wandle at Morden and another in a station goods yard at Merton.

Along the Thames swallows were seen feeding young in the boathouse at Kew in 1940, and young were reared at Ham Common in 1942. The species is now rare below Kingston, and has disappeared as a breeding bird from Richmond Park within the last ten years. A pair bred at Horsendon Hill in 1945 and 1946, but the swallow is nowhere numerous in west Middlesex, even in the more rural districts. In most other rural parts round London, especially near rivers and streams, it is still a common summer resident, although many observers believe that it is still decreasing in numbers.

Swallows occur in all parts of the Area on passage. They may then be seen over the central streets or feeding above the park lakes, although the largest numbers are to be found by the reservoirs and along river valleys. In autumn large numbers gather to roost in reed beds, about 5,000 being estimated at Navestock on September 4th, 1952. The earliest spring record is March 14th, 1943, when a single bird was seen at Loughton by J. A. Simes. The median date of first arrival over forty years (not consecutive) is April 6th. The return movement often begins as early as July, continuing into October. There are many November records, and four in December, the latest being December 28th, 1934, when Miss C. E. Longfield saw a party of six in the Colnbrook valley.

HOUSE MARTIN, *Delichon urbica* (L.). Summer resident, breeding locally in suburban areas and many towns and villages on the outskirts. Widespread on migration.

The house martin has withstood the growth of London more successfully than the swallow. In the last fifty years it has deserted some of its former nesting sites in the inner suburbs and its numbers have declined considerably in others, but there are still colonies within seven miles of St. Paul's and some of the new suburbs have been successfully colonised. A flourishing colony near Ruislip reservoir, for example, was started in 1937, on houses which had been built less than a year.

The house martin had ceased to breed in Inner London before 1900 but it nested then just outside—at Dulwich, Brixton, Peckham Rye and Willesden, for example. On the west, near the Thames, it still nests relatively close to the centre, with flourishing colonies at Barnes and Putney and a smaller one in Hammersmith. Up to 1926 it was common in Finchley and Highgate; since then there has been a marked decrease in Finchley, but in Highgate, after an absence of 15 years, small numbers have nested again in recent years near the ponds. It breeds still in many north-western suburbs, usually in small numbers, but has abandoned nesting sites at Edgware and Mill Hill within the last few years. Further out it is common in many parts of Hertfordshire, but in western Middlesex the colonies are small and scattered, except at some places along the Colne.

In south-west Essex G. Dent has reported a considerable decrease between 1911 and 1941, and in the Epping area the house martin is said to have diminished more than the swallow, though eighteen pairs bred at Chingford in 1946. J. W. Tutt (Turner, 1909) said that the house martin bred freely throughout the south-eastern suburbs, but its numbers have since fallen considerably and the colonies are now small and scattered. It is still common at Bexley and along the Darent valley, and small groups are found along the edge of the Thames marshes from Greenwich to Swanscombe. In Surrey, nests were found at Wandsworth (less than five miles from Charing Cross) and Clapham in the thirties, but the only recent record from these parts is of three nests at Tooting in 1953. There are still colonies along the Thames between Kew and Hampton and there are small colonies in many of the Surrey suburbs and parts of the rural areas.

The local distribution of the house martin would repay further study. A census of four sample areas in the western sector of London (*L.B.R.*, 14:49–57) showed that, though colonies may on occasion be found well away from water, they tend to be more numerous near it. The presence of water usually ensures ample food supplies and mud for the nests, and it seems probable that the former is the more important in determining the distribution of colonies. House martins seem to prefer nest sites in the apex of a gable or on a wall beneath wide eaves, but they can adapt themselves to less favourable sites if food and mud are available.

The house martin occurs in all parts of the Area on passage. In the spring the first arrivals may be seen in early April and sometimes in the last two weeks of March; the earliest recorded date is March 18th, 1950, but the median arrival date over 33 years (not consecutive) is April 12th. The main body arrives in late April and passage continues into May and sometimes early June. The first return movements have been noted in July, continuing until October, with stragglers into November and even December. On

January 10th, 1912, a single house martin was seen at Hampton Court by C. J. Robinson (*B.B.*, 5:255).

SAND MARTIN, *Riparia riparia* (L.). Summer resident, common locally in rural areas and occasionally in the suburbs. Widespread on migration.

The nesting localities of the sand martin around London are, in the main, on or near river valleys, and it is probable that, as in the case of the other hirundines, this is because insect food is found more abundantly near to water. The actual sites are restricted to suitable cliffs or banks, where the subsoil is soft enough for the birds to tunnel their holes, though there has been a growing tendency for them to make use of artificial holes, such as drainpipes, in recent years.

Although the sand martin is remarkably faithful to certain localities, the sites of the colonies change frequently because the banks of sand or gravel tend to crumble or are destroyed by new workings and the filling of pits. It is therefore impossible to give a full list of all recorded sites in the last fifty years, though a detailed account for the years 1900 to 1940 was prepared by Fitter (*L.B.R.* for 1940: 16–18). Gravel pits, which provide banks for nesting and plentiful insect food over the water, are the most common site for sand martin colonies, with 30 examples since 1900, or nearly half the total reported. They have been found throughout the Area, wherever gravel pits occur, though more frequently in Essex, Middlesex and Hertfordshire. New pits are often colonised rapidly as at Old Parkbury, where in June, 1946, 65 nests were found in a working which had only been opened nine months previously and was still being dug. Sandpits, with twenty known colonies, are a second favourite site, and have been recorded most often in Kent and Surrey, many of them in the areas of Upper and Lower Greens and to the south of the chalk downs. Sand martins nested at a sandpit in Ken Wood, only five miles from St. Paul's up to 1926, and in another at Barn Elms until working of the pit caused them to desert in 1924.

The first instance of sand martins using the artificial holes provided by drainpipes was early in the century. Writing in 1912 Johnson said that about ten years before they nested regularly in the dry drainpipes of a railway embankment at Clapham Junction. In the Lea valley they were first reported using the drainpipes in the aqueduct which runs from King George V reservoir in 1929, and now there are a number of small colonies along its length, while some of the former sites in gravel pits in the district have been deserted. In recent years other colonies in drainpipes have been seen in the cement bank of the canal at Harefield, on an island in the Thames near Teddington Lock and along Beverley Brook. A small colony in the gravel of the railway embankment near Earlsfield Station flourished from 1924 to 1935, but the birds deserted when the embankment was altered, returning later to nest in drainpipes in a concrete wall nearby, where they continued to nest until 1944. Although the size of the colony may be limited by the number of drainpipes available, these artificial holes provide easy and secure nesting sites and appear to be growing in favour.

Seven colonies have been recorded in railway embankments, and in 1923 birds were seen taking nesting materials into holes in the brickwork of the platform of Rye House station. More unusual sites have been in military trenches near Gidea Park station in 1917, in the canal bank at Alperton and in a private road-cutting at Brooklands, while in 1929 a pair attempted to nest in a hole in a wharf side near Putney Bridge. Colonies were seen in chalk pits at Beddington in 1909 and at Swanscombe in 1950, but the sand martin appears to be absent from the chalk districts of the North Downs. In the last fifty years only one colony, out of the 75 recorded, has been in a natural site, in a sandy bank of the Thames near Shepperton. Man is thus now a prime factor in the ecology of this species around London.

In spring the first sand martins are seen in late March or early April; the median arrival date over 27 years (not consecutive) being April 2nd. The earliest date is March 18th, 1945, when E. R. Parrinder saw a single bird at Brent reservoir. Passage usually lasts until May. The return movement begins in July, continuing until September, with many October records. The latest is of a bird seen by C. A. White and W. N. Mitchell on November 6th, 1949. Large flocks occur at reservoirs and sewage farms in autumn. Small numbers are seen over park waters of Inner London on passage.

GOLDEN ORIOLE, *Oriolus oriolus* (L.). Scarce spring and autumn visitor: has bred successfully at least once and has attempted to do so on a few other occasions.

The golden oriole has been identified about twenty times in the Area, fifteen of the records being in April, May and June, the rest in August and September. Pairs have been seen on seven occasions and single males on seven. In 1930 a pair bred in Surrey and successfully reared young (*B.B.*, 24:226). The locality was within our Area and pairs have been seen there in at least two subsequent years. On April 27th, 1940, a pair was seen in the grounds of Chiswick House, and a half-finished nest was found. A week later, however, no addition had been made to the nest and the birds were not seen again. A female seen on Wimbledon Common on May 11th may well have been one of the Chiswick birds.

The records naturally reflect the distribution of suitable woodland. In Hertfordshire, for instance, the Watford area is particularly favoured, with five occurrences, three of them in June. A pair was also obtained at Bayford in 1943 (*Journal* Letchworth N.H.S., 3: 18-26; 1943). There are three records also for Wimbledon Common. Briefly summarised the rest of the records are as follows:— Epping Forest 1905, Hampstead about 1908, Kew Gardens 1934, Mitcham 1934, Riverhead 1944, Mill Hill 1947, and Keston where a pair was seen from June 1st–3rd, 1953. In addition there is a somewhat doubtful record at Dartford in 1902.

RAVEN, *Corvus corax* L. Vagrant, no recent records.

Although the raven bred in one or two localities up to the middle of the nineteenth century, in the period under review there are only three reliable records, all within the first ten years. Ticehurst (1909) quotes a record of a pair seen over Eltham in the autumn of 1902 by a Mr. Farn. Bickerton (*Trans.* Herts N.H.S.) refers to a pair which visited Elstree Reservoir on July 27th, 1905 (see also *B.B.*, 1:160). On September 19th, 1907, Walpole-Bond saw and heard two birds over Bromley (Ticehurst, 1909).

Several other records appear to lack authenticity, either because of uncertain identification or suspicion that they relate to escaped or liberated birds. The notes in question appear in *The Field* (100:680), the *Zoologist* (67:398) and the *Essex Naturalist* (20:108). The possibility of the three accepted records relating to escaped birds must also be borne in mind.

CARRION CROW, *Corvus corone* L. Resident, breeding throughout the Area, though less common in parts of the closely-built zone and in a few rural districts where still persecuted.

In the London Area the carrion crow has benefited greatly by the reduction in persecution in the last fifty years. In 1900 it was rare in most rural areas. Thus, in that year, Bucknill said that in Surrey it was much less abundant than in former years, being so persecuted by gamekeepers that it was nowhere common, while in West Kent, according to A. P. Macklin, it had been all but exterminated by keepers in the larger woods (Turner, 1909). It was commoner in Middlesex, where there were fewer preserved estates, though still rare in some of the more rural areas, such as Staines. The suburbs of

London were its main stronghold at this time, and in some, such as Hampstead, it had recently increased (Goodchild, 1913). In Inner London it nested in small numbers, chiefly in Hyde Park and Kensington Gardens, and in 1898 Hudson thought its fate hung in the balance, for the birds attempting to breed in the Royal Parks were shot or had their nests pulled down because of their partiality for mallard eggs and ducklings.

Gamekeeping declined in some of the rural districts during and after the 1914–18 war and there the carrion crow increased. Some years later, however, it was still very unevenly distributed in Essex, the London district being its chief haunt while in most of the county it was uncommon (Glegg, 1929). In Surrey H. E. Pounds rarely saw a carrion crow in the Addington and Farleigh districts up to 1929, but after that date they spread steadily throughout the district, and the increase at Beddington dates from about 1928. In contrast with Pounds's experience Harrisson (1931) estimated that there were 24 pairs within a radius of 1½ miles of Harrow-on-the-Hill.

The Second World War led to a further reduction in the numbers of gamekeepers, and even more striking increases in the number of carrion crows have been reported from many rural districts within the last ten years. The species now appears to be common in all parts of the Area, except where open spaces are few, as in the East End and some boroughs on the south bank of the Thames, where, although it does occur, its numbers are said to be small. The scarcity of breeding carrion crows in the closely built areas is no doubt partly due to the absence of grassland for feeding, but as they will range over considerable distances for food the lack of suitable trees for nesting may also be a factor. However, in a few instances they have adapted themselves to nesting on buildings in London; twice on the Houses of Parliament and on several occasions on the gas-holders at Bromley-by-Bow. In Inner London there has been an increase, and in 1951 there were at least 21 pairs. Though most nests are still found in the parks and the larger open spaces, the carrion crow has shown a greater readiness to nest in the squares in recent years, usually those closed to the public.

In London the carrion crow has been reported feeding on eggs, young birds, small birds, carrion, insects, fresh-water mussels, vegetable matter of many kinds and refuse. It is a regular scavenger along the Thames mud, and has been frequently seen picking food from the surface of the river and the park lakes. In Inner London the carrion crows do much of their feeding on the grass in the parks and the quieter squares. Elsewhere the largest numbers have been observed in parks, such as Bushy and Richmond, and on fields, sewage farms and rubbish dumps. These flocks may be seen in all months of the year, and they have tended to grow larger as the species has increased. In recent years there are many reports of flocks of over fifty birds and several of more than a hundred. The largest flocks have been reported from Richmond Park, where R. W. Hayman (*Bird Life in the Royal Parks*, 1951) states that in January and December, 1950, it was not unusual to see as many as 160 together. The numbers found there in the breeding season are much lower, though a series of counts made at Beddington sewage farm between 1946 and 1949 showed that the average size of the flocks varied little at different seasons, being 57 in the first three months of the year, 56 in the second, 50 in the third and 61 in the last three months. Larger numbers are found at the communal roosts which are described in the chapter on this subject.

There is no evidence of any increase in the total numbers of carrion crows in the Area in the winter months, nor are there any records of migrating birds, though as the residents roam widely small movements of migrants could be easily missed.

HOODED CROW, *Corvus cornix* L. A few still seen regularly every winter but no flock reported for over twenty-five years. Formerly commoner, decrease probably began before 1900 or very early this century.

Though the hooded crow is generally recognised to have decreased considerably as a winter visitor to south-east England, the change is no recent development as it was already scarce when Harting (1866) and Bucknill (1900) wrote their histories of the birds of Middlesex and Surrey respectively. In the early years of this century the hooded crow was seen regularly in the Haileybury and Broxbourne districts of the Lea valley; it was also a winter visitor to the marshes near Dartford (Davis, 1904) and frequently observed in winter on the Blackheath and Greenwich marshes (Turner, 1909). At the same time birds occurred regularly in numbers up to ten at a time in the Limpsfield, Titsey and Woldingham districts of the North Downs. It is probable that they were then regular visitors to all the higher open country of north-east Surrey, though they did not often occur west of Caterham and Godstone. They were unusually numerous in the winter of 1906–07 and were still occurring regularly in this district in 1920, Beadell (1932) counting sixty in the Beddlestead valley on February 22nd. A year later he saw twenty on February 20th at Warlingham. In the decade after the 1914–18 war one or two, and occasionally three, were often seen at low tide along the Thames in Chelsea Reach. Since then, however, there have been no reports of more than six at a time anywhere in the Area.

Undoubtedly the scarcity of observers had much to do with the infrequency of observations away from the North Downs, for when reservoirs and sewage farms were more often watched they soon produced the majority of records. Single birds were seen at the Lea valley reservoirs in six successive winters from 1933–34 to 1938–39. For the same period isolated reports came from the Roding valley and Wanstead Park, Elmers End, Epsom and Watford sewage farms, Bushy Park, Mill Hill and the Barnes and Richmond Park district. At Beddington sewage farm up to three birds were seen in most winters from 1930–31 to 1935–36, and in the last ten years or so hooded crows, usually singly, have been seen in a number of widely separated localities, including Hampstead Heath. In the winter of 1952–53 more were seen than usual and four spent the winter in West Middlesex, often roosting with carrion crows at Perivale Wood. The party of six already mentioned was on the Thames marshes at Aveley.

The first arrivals have been recorded six times in the first half of October but, for thirty-five years in which birds were seen in October or November, the mean arrival date is October 28th, and twenty-four of the first occurrences fall between October 14th and November 4th. There is little definite evidence of direction of movement apart from the party of seven birds seen by Power (1910) flying west at Brixton on October 29th, 1909. While many birds undoubtedly only pass through the Area, some regularly wintered on the North Downs, and probably in other localities, in the first quarter of the century. They normally leave in March but have been seen in April in twelve years and once on May 2nd.

ROOK, *Corvus frugilegus* L. Abundant and widespread resident outside the heavily built-up areas. Some evidence of immigration in autumn.

A complete census of the rookeries of the London Area was made in 1945 and 1946 as part of the war-time Rook Investigation undertaken by the British Trust for Ornithology for the Agricultural Research Council. The results, summarised in the *London Bird Reports* for the census years, showed that a total of 355 rookeries held just under 20,000 birds, an average density of 15.9 birds per square mile compared with just over 30 per square mile over the country as a whole. But average densities may give a totally misleading impression of local distribution. The *London Bird Report* for 1946 included an isopleth map, compiled from the census returns by James Fisher and Dr. R. G. Newton, which showed clearly the distribution of rookeries in the London Area. From the map it can be seen that virtually the whole of the central built-up area, up to six to ten miles from Charing Cross, was completely devoid of rookeries; indeed, in 1945 only three rookeries were located within ten miles of the centre. Outside this "rookless" zone were roughly concentric belts where the number of nests gradually increased until around the greater part of the perimeter a density of 6–12 nests per square mile was reached. In four localities, in the neighbourhood of Watford, North Weald, Eynsford and Godstone, belts of high density, exceeding 24 nests per square mile, overlapped into the Area and in two places within these the density per square mile approached 50.

There are no comparable figures for the early part of the century and although the rook was generally described as abundant it is a matter for conjecture whether it was then more numerous in the country districts than it is now. But in the suburbs it was certainly less rare and nested as close to the centre as Hampstead and Dulwich. In the centre itself, the large rookery in Kensington Gardens had been dispersed in 1880 when 700 tall trees were cut down. Survivors from this colony remained for some years and in 1900 there were twelve nests in Connaught Square, just north of Hyde Park, one by the Prince of Wales Gate and seven in a garden off the Kensington Road. The last two sites were abandoned after 1900 but there is some doubt of the year in which the Connaught Square colony was finally extinguished. R. S. R. Fitter (1949) says that C. A. Cresswell, who lived in the Square, was quite certain that it was deserted after 1903, when eight pairs nested. But correspondents in *Country Life* (Vol. 23, 396) and *The Times* (14.4.06) reported nesting in 1905 and 1906; Charles Dixon said that there were ten nests in 1908, and finally A. E. Haserick wrote in *Country Life* (Vol. 29, 468) that in 1911 three nests were reoccupied after a lapse of three years. Another famous Inner London rookery, in Gray's Inn, which had existed at least since the 18th century, came to an end in 1915—it was said that the rooks objected to the noise of the training of recruits beneath their trees. In the following year four pairs, perhaps from Gray's Inn, built in a plane tree in the Temple. Since then, no nests have been found in Inner London and the rook is the only species which has been forced to abandon nesting regularly in the centre in this century. The ruthless cutting down of trees was probably one of the reasons for the disappearance, but the most likely cause was the increase, as London spread, in the daily journey in search of food.

In the inner suburbs, the rook held out for rather longer. Hampstead seems to have been deserted about 1903 but in the south there were small rookeries at Herne Hill until 1919, at Wandsworth until about 1924 and at Dulwich until about 1930. At the time of the census in 1945, the nearest rookery to St. Paul's Cathedral was at Lee Green, 6¼ miles away, but even this was abandoned in 1947.

There are as yet too few ringing returns to judge how far the resident rooks disperse after the breeding season. Four nestlings or juveniles ringed in the Area have been recovered, three locally but the fourth, ringed at Ware in April, was recovered at Lakenheath, 50 miles north-east, in the following November. An adult found at Hitchin in April had been ringed at Rollright, 55 miles west, in February of the previous year.

In the autumn and winter large numbers of rooks, frequently in company with jackdaws and starlings, are seen feeding on open spaces, ploughed land and rubbish dumps. Some of these may be immigrants. The extent to which rooks from the Continent or from other parts of Britain, pass through or visit the Area in winter is still an open question. As discussed in the chapter on migration there are very few recent records of flocks of rooks passing over London in October. It seems likely that more would have been recorded (even allowing for the difficulty in distinguishing between migratory and roosting movements) if the large east-west immigration in the Thames estuary continued as far as London.

A short account of rook roosts in the London Area is given in the chapter dealing with roosts and flylines.

JACKDAW, *Corvus monedula* L. Common resident, sedentary, nesting in old trees, quarries and buildings, and flocking on arable land in company with rooks and carrion crows. Some evidence of immigration in autumn.

In the more rural parts of our Area the majority of observers report a considerable increase in recent years. In built-up areas numbers vary with available nesting sites, but the bird is fairly common, and in some districts abundant. There have been inevitable local decreases owing to the break-up of estates, the felling of old timber or eviction from buildings, but nesting birds are attached to old haunts, and before leaving a locality will attempt to nest in new and sometimes unsuitable sites. Nesting in quarries has been reported among other places, at Whyteleafe, Riddlesdown and Epsom in Surrey, Harefield in Middlesex, and at Purfleet and other sites near the Thames in Essex and Kent; also in the sand of a railway bank at Coulsdon, and in sandpits at Bromley and Limpsfield.

In Inner London, perhaps rather surprisingly, no advantage has been taken of nesting sites on bombed buildings, although the birds' addiction to ruins and quarries would seem to favour this. Apart from the colony in Kensington Gardens, jackdaws are often seen flying over and even feeding in London squares and small gardens. They are only occasional visitors to Regent's Park, though a flock of probably more than 200 birds passed over in fog on February 14th, 1923 (Seth Smith, *Field* 141:287). The small colony in the south-west corner of Kensington Gardens has been present for many years, although in 1923 it was considered doubtful if any nesting had taken place for two years, owing to trees having been lopped or blown down. Glegg (1935) thought it doubtful if the jackdaw still bred. The first young bird of which we have actual record was seen in 1936, when three or four pairs were present, and young were also recorded in each of the following five years, the colony increasing to six pairs in 1941. In 1946 about a dozen birds were present from July to December, with a maximum of 24 on November 1st. In 1947 nesting was presumed at six different sites in trees; after April 23rd the growth of foliage made observation difficult, but no young birds or parents carrying food were seen, bearing out the poor results noted in previous and later years at this colony. In 1948 not less than four pairs bred, and in 1949 at least three young were identified. The colony remained in existence but no more young were seen until 1954, when two nestlings were found dead beneath a nesting-box.

The association of rooks and jackdaws, both by day and at the night roosts, is well known. For more than fifty years there was a very large roost at Gatton Park, with flight lines from the west over Reigate, from the north over Kingswood and from the south over Redhill. There is some evidence that this roost drew birds from a much larger area. In the Bricket Wood and Colney Street area in 1950 daytime flocks were estimated by Professor E. H. Warmington at up to 2,000 birds. In Richmond Park, where the old timber offers abundant nesting sites, flocks feeding in winter did not formerly exceed about 150 birds, but after the advent of cultivation in the second world war over 600 were counted in each of the years 1948 and 1949. Refuse dumps also are a common feeding ground.

Although the jackdaw is known to be a winter immigrant from the Continent, no seasonal fluctuations in our Area have been reported. In the earlier years of our period Power (1910) on a few occasions noted parties of threes and fours associated with the marked W.–N.W. migration of rooks in October, and previously he had in two different years observed a much larger movement. In 1951 S. Cramp saw about 40 flying S.W. over central London on November 1st, and in 1952 about 250 flying W.S.W. ten minutes after sunrise on October 12th. A jackdaw ringed at Alveborg, Sweden, on June 5th 1939, was recovered at Radlett on March 10th 1940, and presumably belonged to the Scandinavian race, *C.m. monedula*. A full-grown bird ringed at Long Ashton, Bristol, in July 1950, was recovered at London Colney, Herts., 100 miles E.N.E., in April, 1953.

MAGPIE, *Pica pica* (L.). Very rare early in the century; increased slowly during and after the First World War and rapidly from the thirties onwards. Now common in the rural districts and colonising several localities within eight to ten miles of St. Paul's where there is still some open country.

Before the First World War the magpie was extremely scarce in our Area, a few pairs only struggling to survive where they were not being exterminated in the interests of game preservation; seventeen were once counted on a keeper's gibbet near Haileybury. Once common as near London as Wembley Park and Kingsbury, for example, by 1906 magpies were only sparsely distributed as far out as Staines (Kerr). "A small remnant of Herts. magpies" were just maintaining their ground near Watford, while in the Epping Forest district they were very uncommon and only single pairs were reported as far from London as Brentwood and Ongar. In north-west Kent they were "all but exterminated" and at Oxshott the magpie was said to be "one of our rarest breeding birds". Apart from a single pair at Upper Warlingham in 1900 one observer saw none in north-east Surrey until 1909 when there was a pair near Oxted. A gradual spread into this district followed from outside our Area.

In this first decade of the century a few magpies bred in the central parks, but their origin from captivity was fully described in the literature of the time. They provided such incongruous sights as a magpie on the weather vane of Holborn town hall and one walking on the ice on the Serpentine.

The First World War brought the magpie some relief from the gamekeepers. By 1918 six pairs were known near Godstone, and in a slow spread in north-east Surrey birds were seen at Caterham by 1921 and at Tadworth by 1922. By this time magpies were quite common at Hertford, and were numerous at Chelsham in Surrey a few years later. By 1930 it would probably be correct to say that they were widespread in the outer parts of the Area, but were seldom common enough to form large flocks. The Addlestone district appears to have been an exception, as T. H. Harrisson saw at least sixty within a mile of Ongar Hill in September, 1929, and at Hampton a "large flock" was reported on December 30th of the same year.

In the thirties the increase seems to have become much more rapid, although still held in check in some places by persecution, birds being reported on keepers' gibbets for example at Hayes (Kent), Fawkham and Knockholt. Glegg (1935) considered the magpie to be common in Middlesex south of the Grand Junction Canal but uncommon and local north of it, the reason apparently being that the southern district contained many orchards and, in some parts, tall hedges with a corresponding absence of large estates or woodland guarded by keepers. Other observers also have commented that magpies were numerous in south-west Middlesex. Apart possibly from one or two scattered pairs the nearest sites to London before the last war appear to have been at Bushy Park (from 1930), Cranford, Ruislip (first in 1938), Shenley, Cuffley, Cheshunt, Epping Forest (1935–37 only), Addington, Selsdon and Chessington. This excludes attempted breeding at Dulwich in 1938–39 and a pair resident at Ken Wood, undoubtedly escaped from captivity. Birds were seen nearer London outside the breeding season but very seldom in densely inhabited districts.

During and after the last war magpies increased remarkably, presumably to a large extent due to the absence of persecution, but as the species was already on the increase when the war started little impetus would have been needed to send up its numbers. Despite this favourable combination of circumstances the magpie has still not colonised the really built-up districts like its relative the jay, and there is little evidence yet of its becoming as indifferent to man as it is in Scandinavia, for example. Exceptionally it has nested in large gardens in Kingswood, Limpsfield and Tadworth in Surrey, and in South Croydon one developed the habit of visiting a back garden for scraps. It is worth noting that there are places where the bird is still persecuted and in three months in the autumn of 1946 one keeper accounted for 57 at Addington (Pounds, 1952).

The normal inner breeding limit is now Bushy Park, Cranford, Ickenham, Harrow Weald, Edgware, Mill Hill, Totteridge, Barnet, Chingford, Hainault, Havering, Harold Wood, the Ingrebourne valley (exclusive of the built-up areas of Upminster and Rainham), Plumstead marshes, Abbey Wood, Shooters Hill, Chislehurst, Petts Wood, Hayes, Wimbledon Common and Richmond Park. Within the last few years one pair has bred at Finchley and nesting has been attempted on Dulwich and Mitcham Commons. There is a definite tendency to spread in towards London, but the magpie's feeding habits may prevent it from becoming as urbanised as the jay.

NUTCRACKER, *Nucifraga caryocatactes* (L.)

A bird of the slender-billed form (*N.c. macrorhynchus*) was shot at Addington Park, Croydon., on October 13th, 1913, and identified by the late T. A. Coward (*B.B.*, 7:301). The skin is now in the Manchester Museum, where it has been examined by Mr. Howard Bentham (cf. *Zool.*, 71:76, and Croydon N.H.S. *Reports*, 8:33).

Power (1910) claims to have seen a nutcracker flying across the golf course at Lordship Lane, Dulwich, on April 14th, 1905. He says: "I am satisfied as to my correct identification", but gives no details, and some doubt must attach to the record. On July 6th, 1936, a nutcracker was seen at Kew Green by W. M. Greenwell (*B.B.*, 30:93), but was considered to be an escape.

JAY, *Garrulus glandarius* (L.). Resident in all suitable wooded districts, including the Inner London parks. Common in most of the rural parts, often visiting more open country. Sometimes seen in London streets, and occasionally nests in them. Some immigration in winter possible from the Continent.

At the beginning of the century the jay, although well-established in many parts of our Area, was less numerous and widespread than it is to-day. In *Birds in London*, published in 1898, Hudson records that the jay did not then inhabit any of the inner parks and open spaces and that he could find no evidence of its ever having done so, but by 1906 he said that it was a common resident in Kew Gardens. Reports during this period are conflicting: thus Dixon (1909) said it was gradually decreasing, whereas Walpole-Bond in a manuscript annotation to a copy of his *Birds of the Bromley District* wrote that it had increased wonderfully compared with 1901, and Johnson (1912) considered that it was markedly on the increase at Wimbledon. In general, however, numbers were probably low at that time wherever gamekeeping was effective. The decline in game preservation during and since the 1914–18 war has almost certainly been a major factor permitting the subsequent recovery, and the increase in numbers has been particularly marked since the Second World War.

In the outer parks the jay is now abundant and well-established and is a very characteristic bird of Richmond Park. In Hampton Court Park it was first proved to breed in 1933. In the autumn of 1935 large numbers were seen (probably in connection with acorn-gathering) and by 1947 the bird had noticeably increased, as a resident, and this increase has, as elsewhere, been maintained.

Cramp and Teagle (1952) have described the spread of the jay in Inner London, where a pair first spent the summer in 1929. In 1930 Meinertzhagen (*Field*, 179:384) reported a nest in Kensington, which was deserted, and young were seen in 1932. Space does not permit details of the subsequent colonisation to be repeated here, but the jay now breeds annually in most of the Royal Parks and in a number of other open spaces in Inner London, having even made nests in plane trees and on buildings in busy streets. Although it has succeeded in establishing itself in Inner London it has not yet fully, if at all, emancipated itself from its dependence on the oak as a source of winter food. In autumn it spends most of its time collecting acorns, which it buries singly in the ground and retrieves as needed. In Inner London, where oaks are relatively few, this habit is particularly easy to observe, and the birds may be watched hour after hour as they journey to and from the oak trees, each departing bird with a much distended gullet and usually a last acorn held in the bill. Even in districts where oaks are common large numbers of jays may come to the same group of trees to collect acorns, and this fact undoubtedly accounts for most of the sudden local increases noticed at this time of the year. In Inner London bread and other artificial food is eaten in some quantity and regularly stored away, each piece being either buried, thrust deep into a tussock of grass, or more often hidden in some crevice in the bark of a tree.

In London there is intense competition for the acorns, chiefly from woodpigeons, which are as adept at plucking them green from the tree as the jay itself. As a result of this it seems likely that the jays would not manage to hide away so many acorns as those living further out. In spring and early summer their natural insect food is in short supply in the London parks and four fledged young examined in June, 1950, had evidently been fed partly on bread, with unsatisfactory results, for two of them were definitely subnormal and the other two had many defective feathers.

It is possible that immigrant jays from the Continent may reach our Area, as two birds shot by Dr. J. M. Harrison on December 1st, 1934, at Shoreham were considered by him to be of Continental origin (*B.B.*, 29:27).

GREAT TIT, *Parus major* L. Resident and widespread in all but the most heavily built-up districts and breeding in Inner London parks and gardens. Evidence of an influx in autumn, when there is a tendency to wander.

Great tits have been common in the London Area throughout the period covered by this volume, their readiness to accept artificial sites for nesting contributing to their success. Besides using nesting-boxes in private gardens and some public parks, they have taken to suitable holes offered by drain- or vent-pipes, hollow iron railings, letter boxes and ornamental stone vases. They can prove equally resourceful in their search for nesting material. At the Natural History Museum in 1932, R. W. Hayman saw a great tit enter a second floor storeroom through an open window, seize a beakful of hair and tow from a mammal skin lying on the table, and fly with it into the Museum gardens.

In its feeding habits also the great tit's boldness and adaptability serve it well. It comes readily to scraps put out by the householder and occasionally takes food not intended for its consumption. It is, of course, one of the two species of tit most commonly found opening milk bottles to steal the cream. This behaviour appears to have been first noticed in the London Area at Croydon in 1922, but unfortunately the offending tits were not specifically identified. Two years later, however, there are records of both blue and great tits attacking milk bottles at Dartford. It is suggested by James Fisher and R. A. Hinde (*B.B.*, 42: 347–357) that the spread of the habit in the London Area can be traced from Dartford and two other localities, Chalfont St. Giles, 1925, and Richmond in 1929; it is, however, almost certain that there were other source localities. By 1946, two years before the British Trust for Ornithology's enquiry, tits were opening milk bottles at places in the London Area as widely scattered as Harold Wood in Essex and Sipson in Middlesex, Aldenham in Hertfordshire and Oxshott in Surrey.

In Kew Gardens great tits will occasionally take food from the hand, and they would also do so in Kensington Gardens in 1927, according to L. Parmenter (*in litt.*). In a number of urban parks they forage for scraps in the litter baskets.

Birds ringed in the Area have usually been recovered "where ringed" or within a radius of a few miles, but there is some evidence that an influx of this and other species of tit takes place in autumn, as noted in Inner London, for example, between September 23rd and October 28th, 1949. F. D. Power (1910) noticed a passage of five species of tit, including great tit, through his Brixton garden. A suggestion that these movements may be of Continental origin is strengthened by the recovery in the Pas-de-Calais province of France in May, 1954, of a great tit ringed at Sevenoaks, just outside our Area, in early March, 1953. Another ringed near Hayes, Middlesex, on November 24th, 1952, was found near Le Touquet on February 2nd, 1954.

BLUE TIT, *Parus caeruleus* L. Common resident in all parts of the Area, especially in the rural districts and outer suburbs, and nesting even in the inner built-up zone.

The blue tit is London's commonest tit and there is no evidence to suggest that its status has altered to any extent during the half century. It is apparently able to exist in a wider variety of habitats than the great tit, and in Inner London it is not restricted to the parks and large gardens. It regularly frequents the weed-grown bombed sites in winter and has bred in some of the squares, to which the great tit is only a passing visitor. The blue tit is able to live even in that drab, congested and comparatively treeless belt around the city centre, part residential and part industrial, which developed during the last half of the nineteenth century.

The success of this tit in adapting itself to urban conditions is partly due to the degree of tolerance which it shows towards man, and the readiness with which it exploits artificial nesting sites. In the London Area, besides the usual nesting boxes, drainpipes and occasional letter-boxes, blue tits have frequently nested in some of the older types of lamp standard. They will also roost in such sites.

Although confiding, London blue tits do not readily feed from the hand, but they are easily attracted to bird tables, suspended pieces of fat and peanuts, and in the parks they will sometimes hunt for scraps in litter baskets. Reference has already been made (*vide* great tit) to the now widespread habit of milk stealing. Blue tits have been found opening milk-bottles even in Inner London. In November, 1949, a bird tried to remove a cardboard cap from a bottle on an office window sill in Lambeth, and it was learned in 1952 that for at least six years blue tits had made attempts to take milk from bottles delivered to the refreshment stall in Lincoln's Inn Fields.

There are also a few instances from the London Area of that other curious form of behaviour known as 'paper-tearing'. The tendency for tits to enter houses at certain times and "furiously" peck and pull at wallpaper, ceiling paper, paper wrappers and the like has been discussed in two articles in *British Birds* (W. M. Logan Home, 46:16–21 and R. A. Hinde, *ibid.*, 21–23). There were reports of paper tearing in 1949 from Ewell, Bookham and Sutton-at-Hone. Adhesive labels, newspapers, blotting-paper and a fuel licence were among the objects attacked.

The only evidence from ringing data of other than local movements comes from a recovery in January at West Hoathly, Sussex, of a bird ringed the previous month at Carshalton, about twenty miles away. Very few nestlings have been recovered, and most of the recoveries of adults have come from re-trapping in the same place by the original ringer. The incidence of these recoveries, which are principally in gardens, is least in the height of summer and greatest in February and March, which suggests a close correlation with the availability of natural food. While such evidence as ringing provides suggests that blue tits are more or less sedentary or at most local wanderers within a narrow radius, there is a certain amount of visual evidence suggesting a definite autumn movement, such as the exceptionally large autumn influx of tits which was noted in Inner London in 1949. Blue tits were far more numerous than all the other species, and single birds, couples and small parties were seen on tall buildings, scaffolding and bombed sites, as well as in parks and gardens throughout the built-up area. The 'peak' of the passage was reached during the first two weeks of October (*L.B.R.*, 14:14). The source of these birds is unknown: in Kent, outside our area, there are a very few definite records of Continental blue tits (*Parus c. caeruleus*) and immigration has often been suspected (Harrison, 1953), but there is no proof as yet that this is on an appreciable scale.

COAL TIT, *Parus ater* L. A thinly distributed resident, much less numerous than blue or great tits, except perhaps where conifers predominate.

Coal tits have almost certainly decreased close to London since 1900. Although there are few comparative figures of their numbers, on Tooting Graveney Common, for example, H. G. Attlee found only 2–3 pairs in 1948 compared with 8–10 in 1895. Nevertheless, in recent years coal tits have bred within about five miles of St. Paul's at Dulwich, Greenwich Park and Hampstead, and adults have been seen with fledglings or very small young in Kensington Gardens in 1947, in Regent's Park in 1951 and 1953, and in Marlborough Place, N.W.8 in 1953.

Normally the coal tit is commonest where conifers predominate, as on the Bagshot Sands at Oxshott, but pairs are found here and there in closely built-up suburbs like Norwood associated with single or very scattered pine trees. This predilection for conifers is illustrated also by attempted nesting in a suburban garden in the introduced *Cedrus atlantica glauca*. An example of an unnatural nesting site was provided by a pair which reared young in 1924 in a hole of a platform at Mill Hill station, only a foot away from the busy track.

Although frequenting the neighbourhood of houses less than blue or great tits, coal tits do visit bird tables and even Inner London gardens to feed, while in the cold spell of December, 1938, as many as six came to a bird table in St. John's Wood. They will also, though again less frequently than their commoner relatives, occasionally use nest boxes. It is not any avoidance of man but the scarcity of well-grown conifers that makes the coal tit a local species in most localities.

There is little evidence to suggest that passage movements take place through the Area, although unusual numbers of coal tits were seen moving through central London in October, 1930 (*B.B.*, 24:323), and J. N. A. Rignall saw a party of 50–60 in Battersea Park on October 30th, 1954. In winter they join mixed parties of Tits and there are two December accounts of flocks composed entirely of this species, about thirty in each case.

CRESTED TIT, *Parus cristatus* L.

On April 24th, 1904, C. W. Colthrup saw a tit with a marked crest flying about the tops of some tall trees near Croydon. He heard a note which he considered to be that of a crested tit but, as he was not able to get a closer view of the bird, the record was published as a "probable" (*B.B.*, 16:161). The second occurrence is a recent one. On April 10th, 1945, Miss D. Burridge saw a crested tit at close range in trees on marshy ground near Godstone, Surrey. She was able to give full identification details and to compare it with other tits present (*Bird Notes and News*, XXI:100), and there seems to be no doubt about the genuineness of this record. These birds are more likely to have been wanderers from the continent than from Scotland.

MARSH TIT, *Parus palustris* L.

Resident in woodland and scrub throughout the rural area and in the more wooded parts of the suburbs, but only locally common.

Typically the marsh tit prefers birch-clad commons and oak or mixed deciduous woods with a fair amount of secondary growth. It avoids suburban districts where there are only isolated trees and garden vegetation. Any changes in its distribution during the present century have probably been confined to withdrawals outwards from London as suitable habitats disappeared. In the breeding season it is now rare in Middlesex south of a line through Pinner, Stanmore, Mill Hill, Cockfosters and Whitewebbs Park, though it is found in good numbers in the oak and birch woods of Stanmore and Ruislip. In 1951 a pair bred in Osterley Park, and in 1937 an adult was seen feeding four young in the wooded grounds of Holland House. Normally, in Inner London, it is only an occasional autumn and winter visitor, a few being seen in most years.

In the flat plain of south-west Middlesex and in the more low-lying parts of south Essex it is scarce, but it is well distributed in the more wooded parts of Essex.

South of the river the marsh tit bred in Greenwich Park until 1945, and is a local resident in small numbers in the woods beyond Woolwich and Eltham. In 1946 it was still a "sparse resident" at Dulwich, and to the west it has bred on Wimbledon Common, in Richmond Park and up to 1938 in Kew Gardens. Surprisingly few nests are ever reported and it is probable that in some of the localities it is more regular than the records suggest. Further out, suitable habitats are plentiful, particularly in Surrey, and the bird is not uncommon.

The absence of marsh tits in spring and summer from most of the suburban belt, except where there are fair-sized woods, is not apparently due to any fear of man, for they will join other birds at garden bird-tables, and in Ken Wood and Whitewebbs Park, they are fed regularly by the public. In Ken Wood nesting has been suspected in recent years but not proved. Like other tits they tend to wander outside the breeding season, and in St. James's Park in the winter of 1949–50 one spent much of its time foraging in the litter baskets.

WILLOW TIT, *Parus atricapillus* L. Local resident, with a liking for the more wooded commons.

It was not known that the willow tit occurred in this country until 1897, when two specimens obtained at Hampstead were found among skins of marsh tits at the British Museum. In the same year Tring Museum received two birds killed at Coldfall Wood, Finchley, and one of these was taken as the type specimen when the British sub-species (*P.a. kleinschmidti*) was described.

There is no further information until 1905, when Walpole-Bond announced his discovery that some of the "marsh tits" nesting in the Bromley district were, in fact, willow tits. Apart from a single reference in 1910 to the bird being seen at Reigate, no more records are available until 1929. During the next few years willow tits were found building in the "Lower Colne valley" (*B.B.*, 25:163–4) and at Stanmore Common, and birds were seen at Ruislip and in several parts of Surrey. In the later 1930's the species was reported from many new localities distributed all round our Area, in the north most frequently in Epping Forest and the woods to the north-east, and south of the Thames on the numerous Surrey commons. There is little doubt that it was well-established in these localities though few nests were found to prove the matter.

Its status in Middlesex, according to Glegg (1935), was still obscure owing to the difficulty in identification. In 1937 J. M. Harrison reviewed the position in the Sevenoaks district of Kent for the previous 17 years (*S.E.B.R.*, 1937:29), and found little fluctuation in numbers, the ratio of willow tit to marsh tit being about 1:10. The proportion in the Brentwood-Romford area in the late 1930's was found by R. B. Warren to be 1:3 or 4.

Since 1940 records have been numerous, although even now breeding has been proved on comparatively few occasions. The species is perhaps most plentiful in Surrey, where damp, wooded commons provide suitable habitats. Birds are regularly reported from Bookham, the Esher-Oxshott area, and the neighbourhood of Walton-on-the-Hill, Headley and Tadworth. Records for Kent are less numerous but the significance of this is doubtful. North of the Thames, Ruislip Common, Stanmore, the Colne valley between Uxbridge and Rickmansworth, Epping Forest, Mimmshall Wood and Cuffley are favoured localities. As with all the tits birds wander in winter, a favourite haunt in Essex being the overgrown bridle-paths, where they are often seen searching for food on willow-herb (*Chamaenerion*).

LONG-TAILED TIT, *Aegithalos caudatus* (L.). Local resident in those parts of the rural area where there are thickets or bushy commons, and in a few of the larger and "wilder" open spaces in the suburbs. Wanders, often in flocks, in autumn and winter, when it occasionally penetrates Inner London.

The outward spread of London has driven the long-tailed tit from a number of localities where it once bred, and in recent years nesting has not been reported nearer the centre than Hampstead Heath (last in 1951) Kew Gardens (not here apparently since 1938), Wimbledon Common, Shooter's Hill and Bostall Woods, Gilwell Park and Chingford. It is apparently no longer found at Perivale, where it was still regular in 1930 (*L.N.* for 1930, p.98) or at Herne Hill where it was breeding in Power's day (1910). In the rural areas the bird appears to be present in all suitable localities, but the population fluctuates a good deal as the species is particularly vulnerable to the effects of severe winters.

During its autumn and winter wanderings, which are sometimes made in company with tits of other species, the bird has been observed in many of the inner suburbs. Occurrences in Inner London have been numerous, and in 1938 a party, which appeared on October 11th, remained in the area for two months, being most frequently reported from Kensington Gardens. Numerous other records from other parts of the built-up area at the same time indicated a large influx. On October 3rd, 1949, during the period when blue tits were appearing in Inner London in unusual numbers, Professor E. H. Warmington found what may well have been a migratory party of fourteen long-tailed tits, the movements of which he was able to follow across Central London from near St. Paul's Cathedral to Torrington Square, Bloomsbury.

NUTHATCH, *Sitta europaea* L. A fairly common resident throughout most of the suitable woodland and parkland areas, but remarkably scarce in the Essex sector.

At one time the nuthatch undoubtedly enjoyed a wider range. As Glegg pointed out in 1935, it disappeared from many suburban localities in Middlesex during the nine-teenth century. Prior to 1908 it nested at Wembley Park, but it was already rare in the Willesden area by 1907. A. W. Battley recorded in 1900 that nuthatches were formerly plentiful in Hanwell Park but that they had become much scarcer "since the building of more houses in the vicinity". The disintegration of the large estates before the advance of the builder certainly influenced the distribution of the species, but it did not always have the effect of banishing it completely. Here and there, surrounded by suburbs, even of the denser sort, are islands of parkland or woodland where the bird persists, as at Ken Wood, Osterley Park, Dulwich Wood, Greenwich Park and the grounds of Chiswick House, while in 1950 and 1952 at least a pair nested on Streatham Common.

Apparently the Central London parks are no longer suitable. In Yarrell's day (1843) nuthatches bred in Kensington Gardens, but before the end of the century they had become occasional visitors, which is their present status in Inner London now. Fitter (1945) suggests that this desertion of a locality which still provides food and nesting sites may be due to the accumulation of soot on the trees. In Greenwich Park, where the nuthatch was last seen in 1953, the atmospheric pollution is seriously increased by the discharge from a nearby power station, and the recent development of Kidbrooke has perhaps effectively isolated the park from those areas where nuthatches are commoner and from which they might have spread.

The bird is fairly common in the outermost suburbs where large gardens are often adjacent to suitable parks and woods. Over much of western Middlesex its range is restricted by lack of suitable habitats, but it is found in the neighbourhood of Bushy Park and Hampton Court, and is well established between Harefield and Mill Hill. In Kent it is apparently commonest between West Wickham and Dartford, while in 1942 J. M. Harrison considered it an abundant resident in the Sevenoaks district. On the chalk south of Dartford it seems to be comparatively scarce.

The nuthatch is apparently absent from a large part of the Essex sector, although suitable habitats are not lacking. It is resident in Epping Forest and has occurred fairly frequently at Larkswood, Higham's Park and Gilwell Park, but further east it seems to be extremely rare. It is rarely seen at Hainault Forest and, in over twenty year's watching in the Romford-Brentwood district, R. B. Warren only once saw a nuthatch (at Warley in 1948) although he received occasional reports of birds at Thorndon Park and South Weald Park, where a pair did breed in 1953. According to Canon Kuypers it was, before 1939, quite common in Thorndon Park.

TREECREEPER, *Certhia familiaris* L. Resident in all suitable localities, but in small numbers.

Although less exacting in its habitat preference than the nuthatch, the treecreeper is rather thinly and unevenly distributed, and it is only in the more wooded parts of the rural area that it can be considered to be at all common. In the suburbs it occurs occasionally in gardens, parks and other open spaces, and has nested intermittently as near to the centre as Hampstead Heath, Dulwich Wood and Greenwich Park. It has been seen in the breeding season during the last few years at North Ealing and on the commons of Tooting Bec and Streatham, and it has long frequented Wimbledon Common. Birds have been noted out of the breeding season at Highgate Woods and in such open spaces in the inner suburbs as Wanstead Park and Clapham Common.

To Inner London the treecreeper was considered by Holte Macpherson (1929) and Glegg (1935) to be only an occasional visitor, but up to 1954 a few were resident and breeding in Kensington Gardens. Elsewhere in the centre of London, and such other unsuitable areas as parts of south-west Middlesex and the marshes bordering the Thames below London, it is very seldom recorded.

WREN, *Troglodytes troglodytes* (L.). Abundant resident; some evidence of increase in autumn.

Except in the most heavily built-up parts, the wren is common and widespread throughout the Area. As elsewhere, its choice of habitat is catholic, and it can usually be met with wherever there is sufficient low cover. Even in such relatively barren areas as the Thames marshes wrens are not uncommon. J. F. Burton states that they breed commonly along the fringes of the Kent marshes within the Area and in isolated sites well out on the levels; he records a nest inside a hut in the middle of the Stone marshes.

Nearer in, the wren breeds in many of the larger suburban gardens and open spaces, and is resident as close to the centre as Hampstead and Peckham Park. In Inner London, it now nests regularly in Battersea Park, where it has increased since the war, less regularly in Kensington Gardens and Regent's Park and probably in the St. John's Wood area.

There is little evidence of changes of status of the wren in the period under review. It is a hardy species and although some observers have recorded fewer wrens in their district after severe cold spells (e.g., 1939–40) others have considered the population unchanged; it seems certain that a quick recovery is made from any temporary set-back.

Little is known of the movements of wrens in the London Area. The breeding birds appear to be resident, but it seems likely that there is an influx from the outside in October and November. This autumn increase is most apparent in Inner London, where wrens occur in places where they are known not to be resident. For example, one was seen in the grounds of Temple Church on several dates between October 10th and November 13th 1944, and near the same place on October 16th and November 13th, 1946. At the bombed site in Cripplegate, in the years 1950–52 wrens were first reported between October 15th and 24th, remaining until April or early May, on one occasion as many as four being seen. It might have been expected that a few pairs of wrens would have colonised the bombed sites, where places for nesting, and food, must be quite plentiful, but none has yet been seen in summer.

DIPPER, *Cinclus cinclus* (L.)

The dipper has been reliably reported four times in the London Area, three of the records being in spring. On March 28th, 1915, during very cold weather, M. V. Wenner saw one on the River Mole near Leatherhead (*B.B.*, 8:292), and another was seen in the same area on May 3rd, 1926, by P. F. Dagger (*B.B.*, 20:107). Rowan reported seeing a dipper on a flooded field near Hatfield, Herts. on April 5th, 1916, (*B.B.*, 10:34). Finally, W. Naunton Rushen refers to one seen in Kelsey Park, Beckenham a few years prior to 1926 (*Field*, 149:676).

MISTLE THRUSH, *Turdus viscivorus* L. Well-distributed even in the built-up areas where there is some open ground for feeding. Has increased considerably in Central London and the inner suburbs.

Bucknill in 1900 wrote that in Surrey the mistle thrush decreased rapidly in numbers on approaching the metropolitan area, within which it was more often noticed during the winter months than in the nesting season. The species was extending its range rapidly in the outlying parts of the British Isles in the nineteenth century (Alexander and Lack, 1944), and in our own Area Bickerton, writing in the annual report on birds in Hertfordshire for 1903, commented on a decided increase in the previous two years, while Kerr (1906) spoke similarly of a considerable increase of late years. At that time it was breeding in Kensington Gardens, but as late as 1929 there were still only a few pairs nesting in Inner London, where it now breeds in most of the parks and some other open spaces such as the squares (Cramp and Teagle, 1952). These authors suggest that the increase in London may be due in part to the extermination of the grey squirrel, whose depredations on the nests of such conspicuous birds are well known.

Interesting examples of adaptation to an urban life are singing from the top of a chimney in Campden Hill Road, and nests situated close to busy London pavements, in tubular scaffolding at the Temple, in the iron canopy of a statue at Hammersmith and on the scaffolding erected in 1953 for the Coronation; near Richmond Gate a pair nested on a window ledge only eight feet from the ground.

Mistle thrushes flock very early in the summer when the young are fledged, and as many as 89 were seen at Beddington sewage farm on June 26th, 1932, where L. Parmenter found them to be regular visitors at this season to the freshly-mown fields, probably to feed on exposed slugs and snails. As the year progresses flocks become more noticeable, *e.g.* about 150 at Caterham on August 3rd, 1919, and "numbers" going south at Ewell on August 14th, 1923. Reports of movements, southward whenever the direction has been noted, increase in September when an influx has often been noticed

In early October large numbers gather on the North Downs to feed on the yew berries, and a flock of about 250 was seen on Mickleham Downs on October 10th, 1937. Mr. V. R. Garrett, who has studied the arrivals of Turdidae on Hampstead Heath, has found that the new arrivals are usually very unsettled and vocal.

Large movements may occur at any time in the early months, as shown by such comments as a "big influx, very excited and voracious" at Hampstead on November 11th, 1946; "remarkable rush" in Hampton and Bushy Parks on November 27th, 1929; "fully 1,000 birds" at Selsdon on December 6th, 1942. Large numbers are not often reported after the turn of the year—exceptionally, about 400 at South Croydon on January 22nd, 1946. In general terms, the movements would seem to consist of family flocking after the nesting season, followed by wandering or a southward movement in early summer and late autumn, with an immigration, possibly of Continental origin, in the late autumn and early winter.

FIELDFARE, *Turdus pilaris* L. A winter visitor whose numbers vary considerably from year to year; westerly movements are a feature of hard weather in December when some birds come into the built-up area.

A few fieldfares are often seen well in advance of the main body and, exceptionally, odd birds have been reported as early as August 9th and 28th and September 4th and 9th. First arrivals are noted most frequently in the second half of October, but it is unusual for numbers to be very large at this season and the birds either pass on or disperse quickly. Their direction at this season varies from S.W. to N.W., and at Bexley, in particular, there has been a marked movement W.S.W. in recent Novembers. Sometimes in December a pronounced westerly movement takes place associated with the onset of hard weather. In 1934 many hundreds were flying W. or S.W. on December 16th at Woldingham and passage was also noticed over Epsom Downs. An influx at this season was even more marked in 1946, when some 2–3,000 were seen on December 15th in yew-trees in Norbury Park. The previous year several large flocks had passed south-west at Wimbledon on December 26th, and in 1947 about 2000 were present at Berwick Pond, near Rainham, on the same date. A general increase with the advent of cold weather was also noted on December 22nd, 1938.

While these large flocks do not usually remain intact in our Area, numbers in the earlier part of the year are normally much higher than in the first few months of the winter. In the unusually severe conditions of early 1947 the flock at Beddington sewage farm was conservatively estimated at 2,500 on February 6th. Return passage is often noted in March and April; flocks at this time seldom consist of more than a hundred birds, but on April 26th, 1953, about 1,000 flew N.W. over Fawkham Valley in Kent. In some years this passage may continue into the first half of May, and in 1943 a single bird remained at Brentwood until May 27th.

Fieldfares occur occasionally in Inner London but are more often seen flying over. They are not so often seen as redwings in suburban districts in spells of very hard weather.

SONG THRUSH, *Turdus ericetorum* Turton. Common and widespread resident but decreased markedly, especially in the built-up areas, since the beginning of the century. Many are sedentary but some disperse in autumn.

At the beginning of the century the song thrush was apparently a very numerous species in and near London. Finn wrote in 1907 that the song thrush and the blackbird could hardly be commoner anywhere, and in 1908 J. E. Whiting knew of no place where the present species was more in evidence than at Hampstead. It was fairly common in the inner parks, increasing in Hertfordshire and, according to A. P. Macklin, greatly outnumbered the blackbird in the more populated parts of West Kent (Turner, 1909). At Blackheath, Witherby (1894) found about three nests of the song thrush to one of the blackbird, and C. L. Collenette in the period 1904–11 recorded 97 nests of this species to 94 of the blackbird around Woodford. Piggott, writing in the *Saturday Review* of 1902, said that the blackbird was less common than the thrush, while at Harrow the two species were said to be about equally common. From these comparisons it seems fair to conclude on present-day evidence, even after allowing for the increase of the blackbird, that the song thrush has declined considerably in numbers.

When the process started is uncertain, but Collenette is of the opinion that, in the decade after the First World War, blackbirds were probably about five times as numerous as song thrushes at Woodford, and that this resulted from a decrease of the latter and not from an increase of blackbirds. In the thirties various observers commented that the blackbird was the more numerous of the two species. Winter counts obviously do not reflect the relative breeding status, but it is none the less interesting that a series of twenty counts by Howard Bentham in the Tadworth and Walton districts, made between October and February inclusive, in the years 1947–49, gave a ratio for blackbirds to song thrushes of four to one; four breeding-season counts in 1949 in the same district gave almost exactly the same proportion, though possibly biased in favour of the blackbird through following closely on the hard winter of 1946—47, which had a much more serious effect on song thrushes than on blackbirds.

The song thrush still breeds in all the large parks in Inner London as well as in parts where there are large gardens, but it is now rare in the squares, in many of which the blackbird is well-established. Exceptionally, one was once seen feeding in the gutter in the Haymarket in cold weather.

Ringing recoveries show that many of the birds occurring in gardens or built-up areas are sedentary and that such movements as there may be have no pronounced directional trend, except for three birds ringed as nestlings in 1920 and 1921 which were recovered in France during their first winter and one young one ringed in May, 1950, which was recovered at Caen in November, 1953. There is little evidence of visible migration, but at Hampstead Heath V. R. Garret thas repeatedly noted small flocks of immigrants in late September or in October feeding on rowan trees.

REDWING, *Turdus musicus* L. A winter visitor and passage migrant which is often heard in the late autumn passing over London; much more frequent than the fieldfare in Inner London and the suburbs.

The average date for first appearance during the inter-war years was October 9th, with the earliest record on September 20th, but in few years are flocks of any size seen before the middle of October. About 5,000 passed S.W. over Bookham Common on November 9th, 1952, in just under five hours. If passage movements are excluded, the largest concentrations occur in the second half of the winter. Flocks of up to three hundred or so are found in many localities, but observations of larger numbers come notably from Beddington sewage farm, where redwings were exceptionally numerous in the hard weather of early 1947, estimates on February 8th ranging from one to two thousand. Flocks of a thousand or more have also been seen in the scrub bordering Stone Marshes, and there were some 3,000 there in hawthorn thickets on February 4th, 1951. At Epsom sewage farm about five hundred were present on February 3rd, 1940, again during a period of hard weather.

These figures are only given as examples, and at such times redwings are not infrequently seen along the tow-path and tide-line of the Thames in the built-up area, while others visit suburban gardens and the inner parks. In February, 1917, some were seen searching for food on the mud at low tide at Chiswick and running along the pavement when the tide was up. More recently a cold spell in the second half of December, 1938, resulted in a heavy passage of redwings over central London and the appearance of small numbers in many unusual places. They occur much more frequently than field-fares in the central area.

Most of the winter residents have left before the end of March, but there are few years in which some are not seen in the first half of April. It is much more unusual for any to be seen after this, though exceptionally there was one at Larks Wood, Chingford, on May 15th, 1931. The average departure time of redwings is thus appreciably earlier than that of fieldfares, which are not infrequently seen in May.

RING OUZEL, *Turdus torquatus* L. A casual visitor on both spring and autumn migration, chiefly to the higher ground in the south of the Area. Possibly slightly less frequent in recent years.

The ring ouzel has decreased markedly in the British Isles during the present century (Alexander and Lack, 1944), while in 1900 Bucknill wrote that numbers on migration had largely decreased because of the encroachment of building on the higher Surrey hills. It is to be expected, therefore, that its visits should have become less frequent as time went on. The position is complicated, however, as a large proportion of the records come from two observers on the North Downs, C. H. Bentham and the late Richard Kearton, and tend to be grouped in the periods when they were most active. It is more than possible, moreover, that the greater number of observers in the last twenty years may have resulted in a higher proportion of the occurrences being recorded.

In fact, of forty-four records up to 1950 twenty-seven were in the first quarter of the century and seventeen in the second quarter; twenty-nine of these notes refer to Surrey, eleven to Middlesex, three to Kent and one to Essex. In the spring migration, fourteen of the eighteen records have been in April while of the twenty-four observations in autumn or early winter twelve have been in September and eight in October. In the years 1951–53 there were eleven spring records and three in autumn; in addition there were ring ouzels on Walton Heath for over three weeks in the autumn of 1951 with a maximum of 10 on October 8th.

Ring ouzels have been seen most often on the North Downs, where their natural breeding haunts are in places fairly well reproduced in miniature, as at Headley and Caterham, or on the heaths overlooking the gentle northern slopes of the downs. There are occasional records for the inner built-up areas, such as Brixton (1900), Walthamstow (1903), Tooting (1907), Kensington Gardens (1922 and 1951), Clapton (1924), South Kensington (1952) and Hampstead (1909–10 when a pair wintered, 1926, 1928, 1951 and 1952). There are several notes of birds feeding on berry-bearing shrubs in suburban gardens.

BLACKBIRD, *Turdus merula* L. Abundant resident which has greatly increased in numbers in London and the suburbs; breeds freely in suitable sites in Inner London.

The relative abundance of this species and of the song thrush has already been dis-cussed, and there is no question that the blackbird has increased very considerably dur-ing the present century, whereas any change in the population of the song thrush has been in the opposite direction. Even in 1900 Bucknill considered that the blackbird pene-trated the thickly populated districts in greater numbers than the thrush. In Inner London a spread from the parks to many of the squares and gardens seems to have taken place in the late thirties. Cramp & Teagle (1950) have shown that in the winter of 1948–49 blackbirds were almost five times as numerous in Kensington Gardens as in the winter of 1925–26. For the same park in 1945 E. M. Nicholson considered that it was about three times as common as the song thrush, though figures for this park and St. James's and Green Parks in the winter of 1949–50 suggest a very much higher ratio in favour of the blackbird, which was in all the parks the most numerous land species after the house sparrow (Cramp & Teagle, 1952A).

There can be little doubt that the blackbird is a hardier species than the song thrush and has a wider feeding range. Its adaptability to urban and suburban conditions is shown by the frequent use of buildings as song-posts, the presence of birds on several occasions on the roof-gardens of the big Kensington stores, observation of a bird foraging inside a litter basket in Inner London and the breeding of as many as eleven pairs in the bombed areas of Cripplegate in 1952.

No large flocks of blackbirds have been reported in the Area even during the annual October and November immigration of Turdidae, with the result that it is difficult to be sure that small parties seen do not merely represent a local concentration. However, V. R. Garrett has noticed a marked influx on Hampstead Heath in the second half of October and in November, and small parties of probable immigrants have been seen at other localities in these two months. Concentrations are sometimes larger at roosts and on December 16th, 1950, 252 were counted flying from one direction into a roost at Ken Wood. Another roost of 200–300 has been observed at Ruislip, and doubtless there are many other similar cases.

From over two hundred and thirty ringing recoveries affecting the London Area there are only three of birds ringed locally and recovered abroad. An adult ringed at Enfield on December 24th, 1925, was found in Belgium on the following October 25th, so that its origin is doubtful, but the recovery in South Norway on March 21st, 1952, of an adult ringed at Richmond in December, 1950, gives a hint of the possible origin of some winter visitors. Whereas a very large proportion of the recoveries merely show that many of the blackbirds are sedentary throughout the year, one juvenile ringed at Wimbledon on May 13th, 1945, was recovered at Brest, France, on January 25th, 1949, and there is a tendency for immature birds to disperse in autumn in the same way as song thrushes. There is always a bias in favour of recoveries at the place of ringing, but even so it appears that only a relatively small proportion of the local population is migratory and that such movement as there is takes the form of a dispersal rather than of true migration.

WHEATEAR, *Oenanthe oenanthe* (L.). Double passage migrant. Never common as a breeding species and now occasional only.

At no time in our period has the wheatear been more than a local and not very common nesting species. North of the Thames, it was rare in the early part of the century, even on migration, and in the whole period there are only three satisfactory breeding records. Glegg (1935) quotes one from Edgware in 1920 and another from Harefield Place Estate in 1930, in which year also a pair nested among old tree stumps in a dump at Bushy Park, as recorded in the Report of the Committee on Bird Sanctuaries in the Royal Parks. In *Bird Notes and News*, 2(2): 32, it is stated that a pair nested, in 1924, in the South African Rock Garden at the Wembley Exhibition but no supporting details are given. A juvenile was seen at Brent reservoir in June, 1944, and another on Hampstead Heath in 1952, but there was no evidence of breeding.

South of the Thames, where there is more high, open ground, the wheatear was once a regular, although somewhat local nesting species. In Kent, Ticehurst (1909) said that a few pairs nested in the valley of the Darent, while Bucknill (1900) stated that in Surrey they bred at such places as Epsom Downs, Reigate, Walton, Banstead, Headley and Chertsey Heaths, Burwood Common, Box, Leith and most of the West Surrey hills. Closer in, a pair or two nested on Wimbledon Common in the early part of the century and they nested annually until 1908 in Richmond Park, where Collenette (1937) has related that their presence was correlated with the preservation of rabbits for shooting. In 1904 the rabbits were killed off and their burrows, outside the plantations, filled in; the wheatears, which had nested in the burrows, "held on in diminishing numbers for a few years before finally forsaking the Park".

Towards the end of the first decade, there seems to have been a general and sharp decrease, for no very obvious reason, in the breeding of wheatears in the southern part of the Area. Birds nested at Epsom and Purley in 1912, on Walton Heath in 1914, and at Caterham in 1917—thereafter, there are no reports of breeding until 1941, when a pair bred on Walton Heath. Since then, there have been two other conclusive breeding records. In 1946 J. F. Burton found the nests of two pairs in piles of bricks on Blackheath; the bricks had been removed by the spring of 1947, but two adults seen with three young on Woolwich Common, about two miles from Blackheath, had probably nested nearby. In 1949, M. D. England found a nest in the Corporation dump at Upper Warlingham.

On passage, wheatears pass through on both the spring and autumn migrations, and there is perhaps a tendency for them to occur slightly more frequently in the autumn. Rather surprisingly, they appear to have been uncommon on migration through the Area in the early part of the century, and it was not until about 1930 that they began to be reported with regularity. In the following twenty years the average dates for the duration of the spring passage are March 22nd to May 14th south of the Thames and March 25th to May 17th in the north. In the autumn, the average dates are August 2nd to October 18th in the south and August 5th to October 3rd in the north. On both passages, wheatears are usually seen singly or in small parties but H. Bentham and others have recorded autumn parties of up to twenty on the Downs. Larger flocks occur exceptionally; in the early morning of April 8th, 1902, A. Holte Macpherson counted about 200 in Hyde Park. They all left during that day. Flocks of 25–30 have been seen twice in Regent's Park, in the spring of 1909 and again on May 6th and 7th, 1930.

As might be expected, wheatears on migration are seen most commonly on the Downs but they also occur at reservoirs, sewage farms, parks and open spaces. A few are seen each year in Inner London, in the parks or the bombed areas. Twice at least, on August 29th, 1907, and August 25th, 1934, migrant wheatears have been seen at Lords, within yards of the wicket while play was in progress.

A number of the passage wheatears, mostly seen in the middle or end of May or in September, have been identified as belonging to the Greenland race, *Oenanthe o. leucorrhoa* (Gm.), and two trapped at Romford sewage farm on May 1st and 2nd, 1954, had the measurements of this race. Birds from Greenland undoubtedly pass through the Area in small numbers each year, but the range of variation of the common wheatear, in size, plumage and perching habits, makes it difficult to assess the value of each report.

BLACK-EARED WHEATEAR, *Oenanthe hispanica* (L.)

A male of the black-throated form of this species was seen by H. C. Holme and Eric Simms in Regent's Park on April 23rd, 1951 (*B.B.*, 46:66–68).

STONECHAT, *Saxicola torquata* (L.). Never common, has decreased and is now a very local resident; but is more widespread on passage and as winter visitor.

In the London Area, the stonechat has always been a little more local and, except in Surrey, less common than the whinchat. One of the reasons may be that although they share some habitats (e.g. commons, railway embankments, wastelands) the stonechat requires a bush or fence or other song post within its territory, and does not normally nest in meadows or rough pasture, which in some parts of the Area are the principal haunts of the whinchat. Moreover, it is peculiarly sensitive to hard winters, which do not affect the fully migratory whinchat.

In the first quarter of the century, the main recorded strongholds of the stonechat were Epsom Common, Walton Heath (up to six pairs), Richmond Park and Mitcham Common in Surrey, Hayes Common and Dartford Heath (up to eleven pairs) in Kent, the banks of the Staines and Littleton reservoirs in Middlesex and irregularly in the more open parts of Epping Forest in Essex. Similar colonies or single nesting pairs were reported from time to time in other parts of the Area on gorse and heather covered commons, bushy wastelands and especially along railway embankments and cuttings. The population always seems to have been considerably less than could have been sustained by the suitable territory and in some parts of the Area, e.g. Hertfordshire, it was very local indeed.

In 1933, when the species was chosen for an intensive study in the London Area, nesting was recorded at seven localities on the North Downs, on Mitcham Common, in Richmond Park and on Wimbledon Common in Surrey, at Wembley and Ruislip in Middlesex, on Chorleywood Common and three sites near Mill Hill in Hertfordshire and near Black Park in Buckinghamshire. No nests were found in Essex or Kent, but a pair or two may have been missed on the Thames marshes, where they have bred since and which at that time were little watched. The breeding population in 1933 was evidently smaller than in the first two decades, but the reduction had not been drastic. Much of the nesting territory (commons, downland, railway embankments) was inviolate and the growth of London had less effect on the stonechat than on some other species, including the whinchat. In some places, indeed, the construction of new factories and other buildings provided, within the precincts, just the kind of wasteland the stonechat favours. Between 1933 and 1950, however, the stonechat suffered a very serious decline in the London Area as in other parts of the country, accelerated by the exceptionally cold winters of 1938–39, 1939–40 and 1946–47. The cumulative effect of these disastrous cold spells was that in the summer of 1947, following one of the most severe winters in living memory, only one pair of stonechats was found nesting in the whole of the Area. In the next seven years stonechats have bred in one or more years at Rainham in Essex, Moor Mill in Hertfordshire, Northolt, Ponders End and possibly Brockley Hill in Middlesex, on the Abbey Wood and Plumstead marshes in Kent and Epsom Common in Surrey, but in no year have there been over four pairs. The number of winter records has increased considerably and it seems likely that the species will re-establish itself, if the climate allows it.

The stonechat appears to be a partial migrant and other observers confirm Howard Bentham's view that most, if not all, of the breeding pairs used to leave the Area in the late summer or autumn. Other stonechats, presumably from outside the Area, arrived throughout September and October; some stayed for the winter, others, apparently, passed on. The return movement is in March. On passage, and in winter, the stonechat is more widespread than in the summer and as well as in the breeding habitats it has been reported at sewage farms, reservoirs, on reed beds, on allotments and in the suburban parks and waste ground. In Inner London, unlike the whinchat, it is exceptionally rare and has been recorded twice only, in Kensington Gardens in 1912 and 1949.

WHINCHAT, *Saxicola rubetra* (L.). Local summer resident, has decreased and is now scarce in the north and very scarce south of the Thames; more widespread on migration.

At the beginning of the century the whinchat was locally common as a nesting species, especially in the northern part of the Area around Enfield. For example, R. B. Lodge (1901) stated that it was exceedingly abundant, "quite one of the commonest birds", and that a pair or two might be seen in every field and meadow. Although this may be exaggerated, it does seem that the whinchat was relatively common wherever wasteland and rough grassland provided suitable nesting sites. The sides of the many railway embankments in North London were especially favoured.

South of the Thames the whinchat appears to have been more local, possibly because the pastures, e.g. on the North Downs, were kept more closely cropped.   However, it nested sparsely on most of the gorse-covered heathlands and on the banks of the reservoirs and similar stretches of rough grass. One of its strongholds was Richmond Park, where up to four pairs nested in practically every year from the beginning of the century until 1940, when the colony was vanquished as the result of military manœuvres.

During the second quarter of the century, there was a slow decline in the numbers of breeding whinchats; the decrease was variously ascribed to the encroachment of building, the uprooting of trees and brambles, the earlier cutting and trimming of railway embankments and the ploughing-up of pastures to grow crops. The decline was particularly pronounced in the Surrey part of the Area, where no breeding was recorded between 1938 and 1951, since when one or two pairs have bred at the Walton gravel pits. In Kent, in summer, whinchats are now reported only on the Thames marshes, where in 1952 there were ten pairs between Abbey Wood and Swanscombe. In Essex also the marshes bordering the Thames are a favourite haunt, as are the surroundings of the Ingrebourne and the Mar Dyke, while there were at least 13 pairs in the Lea valley in 1954, mostly at gravel pits, reservoirs or sewage farms. There are a few scattered pairs in Hertfordshire and Middlesex, but only in the Staines–Perry Oaks district are they at all well established.

On passage the whinchat is more numerous in autumn than in spring; Howard Bentham in the years 1932 to 1948 recorded 37 on spring passage in the Epsom Downs and Walton Heath districts and about 202 in autumn. The spring passage usually begins in the third week of April, the average date for the years 1933 to 1949 being April 18th. Two have been seen in March, the earliest on March 9th, 1930, when H. E. Pounds saw a female near Addington (*B.B.*, 23:306). There is one winter record of a male seen at close range by P. W. Ratcliff at Elmers End sewage farm on December 26th, 1934; although this date is quite exceptional we are fully satisfied with the identification.

In Inner London the whinchat was formerly an occasional visitor to the parks; it is now seen regularly on passage, especially on the bombed sites.

REDSTART, *Phoenicurus phoenicurus* (L.). Summer visitor, rather local, in rural parts of Area; more widespread as a passage migrant.

According to Alexander and Lack (1944) the redstart has been subject to a "very marked decrease throughout southern, eastern and central England", the cause of which is unknown. This statement certainly holds true for the London Area, and while it is clear that the advancing tide of housing development has been responsible for some of the decrease, much of it is unexplained. In the Hampstead and Highgate district, for instance, where it bred not uncommonly till about 1928, it was only a rather uncommon passage migrant until one pair nested in 1954. This district has been less affected by housing development than most, and still contains many large gardens and old trees, which are apparently quite suitable for the redstart. On the other side of London, at Bromley, the redstart had in 1901 much the same status as it has in many parts of the Continent to-day; according to Walpole-Bond it bred in some of the town gardens, in such sites as behind an old box in a potting-shed and the crevice between an ivy stem and the tree-trunk. Similar sites still exist in abundance in both the inner and outer suburbs. Again, in Epping Forest Geoffrey Dent records that the numbers of the common redstart have much diminished since the turn of the century. He attributes this to the growing up of old pollards, shutting out sunlight and resulting in a reduced food supply, and possibly also to an increase in squirrels. However, it would seem more reasonable to attribute the decrease to some cause operating over the whole of southern and eastern England. Examples of the local decrease due to building development occur at Colindale and Edgware, where none bred after 1925, and at Finchley, where a pair bred until 1927 (E. H. Warmington). In Richmond Park a decrease from 20–25 pairs in 1935 and 1936 to about 9 pairs in 1953 has been attributed to extensive lopping of old timber containing nesting holes.

At present the common redstart is a distinctly local breeder in the more well-timbered parts of the Area. The nearest breeding localities to the centre, apart from the Hampstead record already mentioned, are St. Paul's Cray Common, Petts Wood, Shirley Hills and Richmond Park in the south, and Bushy Park, Stanmore Common, near Whitewebbs Park, Enfield and Epping and Hainault Forests in the north. The redstart having abandoned its habit of nesting in garden sheds, its present prime requirement from a habitat is trees with suitable holes. Hence it is usually found in woods, both closed and open, and in parks and park-like country with plenty of old trees, also on heaths and commons. Since 1920 it has definitely not been a suburban bird, in contrast to some other woodland species, such as the greater spotted woodpecker, which has moved into the suburbs as the redstart moved out.

On migration, in both spring and autumn, the redstart is seen in a good many places, including Inner London and the more open parts of the North Downs, where it does not breed. In most years redstarts are first seen in the middle third of April, but very occasionally some have appeared as early as the end of March: Walthamstow Reservoirs, March 17th, 1928; East Dulwich, March 28th, 1909; Richmond Park, March 30th, 1923 and March 31st, 1948. As with most passerine summer visitors, records of departure are many fewer than records of arrival, but the middle third of September seems to be the normal departure period, with a good many staying over till the last third and a few till the beginning of the following month. The three latest dates are: Chingford, October 15th, 1943; West Molesey, October 18th, 1924; and King George V Reservoir, October 28th to November 1st, 1938. Early and late dates in this species present special difficulties in view of the possibility of confusion with the black redstart, but since 1940 at any rate most observers have been conscious of the special care needed to differentiate the two species, and all the above dates are vouched for by reliable observers.

BLACK REDSTART, *Phoenicurus ochruros* (Gmelin). Summer visitor, perhaps occasionally resident; passage migrant and winter visitor of indeterminate status; local.

London is the metropolis not only of man but of the black redstart in the British Isles. In 1926, three years after the beginning of its continuous history as a British breeding species, the black redstart began to breed in Middlesex, and in no year since then have fewer than two pairs bred in the Area. The story begins with three pairs taking up their abode within the Palace of Engineering in the year after the end of the Wembley Exhibition, and nesting on breeze-slab ledges about 18 feet from the ground every year until increasing activity due to war work brought their tenancy to an end after the 1941 breeding season. So far as is known three pairs bred in each year between 1926 and 1941, except in 1937, when there were four pairs. Meanwhile, there was an isolated instance of breeding in a shed at Woolwich Arsenal in 1933, while a cock bird took up territory on the Natural History Museum at South Kensington between April 27th and August 16th, 1927, reappearing briefly on September 16th of the same year. For a short time in the spring (April 30th to May 16th) it was joined by a hen.

The existence of the breeding colony at Wembley, which did not become generally known until 1944, throws an interesting light on the possible origin of the birds which colonised Inner London from 1936 onwards. The first of these was detected by E. M.

Nicholson singing from the roofs of tall buildings near his home off the Horseferry Road, Westminster. For six weeks (April 29th to June 12th, 1936) this bird frequented a neighbourhood where many building operations were in progress, while about two miles away a hen black redstart flew into one of the rooms of the Natural History Museum on May 18th. No black redstarts were reported in Inner London in 1937 or 1938, though the fact that males were seen at Edmonton sewage farm on May 8th, 1938, and at St. John's Wood on May 22nd, 1938, shows that there were some wandering about the Area away from Wembley.

The continuous colonisation of Inner London began, so far as is known, with a cock bird which sang on and around the London University building in Bloomsbury from May 20th to June 22nd, 1939; on June 14th it was seen in company with another bird whose sex was not determined. In 1940 came the first breeding record for Inner London, when a pair brought off two broods within the precincts of Westminster Abbey, and at least five other cocks were reported to be holding territories. The Westminster pair returned in 1941, and a pair bred also in a bombed building in Wandsworth, while four other males held territories in various parts of Inner London. It was perhaps not a complete accident that the year which saw the frustration of the Wembley colony, 1942, proved to be the *annus mirabilis* of the black redstart in Inner London. In addition to pairs breeding at Cripplegate in the City, at Notting Hill and at Wandsworth, at least 19 and perhaps 24 other singing males held territories in various parts of the London built-up area, the great majority of them in the City and Westminster. There seems little doubt that if so many ornithologists had not been otherwise engaged in that year a good many of these singing males would have been proved to possess mates and nests.

There is no space to follow the story of the black redstart as a breeding species hereafter year by year, but the basic facts are shown in the following table:—

Year	No. of breeding pairs	No. of additional singing males
1926	3	–
1927	3	1
1928	3	–
1929	3	–
1930	3	–
1931	3	–
1932	3	–
1933	4	–
1934	3	–
1935	3	–
1936	3	1
1937	4	–
1938	3	1–2
1939	3	1
1940	4	6
1941	5	4
1942	3	19–24
1943	3	18–19
1944	5	12
1945	2–3	10–11
1946	5–6	6–7
1947	6	5–6
1948	8–9	Over 20
1949	14–15	13
1950	15	6
1951	10–11	4–5

After 1951 observation decreased to such an extent that comparative figures would only be misleading.

Thus by the end of the half-century the black redstart appears to have established itself more firmly as a breeding species in Inner London than in any other town in England, except perhaps Dover. Outside London it breeds regularly in one or more of the towns of the south-east coast, occasionally in towns on the East Anglian coast, and exceptionally in other towns; singing males have also held territories as far west and north as Plymouth, Bristol, Cardiff, Liverpool and Edinburgh.

In Inner London, according to N. J. P. Wadley, who has made a special study of the bird's breeding biology, males arrive at the end of March and females in early April, both sexes departing some time between late September and late October. The favourite sites for nests are the upper corners of windows, holes in ceilings or crevices due to missing bricks—all in bombed buildings. The nest may be at any level from six feet below the pavement to the roof of a sixth or seventh floor. The normal clutch is 4–5, but 3 and 6 have both occasionally been recorded. The main food in London is caterpillars, ants, flies and soldier beetles, and, less frequently moths and butterflies. Seeds are eaten more in autumn.

From 1945 onwards the majority of black redstarts' nests in Inner London were always to be found in the large open bombed area around the church of St. Giles, Cripplegate, but throughout the bird's history as a London breeding bird it has from time to time nested in or near Westminster Abbey, the Temple, Fetter Lane, and various other localities, mostly within the City, and all with extensive areas either of garden or of bombed site close at hand. Away from Inner London, pairs have nested from time to time at Wandsworth, Croydon Aerodrome, Beddington cement works, and in 1944 again at Wembley. The new Power Station at Croydon was used by one pair before it was complete, when only about half the exterior brickwork had been done and much of the steel frame was still exposed. However, the constancy with which they stick to the central area, especially the Cripplegate district, and the relative infrequency with which either singing males or breeding pairs have been reported from either the inner or the outer suburbs, remain among the most puzzling features of their spread. It is clear that they need a ledge of some kind to breed on, but while the bombed areas supply a super-abundance of suitable sites, such sites exist almost equally abundantly all over the built-up area. The other thing which the bombed areas provide is an open, rubbly ground surface, where the bird can find ants, flies and other insect food. Again, however, there are similar patches of waste ground and derelict building sites all over the built-up area, and a good many pairs (e.g. Westminster 1940, Cambridge 1937–38, Ipswich 1939) have managed to breed successfully in ordinary unbombed towns, as they do of course over a wide area of western Europe. It is clear that for some years back the black redstart has been gradually infiltrating south-east England, and that a particularly accentuated wave of colonisation in 1942 (helped perhaps by a few birds displaced from Wembley) happened to coincide with conditions in central London that form a kind of black redstarts' paradise. When the rebuilding of the City is complete, it will be most interesting to see if the black redstarts are able to adapt themselves to ordinary town conditions.

Before 1926 the black redstart was only a somewhat scarce migrant in the London Area. It had been seen only sixteen times in all, of which ten were between February 20th and April 10th, an interesting contrast to other inland districts which showed a predominance of autumn reports with a marked peak in the first ten days of November. The most interesting individual records between 1900 and 1926 were an early one at Caterham on September 25th, 1912, a bird which wintered at Hammersmith between December 15th, 1925, and February 13th, 1926, and what may have been an advance-guard of the later invasion, a cock singing at Tadworth on May 20th, 1922.

It was to be expected that this situation would change when the bird began to breed, and the following table shows what happened up to April, 1926, and afterwards:—

Month	No. recorded in 1900–26	No. recorded in 1926–50 away from known breeding sites or occupied territories
September	1	4
October	2	7–8
November	1	10–11
December	1	9
January	1	11
February	3	8
March	5	18
April	3	18

It will be seen that there is still little evidence of autumn passage migration, though the big increase in March and April suggests that there is still a spring passage independent of the birds which are returning to their breeding sites within the Area. The facts strongly suggest that a few of the birds that breed in the Area also winter in it, and in support of this can be cited the number of birds that actually pass the winter in one fairly restricted locality. Three times within our period birds have wintered on the Cripplegate bombed site:— (1) a male from November 28th, 1946, to February 28th, 1947 (the severest winter of the century), a bird whose plumage corresponded closely with that of a cock occupying a breeding territory in London Wall from late March onwards; (2) a cock and a female or immature male which both wintered from November 1949, to February, 1950, the cock later taking up a territory in Jewin Crescent; (3) a cock seen from November, 1950, to January, 1951, in Jewin Crescent, and which was perhaps the same that later occupied the breeding territory there from March 1st onwards, and a brown bird, probably an immature male, which was seen throughout the 1950–51 winter from November to February. There seems little room for doubt that these were all birds that had either occupied territories or (less likely) been born in the Cripplegate area in the seasons prior to those in which they wintered.

There are various other records of birds seen once or for periods of up to three months near or along the Thames in the Hammersmith district. One was the bird seen along the river during the winter before the black redstarts first bred at Wembley; other records at Hendon and Little Stanmore, and also the "redstarts" recorded by T. H. Harrisson at Harrow in October and November, 1928, may well have derived from the Wembley colony. Single birds have also wintered at Mortlake and at Barn Elms since the establishment of that colony but before black redstarts began to breed in central London, and it is obviously impossible to do more than speculate on their origin. At Beddington there were isolated records on October 24th, 1931, and November 18th 1933, and there are instances of birds spending periods of from one to three months in the winters of 1938–39, 1945–46, 1946–47 and 1950–51. The later ones suggest that local birds may have stayed the winter, as they have been seen only two fields away from their breeding sites at the nearby power station and cement works, and this inevitably raises suspicion of breeding in the district at a much earlier date than was recorded.

The only definite evidence of dispersal of locally-bred birds is provided by the recovery at New Southgate on July 26th, 1943, of a juvenile ringed at the Charterhouse only six weeks previously.

NIGHTINGALE, *Luscinia megarhynchos* Brehm. Summer resident and passage migrant; still nests in good numbers where the habitat is suitable.

It is little more than a century since the nightingale nested in Hyde Park, Regent's Park and in other bushy places within five miles of St. Paul's Cathedral. But by 1900 the spread of London (together, perhaps, with the depredations of the bird-catchers) had pushed it out in the north to beyond Hampstead, where it last nested about 1899, and in the south to Lee, where it nested in 1905. Since then the nightingale has continued to recede as London has advanced, and the records are full of accounts, which it would be tedious to detail, of its disappearance as long-favoured haunts were cut down and urbanised. In 1950, the nearest breeding place to the centre was Wimbledon Common, nine miles or so from St. Paul's. But away from the built-up areas, the status of the nightingale has changed very little, and it still abounds on many of the bushy commons and in open woodland with thick undergrowth. London spreads its tentacles a little farther to the south than to the north and it is perhaps easier to find nightingales, close in, in Essex and Hertfordshire than in the nearer parts of Surrey and Kent. Nevertheless, nightingales are common enough in the belt of country between the southern fringe of London (Walton, Epsom, Purley, Beckenham) and the North Downs, and on the Downs themselves up to about 400 feet.

The first arrival of nightingales in the Area normally occurs in the second half of April; the average of 38 years (not consecutive) for first arrivals south of the Thames is April 16th and the average of 48 years for the north is two days later, April 18th. The earliest dates recorded are March 22nd, 1901 (Winchmore Hill, P. J. Hanson) and March 26th, 1908 (Barnes Common, S. W. Golding, *Country-Side*, 6:334). Both of these dates are earlier than those recorded in *The Handbook*.

The main arrival is in early May and at this time nightingales are frequently heard singing in bushy places away from their breeding haunts. But even on migration they occur only rarely in Inner London—'nightingales' reported in song in London streets and squares usually turn out to be some other species or, as on one occasion at least, a gramophone record! The only satisfactory record of a nightingale in Inner London since the Second World War is of one singing near Winfield House, Regent's Park, on April 26th, 1950.

The nightingale is a skulking species with a very short song period, and the date of departure from the Area is far from certain. There are a very few records of birds seen in August and two only in September, the latest being September 18th, 1949, on which date Howard Bentham saw one on Walton Heath.

BLUETHROAT, *Cyanosylvia svecica* (L.). Rare passage migrant.

There have been two certain occurrences of bluethroats in the London Area since 1900, and in one of these the sub-species was determined. On March 4th, 1942, M. G. Ridpath had an excellent view of a male of the red-spotted form at Aldenham Reservoir (*B.B.*, 35:273) and on September 19th and 20th, 1936, a number of observers saw an immature bird at Walthamstow reservoirs.

In the *Zoologist* (62:263) a bluethroat was reported to have been seen by E. C. Chubb on Sheen Common on June 17th, 1904 (cf. *B.B.*, 1:55), but on subsequent enquiries made by Gordon Dalgliesh, the writer admitted that he had probably been mistaken (H. Bentham, *in litt.*).

ROBIN, *Erithacus rubecula* (L.). Common resident; some evidence of passage migration in the autumn.

The breeding status of the robin in the London Area is not unlike that of the blackbird and chaffinch; it is common and widespread in all but the most heavily built-up areas, the marshlands and a few other places where the habitat is totally unsuitable. In Inner London, the robin nests in most of the parks and, outside the breeding season, it occurs in some of the larger squares and on the bombed sites. There is little doubt that the enormous London population of cats is partly responsible for the poor breeding success of robins in the built-up areas—A. Holte Macpherson (1929) said that comparatively few of the young bred in the parks reach maturity owing to the depredations of cats. In the suburbs, the robin is common wherever there is sufficient open space and cover; nest sites include shelves in outbuildings, ivy or creeper growing on houses or garden walls and holes in banks or trees. As in other districts, London robins have been recorded nesting in a wide variety of "unusual" situations—nests inside buildings include one in the greenhouses in Kew Gardens, in the dressing-room of a football club and on a ledge in a public lavatory.

The food of robins in London is much as elsewhere; they are, of course, frequent visitors to bird tables for kitchen scraps and bread crumbs. A more unusual diet was recorded by P. F. Bunyard (*Bull*. B.O.C., XLIV:46) who observed a robin at Fortis Green in 1925 frequently feeding on putty, which appeared to pass through it in the form of undigested pellets.

Judging by the ringing returns London robins seem to be almost entirely sedentary. All the adults ringed and subsequently recovered have been found at or very near the place of ringing—as an example, a bird ringed at Streatham in October, 1921, was re-trapped there later in the same month, in June of the next year, in September and October, 1923 and, finally, in April, 1925. Eight nestling or juvenile robins have been recovered and of these seven were found where ringed; a juvenile ringed at Woodford Green in early August, 1930, was re-trapped eight times up to May, 1931. The eighth juvenile, however, was a notable exception; it was ringed at Woodford Green on May 10th, 1938, and was found in France, at Guéthary, Basses Pyrénées, on September 16th of the same year. It was only the fourth British ringed robin to be recovered abroad.

In the autumn and winter, robins are frequently seen in suburban gardens and parks and other places where they have not bred. It seems likely that this apparent increase is caused by a very local scatter of resident adults and young after the breeding season, rather than by an immigration of British robins from other areas. Lack, from an analysis of the ringing returns, has shown in *The Life of the Robin* (1943) that extremely few British robins migrate more than a few miles at any stage of their life. In some years, however, there does seem to be a definite migration of robins through the Area in September and October. Rudge Harding in *Country-Side* for February, 1921, records a large influx in St. James's Park on September 20th, 1920, and states that the birds were gone by the 27th; L. Parmenter noted a sudden increase at Beddington sewage farm in September, 1932, and T. Bispham saw a small but definite passage along the Thames tow-path at Barnes on October 11th, 1943. At this time of the year robins of the Continental race (*Erithacus r.rubecula*) are passing down the East Coast, in some years in very large numbers, and it is not unlikely that some of these may come inland as far as London. Most observers would be chary of identifying Continental robins in the field and the only positive evidence of their occurrence is from Sevenoaks, just outside our area, where Dr. J. M. Harrison obtained specimens and confirmed their presence among unusual numbers of robins in the winter of 1940–41.

GRASSHOPPER WARBLER, *Locustella naevia* (Boddaert). Summer visitor, extremely local; also uncommon passage migrant.

For no other breeding bird in the London Area is our information so incomplete as for the grasshopper warbler. It is such a skulking bird that the overwhelming majority of the records consist of "heard singing" only. Records of nests found are very few indeed, and all too often one is left puzzling about a bird that has been heard singing for a period of two or three weeks. Whatever the status of these records, the statements of Bucknill and Ticehurst about the relative abundance of the bird in northern Surrey and north-west Kent in the 1890's suggest that it has decreased substantially in that part of the Area in the past sixty years. North of the Thames, however, Glegg's caution about accepting breeding records for Essex and Middlesex leaves his successors in the dark as to whether there has been little change or a genuine decrease. It is significant at any rate that J. & G. D. Cranfield used to know the bird as a regular visitor to certain parts of Enfield Chase up to, but not since, 1924.

At the present day there are only three localities in the Area where one can go with a reasonable expectation of hearing the grasshopper warbler in the breeding season: Ashtead Common, the Bookham Commons and the Colne valley between Uxbridge and Rickmansworth. Though nests are not found every year in these districts there is no reason to suppose that breeding does not occur annually. Grasshopper warblers were regular at Ruislip until 1942 when the nesting area was bulldozed; nowhere else have they even been heard regularly in the breeding season over a period of years, though in most years a few are heard reeling somewhere in the Area on spring passage or in the early part of the breeding season, and in 1954 three pairs were suspected of nesting at Brookman's Park.

The habitat favoured by the grasshopper warbler, rough tussocky and brambly heathland, and marshy ground with low scrub, is perhaps the most vulnerable of all habitats in the neighbourhood of London, and the cultivation of large parts of both Epsom and Ruislip Commons during the recent war had a disastrous effect. Thus H. J. Hoffmann reports that on Epsom Common the population decreased from 15–20 pairs in 1938 to only four pairs in 1948.

In certain parts of the Area the grasshopper warbler is exceptionally scarce. Thus the only record for the Kentish part of the Area in the past twenty years, is of one singing near Sidcup on July 10th, 1946, although, according to Ticehurst, it seems to have been not uncommon in 1909. In Essex too, away from the Lea—Stort valleys and Epping Forest the only recent records are for Upminster on April 30th, 1946, and for Berwick Pond near Rainham on three dates in May, 1949. There are no records at all for Inner London, though birds have twice turned up on migration at Wimbledon in the past ten years, and in April, 1942, a pair were seen at Dulwich.

In many years the grasshopper warbler is not recorded until May, but the last third of April is probably its true arrival period. It has only three times appeared before April 21st, the earliest of these dates being April 14th, 1948, at Bookham. About the departure of the grasshopper warbler we know next to nothing. There are very few records after the end of July, the latest being for Beddington sewage farm where a grasshopper warbler was seen on September 4th, 1953, when there was an influx of warblers after a period of wind from the north-west. The last date for a breeding locality is August 19th.

REED WARBLER, *Acrocephalus scirpaceus* (Hermann). Summer visitor, local, but common and even abundant in suitable localities.

There is no evidence of other than local fluctuations in the reed warbler populations of the Area since 1900, though in the period since 1800 there has been a substantial decline in the numbers of a bird that was once common along the Thames at Battersea, on the marshes of Deptford and Bermondsey, and among the flooded ballast-pits of Hammersmith and Shepherd's Bush. Though it will also nest among the hairy willow-herb (*Epilobium hirsutum*), the reed-mace (*Typha latifolia*), and other tall marsh plants, the distribution of the reed warbler is very largely that of the reed (*Phragmites communis*), which is its favourite nesting site. Hence the bird is found along river valleys, around ponds and gravel pits and on sewage farms. It is perhaps nowhere more abundant than along the Thames marshes downstream from Dagenham and Plumstead; one ten-acre reed-bed on Abbey Wood marshes was estimated to hold 130–150 pairs in 1949. It is also tolerably common in the valley of the Lea where there were about a hundred pairs at gravel pits and sewage farms in 1954. Until the last war, when the vegetation was drastically cut down, there was a flourishing colony in an unusual site at the Waltham-stow reservoirs where in 1930, for example, eleven nests were found, all in privet or elder (*Essex Nat.*, 24:194–5). A notable gravel pit colony was the one at Mayesbrook Park near Barking, where as recently as 1949 there were twenty pairs or so in an area of reeds not over two acres in extent .The reed warbler is also found along almost the whole length of the Colne valley, which is studded with gravel pits. On the other hand, it is scarce or unknown, except as an uncommon passage migrant, over most of the relatively waterless North Downs, and in the rural parts of Hertfordshire away from the valleys of the Lea and the Colne.

In Inner London the reed warbler was once a not too infrequent passage migrant in the parks, but its reported occurrences have fallen off in recent years; there have been only two since 1928. Until a misguided local authority cleaned the Leg of Mutton Pond on Hampstead Heath of "rushes" (presumably reed-mace) about thirty years ago, a few reed warblers used to breed there regularly, but since 1930 only a few passage birds have been heard singing there, the last of them in May, 1949. On Chiswick Eyot the reed warbler held out longer, for a pair bred there as recently as 1944, and in the last few years a pair has bred at a small pond at Barn Elms on the opposite side of the river.

The reed warbler is a late migrant, the advance guard usually appearing in the last third of April and the main body in the first third of May. The earliest date on record is April 14th, 1935, at Warlingham. At the other end of the season so few departure dates have been recorded that generalisation is difficult. In most years the last bird is seen in August, but a good many have straggled into September, and there are three records for October and one for November, all at Beddington or Mitcham, viz. October 9th, 1938, October 14th, 1943, October 15th, 1944, and November 6th, 1938. This last is ten days later than the latest dated cited in *The Handbook of British Birds*. Both the late records in 1938 were made by Dr. G. Beven who is very familiar with the species.

MARSH WARBLER, *Acrocephalus palustris* (Bechstein). Very rare passage migrant. Has bred occasionally.

In the first few years of the present century there were three records of marsh warblers breeding in the country around Staines. In June, 1903, a nest was found at Harefield by W. H. Smith and was shown to J. E. Harting who confirmed its identity (*Field*, 102:138). In June, 1907, G. W. Kerr found two nests both with four eggs in an osier bed near Thorpe, on the Surrey side of the Thames (*B.B.*, 1:186). Two years later, near Wraysbury, slightly outside the limits of our Area, the same observer found a nest in a dense nettle bed containing two eggs of the marsh warbler and one of the cuckoo, and a fortnight afterwards E. Pettitt found another a few yards away in which were four marsh warbler's and one cuckoo's egg (*Zoologist*, 67:397).

One must assume that these well-known observers, being constantly on the alert for the re-appearance of marsh warblers at these several breeding sites, would have put on record any other cases of nesting known to them, and therefore it would seem that the occurrences listed above represent no more than sporadic breeding. The next occasion was in 1931 when a pair nested at Chalfont Park (*Report* of Oxford Orn. Soc. for 1931, p.45). In the following year, at "a locality in Middlesex" a male was seen and heard by several observers from June 4th until July 2nd but no nest was found (Glegg, 1935). On

June 6th, 1949, J. F. Burton heard and saw a male marsh warbler on Plumstead Marshes and in 1952 a pair was watched on Swanscombe marshes feeding two young: an empty nest nearby was identified as belonging to this species.

One can call to mind many places within the Area that would appear to fulfil the habitat requirements of this uncommon species as given in *The Handbook,* but, although the possibility of pairs being present in such likely places should never be overlooked the distribution of the marsh warbler in south-eastern England is extremely local: only in one part of Kent and at a few localities in Sussex has it been found at all regularly during our period.

There are only two other records. E. K. Ford identified as a marsh warbler a bird watched almost daily from April 24th to May 8th, 1906, near the Pen Ponds, Richmond Park (*Zoologist,* 1907:98). The editors of *British Birds,* however, treated the record with reserve on account of the very early date on which the bird was first seen, and placed it in square brackets (*B.B.,* 1:84). On June 5th, 1924, H. G. Alexander saw and heard a marsh warbler in Kensington Gardens near the Long Water (*B.B.,* 18:242).

SEDGE WARBLER, *Acrocephalus schoenobaenus* (L.). Summer resident, widespread wherever there is water; also passage migrant.

Several observers record a decrease in the numbers of the sedge warbler during this century, but it does not appear to be a very serious one. What has mainly happened is a retreat from places now built over. Thus in 1908 it used to breed along the stream running northward from Hampstead Lane to East Finchley; in 1901 and perhaps other years it bred in Dulwich Park; as late as 1927–30 it was breeding on the Brent at Twyford Abbey till the river was both diverted and polluted; at least till 1934 and possibly later it bred on Chiswick Eyot. The disappearance of the sedge warbler as a breeding bird from Epsom sewage farm about 1938, recorded by Howard Bentham in 1948, is more difficult to account for, and indeed later observations suggest that a pair or two may still breed there in some years.

The sedge warbler is more catholic than the reed warbler in its habitat requirements, and will nest in hedges or thick herbage near lakes, reservoirs, ponds, rivers, streams, brooks, sewage farms, indeed almost any kind of water or even damp patches of ground. It will also occasionally, and more often than its congener, nest right away from water. Apart from the North Downs, there can be few square miles so waterless as to hold no breeding sedge warblers, except of course in Inner London and the suburbs. On the Abbey Wood and Plumstead marshes, however, where most of the available cover consists of reed-beds, it is less common than the reed warbler, which is dominant in this habitat.

In Inner London the sedge warbler is a passage migrant only, being reported not infrequently in spring and rather less often in autumn, when its presence is not betrayed by its song. It appears mostly in the parks, but also from time to time on the bombed sites; one record on an odd date is of a bird seen by L. R. Evans at Camberwell on July 24th, 1945. In spring the advance guard of sedge warblers arrive during the middle third of April (earliest date, April 6th, 1951, at Godstone), and the main body appear during the last third of the month. In autumn, September sedge warblers are not at all unusual, and there are nearly a dozen records for the first third of October. The two latest stragglers were recorded at Ruxley gravel pit near Sidcup on October 16th, 1949, and in Richmond Park on October 23rd, 1938. The latter date is only three days before the latest one given in *The Handbook of British Birds.* Evidence from ringing returns as to the source of passage migrants is scanty, consisting of one ringed at Bedford on July 14th, 1948, and recovered at Greenford on the following August 31st, and one ringed at

Driffield in East Yorkshire on June 11th, 1949, and recovered at Sidcup in August of the same year.

AQUATIC WARBLER, *Acrocephalus paludicola* (Vieillot).
    An aquatic warbler was seen at close range and satisfactorily identified on the causeway of Staines reservoirs by Donald Gunn on August 6th, 1924 (*Field.*, 144:640). The only other record is of one at Perry Oaks on August 25th and 26th, 1951, which was first seen by H. C. Holme and later by several other observers (*B.B.*, 45:416).

MELODIOUS WARBLER, *Hippolais polyglotta* (Vieillot)
    or
ICTERINE WARBLER, *Hippolais icterina* (Vieillot)
    A bird which was evidently one or other of these two very similar warblers was seen near Connaught Water, Epping Forest, on April 25th, 1948, by D. Lea and J. R. Spencer. Unfortunately the description of the song was not conclusive, as it contained characteristics of both species, and it was not possible, therefore, to assign the bird definitely to either species (cf. *L.B.R.*, 13:13).

BLACKCAP, *Sylvia atricapilla* (L.). Summer visitor, widespread and fairly common.
    The status of the blackcap is very similar to that of its close relative the garden warbler, but the blackcap does not seem to require such thick cover and is consequently more able to live in some suburban gardens and tends to nest rather nearer to the centre of London. Thus in recent years it has bred, at least in one or two years, in Charlton, Blackheath, Greenwich Park, Streatham Common, Camberwell, Barnes and, in Inner London, in Holland House grounds. In 1953 two-three pairs bred in a derelict garden area in St. John's Wood Park, and there are normally about 12 pairs on Hampstead Heath and in Ken Wood. It is not possible to make any general statement about the relative abundance of the blackcap and garden warbler, for both species fluctuate in numbers from year to year, nor is it necessarily the case that one is common when the other is scarce, though this sometimes does happen.
    As a migrant the blackcap arrives distinctly earlier, though it does not stay much later than the garden warbler. The first birds may be seen or heard either in the last third of March or the first third of April, the main body arriving later in the month. The earliest dates are:– Bickley, March 20th, 1948; Richmond Park, March 21st, 1948; Walton-on-Thames, March 22nd, 1938; Reigate, March 23rd, 1937. Some of these early birds produce remarkably early nests, such as a clutch of three at Sutton on April 29th, 1935, and one of five at West Kempton reservoir on April 30th, 1950, which were two or three weeks ahead of schedule. At the other end of the season, blackcaps seem to stay well on into September and even into the first few days of October, but records are fewer as the bird is silent at this time of year. The latest records are for Banstead Heath on October 6th, 1949, and Tooting Common on October 21st, 1901.
    Wintering in Britain is by no means uncommon in this species, even so far north as Scotland, and it is rather surprising that only four instances are on record for the London Area during our period:— two hens at St. Albans daily in February, 1902; and males at Croxley Green from February 27th, 1936 onwards; at East Twickenham several times between January 20th and February 22nd, 1945, and at Catford from December 25th, 1952, to January 15th, 1953.

GARDEN WARBLER, *Sylvia borin* (Boddaert). Summer visitor, widespread and fairly common.
    Now, as in 1900, the garden warbler is to be found throughout the Area wherever

there are bushes and bramble-brakes, and especially in parks, shrubberies, large gardens, woods and commons. It is not particularly numerous in the ordinary agricultural countryside, with fields and hedges. It has, of course, in some places retreated before the advance of the builder; thus it appears no longer to breed at Lee or on Tooting Common, as it did at the outset of our period. Its present inner limit towards central London is the ring of large open spaces which features so largely in these pages: Bostall Woods, Shooters Hill, Dulwich Woods, Wimbledon Common, Richmond Park, Ham Common (but not Kew Gardens) and Epping Forest. Garden warblers bred in the Hampstead Heath, Ken Wood area until 1950 when there were about five pairs, but they have not nested since, although blackcaps are still well established. In 1953, however, a pair was seen on July 17th in St. John's Wood Park with two juveniles.

In Inner London it is an almost regular passage migrant in the parks in spring, and doubtless because it does not normally sing at that season is reported rather less often in autumn in the parks, on bombed sites or in City churchyards. The first stragglers of the spring migrants appear between April 8th and 10th in some years, the earliest being one seen by Miss D. A. Rook on Epsom Common on March 27th, 1954; normally the advance guard is heard in the middle third of April, while the main body arrive at the end of the month or at the beginning of May. In autumn there are no records after the middle third of September, except for a bird heard singing at Gilwell Park by Miss A. Hibbert-Ware up to October 10th, 1930, and one at Stone on October 17th, 1954. The only instance of a garden warbler apparently wintering in the British Isles comes from the London Area. On February 27th, 1945, G. Warburg heard subsong from a bird in a garden in Hampstead Garden Suburb, and on March 10th he heard the bird again in full song (*B.B.*, 38:255). After the publication of his note a policeman told him that he had heard a warbler singing near the same place in January. The record is the more remarkable in that the weather of January, 1945, was severe. The previous earliest date for the garden warbler in the British Isles was March 20th.

WHITETHROAT, *Sylvia communis* Latham. Summer visitor and passage migrant; common and widespread except in built-up areas.

Apart from the retreat before the advance of the builder that characterises the distribution of the majority of the breeding birds of the Area, there is little evidence of any change in the status or relative abundance of the common whitethroat since 1900. Like many other birds, it is subject to inexplicable local fluctuations in numbers. Thus Ticehurst (1909) records that it was then less numerous in the Sevenoaks district than ten years previously, and J. M. Harrison, writing of the same district in *The South-Eastern Bird Report* for 1940, reported that in that year it was present in unusual numbers and outnumbered the lesser whitethroat, to which it had been inferior in numbers for some years. It is distinctly unusual for the common not to outnumber the lesser whitethroat in any moderately rural district in the London Area.

The whitethroat's habitat preference is for low tangled vegetation, bramble brakes, beds of nettles or other coarse herbage. The bird may be found breeding almost wherever there is an undisturbed patch of such vegetation in the Area, except within a ring constituted by the following places where it breeds or has bred within the past ten years: Greenwich Marshes, Greenwich Park (1947), Shooters Hill, Eltham Park, Dulwich Woods, Streatham Common, Mitcham Common, Wimbledon Common, Richmond Park, Hanger Hill, Horsendon Hill, Hampstead Heath, Ilford, Mayesbrook Park. Inside this boundary the whitethroat is only a passage migrant, commoner in spring than in autumn (or at any rate more commonly recorded, because more vocal), and is seen especially in parks, on commons and bombed sites, and more rarely in gardens. As late as 1928, however, E. B. Evans stated that it was fairly common in summer on

Tooting Bec Common. In 1924 A. Holte Macpherson thought that a pair might have nested in Kensington Gardens, and in 1953 a pair bred successfully in Regent's Park.

The last third of April is the time when most London bird-watchers see their first whitethroat, but not a few arrive during the middle third, and a few even at the beginning of the month: early dates, Cheshunt, April 3rd, 1940; Cripplegate, April 5th, 1947. At the other end of the season there is some evidence of a passage movement during August and early September. Stragglers are seen until the end of September, and there are four October records, the two latest being at Harrow on October 12th, 1939, and at Edmonton sewage farm on October 14th, 1934. One of the only two winter records of the whitethroat for the British Isles relates to the Area: on January 17th, 1948, J. A Bailey saw a cock bird in a hedgerow at Poyle (*B.B.*, 43:85).

Three nestlings ringed in the Area have been recovered abroad as follows:—

Ringed West Byfleet	26.5.23	Recovered Portugal	4.10.29
„ Ruislip	6.7.50	„ Nr. Cherbourg	6.5.51
„ Upminster	2.6.52	„ Logrono, Spain	23.8.52

LESSER WHITETHROAT, *Sylvia curruca* (L.). Summer visitor, widespread but rather sparsely distributed; also passage migrant especially in spring.

The determination of the status of the lesser whitethroat is more than usually dependent on the unsafe criterion of the presence of singing males during the breeding season. However, the proportion of nests found to singing males holding territories is much too small to reflect biological reality, so we are obliged to accept the singing males as a rough and ready guide. There is no evidence of any general change in the status of the lesser whitethroat in the Area during our period. Unlike the common whitethroat, it is a bird of scrubland and requires fairly tall trees for its song-posts. In more rural districts it frequents the edges of woods, tall straggly hedgerows, well-timbered heaths and commons with plenty of rough undergrowth, and similar places.

Though its inner ring of regular breeding haunts does not differ substantially from that of the common whitethroat, a few pairs are sometimes present closer in to the centre, and definite breeding records are available for Holland House grounds in 1915, Kensington Gardens in 1921, Tooting Common in 1926, Wandsworth Common in 1942 and Finchley in 1951. The bird has been heard singing in the grounds of Holland House in so many other years that there seems little doubt that between 1910 and 1940 at any rate it was breeding there fairly regularly. Males have also held territories in Kensington Gardens in more than one other breeding season. Lesser whitethroats bred regularly on Hampstead Heath until about 1946, and are still present in the breeding season in some years.

It seems probable, from the large number of records in late April and early May, that a good many lesser whitethroats pass through the Area on their way further north at that season; in autumn, however, the silent and skulking habits of the bird are less likely to bring it to the attention of a bird-watcher. Only stragglers arrive during the middle third of April (early dates, Springfield Park, April 11th, 1926; Downe, April 13th, 1936), the main body appearing towards the end of the month and in May. In autumn there is a scatter of the comparatively few records right through September, and one was seen by G. Taylor on Hampstead Heath on October 4th, 1951. Glegg (1935) cited three October records for Middlesex, without saying whether they were before or after 1900.

DARTFORD WARBLER, *Sylvia undata* (Boddaert). Formerly very local breeding species in Surrey, but not recorded at all since 1939.

Once resident on most commons to the south of London and on several to the north of it, the Dartford warbler within the present century has bred only in three localities in the Area, at Batchworth (Herts) about May, 1904, and on Wimbledon Common and Walton Heath on several occasions. It has not bred or been seen in the breeding season in Kew Gardens since about 1880, on Wandsworth Common since 1881 or on Hayes Common since 1891. In 1901 Bucknill and Gurney, writing in the *Zoologist*, considered the Dartford warbler to be extinct on Walton and Reigate Heaths, but in May, 1904, one was seen near Colley Hill, and in April, 1908, Howard Bentham saw a cock on Limpsfield Common. Shortly afterwards the bird was discovered on two separate Surrey commons. After watching two or three pairs for several years E. G. Waddilove found a nest in a furze-bush on Putney Heath in 1910, and the birds were present in each subsequent year till at least 1913. This was an old haunt, as the birds were seen several times on the adjacent Wimbledon Common in the 1890's.

On Walton and Banstead Heaths Bentham saw one or two birds on seven different occasions between October 24th and December 13th during the years 1912–14, while Captain C. S. Meares disturbed several birds during manœuvres on Walton Heath on many occasions during the autumn of 1915. The bird seems to have disappeared again after the hard winter of 1916–17, for Bentham records no more till 1927, when he saw one pair, and 1928, when a pair certainly nested. The 1929–30 winter seems to have exterminated them, and the next record for Walton Heath is of a pair, evidently nesting, in July, 1933. In April, 1935, Bentham found two nests. Two pairs nested again in 1936, and in the following year three cocks were seen on April 23rd. In 1938 no fewer than eight pairs were located in the breeding season, but the cold snap of December, 1938, appears to be reflected in the reduction in 1939, when there were three pairs on the adjacent Headley Heath, two cocks on Walton Heath in March, and a single bird there on July 4th. With the three hard winters from 1939–40 to 1941–42, and the ploughing up of parts of the heath, the curtain descended once more, and none have been seen since.

In October, 1935, a cock Dartford warbler was again seen on Wimbledon Common. In 1936 a pair brought off two broods of four young each, and at least one bird stayed on the Common until the end of December. The following year a cock returned in mid-March, and sang at one time from the top of a Lombardy poplar on Putney Heath; it remained till mid-June without finding a mate. A cock, possibly the same bird, was seen in Richmond Park and on Wimbledon Common between December 19th, 1937, and February 25th, 1938. In August, 1938, a female turned up at Wimbledon again, and a cock also appeared in October and was seen with the hen, but neither appears to have survived the blizzard of December, 1938.

Wanderers, perhaps from Walton Heath or Wimbledon Common, were seen on Epsom Common in the autumns of 1937–38:— a pair on October 26th, and a single bird up to December 24th, 1937, and again one on December 14th, 1938. It is evident that this species has the habit of wandering from its breeding haunts in the autumn, and it is on this habit that we must base our hopes of the Dartford warbler returning to breed in the London Area.

WILLOW WARBLER, *Phylloscopus trochilus* (L.). Widespread and common summer visitor, and passage migrant.

The willow warbler is commoner and more widely distributed than the chiffchaff, its willingness to sing from a lower perch allowing it more latitude in its choice of habitat. It is particularly common in birchwoods and on heaths covered with low birch scrub. It is also much the commoner of the two in large suburban gardens. The willow warbler has also bred more often in Inner London, both in the grounds of Holland House, where one was seen carrying food in 1953, and in the Central Parks. Breeding has been definitely recorded from Hyde Park and Kensington Gardens (1921–23) and Regent's Park (1935 and 1954—2 pairs) and doubtless has occurred unrecorded in other years, especially in Regent's Park.

In most years the willow warbler appears in the Area during the first third of April, though intensive observation in recent years has also yielded a good many late March records, the earliest being on March 16th, 1952, at Beckenham. At the other end of the season willow warblers appear to pass through the London parks in some numbers in August and early September, and most people hear their last bird in the middle third of September. Late September and even October birds are, however, by no means infrequent, and there are three records for November: Bushey Heath, on November 3rd, 1929 (T. B. Andrews), Sutton, on November 11th, 1931 (F. W. Frohawk), and Staines Moor on November 24th, 1940 (G. Carmichael Low). One observed singing in St. James's Park on February 13th, 1935 (*Field*, 165:445) had presumably wintered.

The only evidence that all birds which pass through the Area do not belong to the type subspecies is of one found freshly dead at Aldenham by P. R. Knipe on April 25th, 1949. This was submitted to the Head of the Bird Room at the British Museum (Natural History), who replied: "it appears to match more closely the characteristics of the Northern Willow Warbler. I think there can be little doubt that it is that race." The race referred to was presumably *P.t acredula*, which occurs over most of Scandinavia. One showing distinct characteristics of this race was seen by E. H. Gillham at Shoreham on April 13th, 1952.

CHIFFCHAFF, *Phylloscopus collybita* (Vieillot). Widespread summer visitor and passage migrant.

There is no evidence of other than purely local changes in the status of the chiffchaff in the Area since 1900. H. G. Attlee records that it nested on the south-east side of Tooting Graveney Common up to 1905 and in Furzedown Park until 1906. However, L. R. Evans reported chiffchaffs throughout the breeding season at Dulwich, Peckham and Camberwell in 1945, and according to J. F. Burton many pairs bred between 1942 and 1950 in Bostall Woods, Eltham, Shooters Hill and Southend, while a few pairs also bred in Greenwich Park, Blackheath, Charlton, Kidbrooke and Lee. While, therefore, the chiffchaff may have forsaken some south London open spaces at the outset of our period, it is still well established on others at the end of it. It is also a familiar breeding species in the major open spaces of Hampstead Heath with Ken Wood, Richmond Park with Wimbledon Common, and Kew Gardens. In Inner London it has often been heard singing in summer in the grounds of Holland House, but the only known nest was found by Eric Simms in 1937. In the rural parts of the Area, "the unsuburbanised districts" as one county avifaunist delicately put it, the chiffchaff is common enough in well-timbered localities, needing a combination of trees at least 15 feet tall to sing from and some kind of undergrowth to build its nest in. All observers agree that where both species occur together the chiffchaff is invariably less numerous than the willow warbler.

In places where the chiffchaff does not breed, such as the central parks, it is a regular passage migrant, less common in spring than in autumn, when it passes through two or three weeks later than the willow warbler. The first chiffchaffs are normally seen during the last third of March, though individuals not infrequently appear from the 15th or 16th onwards; Glegg (1935) mentions one on March 2nd, and there was one at Hersham on February 28th, 1954. Chiffchaffs have been seen three times in winter: one by Lord Hurcomb and E. M. Nicholson at Walton-on-Thames on February 1st, 1948; one on Stone marshes on January 3rd, 1953, which was feeding on aphids (Burton and Jones, *B.B.*, 46:457); and one seen at South Norwood Lake by R. H. Winterbottom on December 15th, 1954. In a normal year the last chiffchaff is heard in the first third of October, very often between the 4th and 6th. The only exceptionally late date, apart from the wintering records, appears to be October 28th, 1935, when two were seen in Ken Wood by Mrs. H. M. Rait Kerr.

WOOD WARBLER, *Phylloscopus sibilatrix* (Bechstein). Summer visitor, local but breeding in most suitable localities.

There is no evidence of any change in the status of the wood warbler in the Area since 1900, other than purely local fluctuations. Its habitat requirements are somewhat fastidious, consisting of a wood or well-timbered heath with comparatively little undergrowth. These requirements are best satisfied in beechwoods, birchwoods and dry oakwoods, so that it is in these rather than in the predominant damp oakwoods of the clay districts that the wood warbler is to be sought. Beechwoods are found commonly on the North Downs and locally in Epping Forest; birchwoods and dry oakwoods on the various sandy formations, such as those of north-west Kent and mid-north Surrey, and these indeed are among the districts where the wood warbler is commonest in the Area. It is fortunate that the bird does not like much undergrowth, for this is the first casualty when a wood is thrown open to the public. In Highgate Wood, for instance, formerly a dry oakwood with the usual sparse brambles, there is now no vegetation at all under the trees, except in one railed-off sanctuary. Here the wood warbler persisted until about 20 years ago, and an occasional singing male still turns up in spring. However, the wood warbler still does breed in woods and heaths as near the centre as Shooters Hill, Elmstead Wood, Hayes Common, Shirley Hills, Wimbledon Common, Putney Heath, Richmond Park, Ken Wood (as recently as 1954 but not regularly) and Epping Forest.

It fairly often appears on spring passage in places where it does not breed, but hardly ever in autumn. In Inner London it is distinctly uncommon even on passage and those that do occur are usually in the parks. In 1944, however, one sang all day in Lincoln's Inn on April 23rd, and was seen there again on May 7th. In spring most birds arrive in the last third of April, and a few between the 14th and the 20th. The only three earlier ones were on April 9th (Ruislip, 1949), 11th and 12th. At the other end of the season many years pass without a wood warbler being recorded after the end of July, and there are indeed only three records later than August 23rd, viz: two on September 2nd in 1945 and 1951, and one in Bushy Park on October 3rd, 1929. The latter date is only two days earlier than the latest date for the British Isles in *The Handbook*.

YELLOW-BROWED WARBLER, *Phylloscopus inornatus* (Blyth)

The late F. W. Frohawk reported seeing a yellow-browed warbler in song in his garden at Sutton, on October 10th, 1930 (*B.B.*, 24:159).

GOLDCREST, *Regulus regulus* (L.). A local breeding species which is probably commonest on the Surrey heaths and slopes of the North Downs. Widely distributed in autumn and winter, an influx commencing late in September and reaching a maximum in second half October and early November.

There is little ground for supposing that there has been any permanent change in the breeding status of the goldcrest (*R.r. anglorum*) during the half century, and numbers are principally dependent on the incidence of exceptionally severe winters after which they may be seriously reduced. As the nest is not easily found, especially in heavily populated districts, the few definite nesting records are apt to be misleading, but even so in many parts of the Area, especially north of the Thames, goldcrests seem to have a patchy and irregular breeding distribution that is perhaps not entirely surprising in view of the scarcity of coniferous woods. Even so it is probable that small numbers of goldcrests are much more widespread in suitable sites than the few localities recorded would suggest.

In Kent and Surrey they breed more freely, though few nests are found and no estimate of breeding density in favourable sites has been attempted.

Much more information is available on the very marked influx that takes place in autumn, when goldcrests may be heard in suburban gardens and regularly in small numbers in Inner London. The first reports of appearance in new localities are usually in September, but it is from the middle of October on into November that the large numbers are encountered. For example, in Hainault Forest one year on October 17th many parties were seen totalling probably several hundred birds, and in late October in another year in Epping Forest goldcrests were in flocks of up to forty. A marked influx has been noticed in several years in Bushy Park in early November. It is very likely that many of these birds are of Continental origin as the immigration is well-known along the shores of North Kent. A definite specimen of the typical race (*R.r. regulus*) was taken by Dr. J. M. Harrison at Sevenoaks in 1937 on November 7th (*S.E.B.R.*, 1937:28). There is some suggestion that numbers increase again in March, at a time when redpolls and siskins are also noted on passage, but it is not possible to be more precise about the return movement.

FIRECREST, *Regulus ignicapillus* (Temminck).

Scarce winter visitor, possibly regular in small numbers.

Although the firecrest was only recorded twice in the earlier years of the century, later evidence suggests that a few may visit the Area in most winters. There have been about twenty-eight occurrences, covering all months from September to April inclusive, the highest numbers being in December and January.

The firecrest has been seen mostly in open woodland with silver birch, hawthorn and other small trees up to about fifteen feet in height, or on open commonland with small trees, bushes, brambles, gorse and bracken. On Ruislip Common it was seen in four out of the seven winters between 1938–39 and 1944–45, on Wimbledon Common in 1905, 1926 and 1950, and in that part of north-east Surrey which lies in the triangle Croydon–Limpsfield–Leatherhead it was reported eleven times in seven different years. Other notes have come from Bushey, Stanmore, Epping Forest, Abbey Wood, Sidcup, Hayes and Chislehurst.

Most of the reports are of one or two birds only, but at Ruislip on January 23rd 1944, Dr. Philipson identified two firecrests in a flock of eleven similar birds, and he thought from their calls that six others were of the same species.

SPOTTED FLYCATCHER, *Muscicapa striata* (Pallas). Widely distributed summer resident, breeding not uncommonly in the rural fringe, the suburbs and the parks and other open spaces of Inner London. On autumn passage sometimes seen in parties.

The status of the spotted flycatcher in and around London in the first twenty years of our period was probably not very different from what it is now. It was regular enough for its arrival each year to be carefully noted and familiar enough to be described as common or very frequent. In Inner London two or three pairs were known to be breeding in some of the Royal Parks, while in the suburbs, which in those days were much less extensive than they are now, it was nesting at Brixton, Lee, Tooting and elsewhere. The scattered outer settlements of the closing years of the last century became progressively linked by development, and houses and gardens appeared where previously there were green fields, crops and coppices (see maps in Fitter, 1945, pp. 102–3). Harrow in 1903 for example, was almost rural and Price (1903) came upon nine or ten nests in a season. Now that Harrow is engulfed by the tide of suburban building the spotted flycatcher still breeds there, often in gardens, and there is no indication that it is any the worse for the change in habitat. Suitable food supplies and nesting sites doubtless play their usual important part in the distribution of this species as much as in any other, and the vicinity of human dwellings, farmsteads and such developments as are commonly to be expected in an urban or suburban community provide a sufficiency of both.

It is difficult to think of any part of the London Area, except perhaps the more densely built-up districts of the centre and the comparatively few tracts of open, treeless heath, common or marsh, where the sight of a spotted flycatcher would occasion any surprise. Although not present in obviously large numbers, and certainly much fewer than many other summer visitors to the Area, they may nevertheless be seen wherever a sheltered spot encourages an abundance of the small flying insects that form their food. Yet one hesitates to call them common, loose though this term has become. Many apparently suitable places never or seldom attract them, while others are frequented year after year. If any habitat preference may be detected, private gardens and parkland, even quite small inner suburban parks with little or no undergrowth, seem to be among those sites most favoured.

At the centre of London, in the extensive Royal Parks, spotted flycatchers nest annually now as they did fifty years ago. They nest too in some of the squares of Mayfair and Bloomsbury, and in such secluded retreats as Lincoln's Inn Fields and the gardens at Lambeth and Chelsea. On passage they pass through London squares and bombed sites where they do not breed, and parties of twenty or thirty, or even more, may be seen in autumn in many types of country. Of the migrations abroad of London birds our direct knowledge is limited to the recovery in Portugal, in October, 1949, of one ringed as a nestling two years previously at Tadworth.

PIED FLYCATCHER, *Muscicapa hypoleuca* (Pallas). Regular double passage migrant, most frequent in autumn.

A hundred years ago, or thereabouts, a pair or two of pied flycatchers might have been found nesting in the London Area. But such southerly breeding was always exceptional, and no nesting in the Area has been noticed since 1889 when the brother of H. F. Witherby found a nest at Mottingham (*Trans.* West Kent Sci. Soc. for 1895). The few nesting records for Surrey are all long before 1900.

Bucknill knew the bird in 1900 only as a rare straggler and not, as it is now, as a regular migrant. He suspected that in the days when an odd pair stayed to nest this fly-catcher was rather less of a passage rarity than it was in his time, but he and his con-temporaries were not aided by a large number of observers as we are to-day, and pied flycatchers were only noted in six of the first twenty-four years of our period. Since then there have been only four years without a record, and in recent years they have been seen with increasing frequency; in 1952, for example, they were observed in three localities in spring and fourteen in autumn.

They are noticed most often in the rural fringe or larger open spaces, rarely being seen in gardens, and it is probably the regularity of observation in suburban districts and Inner London that is responsible for their featuring so largely in the records of pied flycatchers in recent years, when Hampstead Heath and Regent's Park have been among the best places to find them. Other Inner London parks and such places as Barn Elms, Catford, Peckham and West Ham have also been visited. Elsewhere, the records are mostly from the ring of woods and wooded commons, such as those at Epping, Ruislip, Esher, Tadworth, Wimbledon and Keston, and from the larger parks such as Richmond and Bushy.

Usually they have occurred in ones or twos, but there were six on Hampstead Heath in the autumn of 1950, up to 15 in Regent's Park between August 31st and September 11th, 1951, and a maximum of seven at the same place in the autumn of 1952.

April and May, August and September are the normal months of passage, and at one time the spring visits were hardly, if at all, fewer than those in autumn. In the years 1951–53 however, pied flycatchers were seen at more than twice as many localities in autumn as in spring, and since the autumn birds are less conspicuous there must be more than a suspicion that this is merely due to better observation. Since 1929 there have been five occurrences in June and three in October.

RED-BREASTED FLYCATCHER, *Muscicapa parva* Bechstein
An adult male red-breasted flycatcher was watched for half an hour by Mr. and Mrs. J. T. Hagarty near the mouth of the River Darent on September 12th, 1954 (*L.B.R.*, 19:37).

HEDGE SPARROW, *Prunella modularis* (L.). Common resident in all but the most densely built-up parts.
Although the hedge sparrow is perhaps not the commonest of London birds, it is certainly one of the most widely distributed. Like the robin, it nests in most of the central parks and in most of the larger gardens in the suburbs. In the rural parts, it can be seen along the hedgerows, on the bushy commons, at the edges of woodland and in other places with sufficient cover.
The history of the hedge sparrow in London in our period is like its appearance and nature, plain and rather dull; there is no evidence of any change of status and cold winters do not appear to have affected its numbers to any marked degree. It is one of the most sedentary of birds and there is nothing to suggest any movement of the resident population—the few recoveries of ringed birds are all at or near the place of ringing. The only suggestion of migration through the Area comes from Power (1910), who said that in October they could be seen moving slowly westwards from garden to garden, usually in parties of four to six. Power also recorded that Kennington Park "seemed to be alive with them" on October 5th, 1904.
In London, as in other parts of south-eastern England, the hedge sparrow is the chief fosterer of the cuckoo.

MEADOW PIPIT, *Anthus pratensis* (L.). Scarce and local resident; abundant and widespread passage migrant and winter visitor.
It is not easy to determine the breeding status of the meadow pipit in the early part of the century, partly, perhaps, because its abundance in the autumn and winter blinded some observers to its scarcity in the summer months. Dixon (1909) claimed that within fifteen miles of St. Paul's it was commoner and much more widely distributed than the tree pipit and said that "it would be impossible to mention all the places in the more rural suburbs where (it) nested". There is very little definite evidence of breeding in the first two decades, however, either from our own records or from other sources. In Middlesex, G. W. Kerr said of the Staines district that there were large numbers in winter but none in summer and other observers said the same of Hanwell, Winchmore Hill and other areas; nesting was recorded only at Harrow, Enfield and Edmonton. A nest at Watford, in 1902, was the only record for Hertfordshire, inside our Area. In Essex, the meadow pipit appears to have been equally scarce even, rather surprisingly, in the more open parts of Epping Forest; nesting was recorded at Chigwell and Loughton in 1906 and 1907 respectively but nowhere else before 1920. Ticehurst (1909) said that in Kent, it was comparatively rare around Bromley but bred sparingly at Keston and Hayes. Only in Surrey, on the rough grasslands of the open downs, does the meadow pipit appear to have been at all common; closer in, it was recorded in 1909 as breeding on Mitcham Common in small numbers, but in Richmond Park, where the tree pipit was fairly common, the meadow pipit was described as essentially a winter visitor and seldom seen in summer (L. B. Mouritz, *Zool.*, 63:349).

At the present time the meadow pipit is still a scarce and local nesting species although it is now recorded as nesting from rather more localities than at the beginning of the century. This 'increase' may be, in part, a reflection of the vast increase in observers, but the construction of the reservoirs, with their grassy banks, and the reversion of arable land to pasture between the wars undoubtedly provided additional habitats. North of the Thames, the meadow pipit now breeds sparingly in the marshy fields bordering the Colne and the Lea and occasionally on the larger open areas, e.g. at Stanmore and Chingford; in 1950 it was suspected of breeding on Hampstead Heath. In the south, it is fairly common in the Epsom district, according to Howard Bentham, although plough-ing has greatly affected its numbers. It still nests locally on the Downs, on some of the Surrey sewage farms and commons, including Streatham and Wimbledon and in Rich-mond Park, which it apparently colonised in the 1920s. In Kent, the growth of silver birches caused the meadow pipit to abandon Hayes and Keston Commons about 1939, but a pair or two nests at Elmers End sewage farm. On the Thames marshes it breeds in small numbers eastwards from about Barking Creek in the north and Plumstead in the south.

As a passage migrant and winter visitor, the meadow pipit has always been abundant and widespread, and from September to March birds can be seen in some numbers at sewage farms, reservoirs, railway embankments, on open pasture and root fields and on rough ground right into the centre of London. The sewage farms, where they feed on the filter beds, probably attract the largest concentrations in the winter; between 700 and 750 were counted by E. Mann at the Edmonton farm on December 24th, 1933. The autumn passage is at its peak from mid-September to the end of October and at this time small flocks can often be seen passing over, especially in the early hours of the morn-ing. The movement appears to be on a broad front, and has been seen from tall buildings in Trafalgar Square, and elsewhere in central London as well as in the suburbs. Along the Thames 346 passed west in one hour on one morning at the end of October. With the prevailing westerly winds, the direction of the movement is westerly but with easterly winds some meadow pipits have been observed flying in the opposite direction. With headwinds, the height of flight is often under 200 feet but with light or following winds the birds may pass over at too great a height for observation, e.g. L. Parmenter heard meadow pipits passing over Kensington Gardens practically continuously for half an hour in the morning of September 22nd, 1929, but saw only one small party and two single birds. It is not certain whether these migrating flocks, which are presumably com-posed of Continental immigrants, pass on without alighting or whether some come down to feed or to spend the winter. Undoubtedly the population of meadow pipits in the Lon-don Area is greater in September and October than at any other period and by the beginning of November numbers have decreased to their winter level. The return move-ment takes place in March and April. Although the passage in spring is not so obvious as in the autumn and visual migration has not been recorded, it is often apparent that a movement is in progress. For example, a flock of fifty in Hyde Park near Marble Arch on March 29th, 1926, were so tired that they allowed approach to within eight feet. In 1952 there were at least 50, and possibly 100, meadow pipits on the bombed sites in Cripplegate on March 31st, while there were about 400 on Hampstead Heath on April 8th. In the same period parties were seen feeding on the Thames mud and large numbers were recorded at Beddington.

Severe weather in the winter months sometimes brings an influx of meadow pipits, often accompanying skylarks, into the Area. In February, 1917, they fed, with redwings, on the tide edge at Chiswick and retreated to the pavements when the tide was high. In the 1938 cold spell meadow pipits were seen by the tideway at Hammersmith and in the snow-covered streets at Hampstead, Beulah Hill and Epsom, where four were found lying helpless in the road. At Loughton some were eating the seeds of a fox-tail grass, *Alopecurus*, sticking above the snow.

Wintering meadow pipits have been observed roosting in reed-beds at three localities in the Area, once in company with pied wagtails. At the Brent reservoir, and no doubt elsewhere, they roost in the long grass. Roosting has also been reported in bracken.

TREE PIPIT, *Anthus trivialis* (L.). Fairly common summer resident; more widespread on passage.

Ticehurst (1909) said that the tree pipit was a fairly numerous summer resident in Kent, but somewhat local and nowhere abundant. The same remarks would have applied to most other parts of the Area at that time and are equally applicable now, although local fluctuations have occurred in some of the intervening years. For example, G. Dent stated in 1939 that there had been a marked decrease in recent years in S.W. Essex; he suggested that the reasons might be closer grazing and the disappearance of some of the open, heathy parts of Epping Forest, where previously it was common. But in 1941 the same observer reported that tree pipits were exceptionally abundant. Similar increases in the 1940's, compared with the pre-war years, were noted in other parts of the Area (Staines, Addington, Caterham, Sevenoaks), and from 1946 to 1951 breeding was suspected in Ken Wood after many years' absence. In 1954 one pair was definitely proved to breed. On the other hand, they were reported as less common, in 1946, in Richmond Park, presumably because some of their favourite territories had been ploughed up.

Around London, as elsewhere, the tree pipit favours especially the commons and heaths, open woodlands, grasslands with scattered trees, and hillsides (e.g. the North Downs), and it can be found along many of the railway cuttings—of which there must be more to the square mile than in most other parts of Britain.

The first tree pipits usually arrive in the Area in the first or second week of April. Early arrivals have been reported in the last few days of March, but a report of tree pipits on Mitcham Common on March 19th, 1933, published in *B.B.*, 26:364, has since been withdrawn by the observer, who now considers the birds more likely to have been first-year meadow pipits, which have flesh-coloured legs.

On passage, the tree pipit is sometimes seen away from its breeding habitats—as, for instance, the one seen in the College Garden adjoining Westminster Abbey on May 6th, 1950. Elsewhere in Inner London, tree pipits occur occasionally in the central parks, usually on the spring migration, but they are not so frequent as formerly.

ROCK PIPIT, *Anthus spinoletta petrosus* (Montagu)
WATER PIPIT, *Anthus spinoletta spinoletta* L.

The rock pipit is an occasional visitor on passage and in winter, but regular on Thames marshes below Crayford Ness; the water pipit is a very rare vagrant.

The first definite "inland" record of the rock pipit in the London Area in this century was on October 28th, 1923, when C. S. Bayne, W. E. Glegg and P. J. Hanson identified one at Elstree reservoir. Since then, and excluding for the moment the North Kent marshes, there have been over sixty dated occurrences, mostly at the Barn Elms, Staines and Lea valley reservoirs. In 1952 they were seen at five localities, and in two of them in both spring and autumn, but in most years there are only about three records. A party of six at Barn Elms on October 5th, 1954, is the largest away from the lower Thames.

An analysis of 65 records away from the marshes gives the following distribution, which shows that the main passage is evidently in October, agreeing with the time of arrival on the Thames estuary:—

August 1	November 5	February 8
September 1	December 12	March 7
October 22	January 5	April 4

Apart from the reservoirs mentioned above, rock pipits have occasionally been noted at other waters in the Thames and Lea Valleys and three times by the Thames itself above Hammersmith. On the lower reaches of the Thames J. F. Burton and others have discovered in recent years that the rock pipit is a regular and fairly numerous October–February visitor along the river walls, foreshores and saltings from Northfleet as far up as Crayford Ness, as many as 80 or more having been recorded on Swanscombe marshes on October 26th, 1952. Prior to 1949, these marshes were very little watched but rock pipits are regular visitors to the more popular North Kent marshes just outside our area. On the Essex side little is known of the status of the rock pipit apart from a statement by P. W. Horn (1921) that they were regular in winter on the Thurrock marshes.

The water pipit (*Anthus s. spinoletta*) has been seen six times in the London Area. Mrs. H. M. Rait Kerr saw one at Walthamstow reservoirs on March 30th, 1938; C. C. Rose and W. H. D. Wince had good views of one on the causeway at Staines Reservoir on October 15th, 1949; J. F. Burton and K. H. Palmer saw a water pipit among rock pipits on the Stone marshes on December 24th, 1950, and another (or perhaps the same bird) six miles away on the Abbey Wood marshes on December 31st, 1950. One was seen by F. H. Jones and H. Medhurst at King George VI reservoir in early October, 1952, and another on Staines Moor on April 3rd, 1954.

PIED WAGTAIL, *Motacilla alba yarrellii* Gould
WHITE WAGTAIL, *Motacilla alba alba* L.

The pied wagtail is resident and widespread in a variety of habitats in town, suburbs and country; the white wagtail is a regular double passage migrant in small numbers, mostly recognised in spring.

At all periods during the present century the pied wagtail has been common throughout the London Area. It occurs in most types of habitat, woodlands and dry open heath being probably the least favoured although the moister parts of some of our heath-like commons attract it, especially for roosting. Even the mass of building in the centre of London is frequented, and since the war there have been almost annual records of its breeding on the bombed sites, where it has nested in the nooks and crannies of the broken masonry and feeds among the willow-herb and other wild plants which appeared there in such profusion. It may be seen foraging in the streets both of town and suburbs, and in some places it roosts, sometimes in numbers up to two or three hundred, in busy thoroughfares and may be seen lining the rooftops at dusk before dropping into the pavement trees. Numbers at the more usual roosting sites in reed-beds have reached 500.

Apart from the communal roosts its largest numbers occur on autumn passage and in winter on agricultural land, and at some of the sewage farms where flocks of perhaps fifty occur on the humus tanks and irrigated fields. On ploughed land near Claygate in November, 1943, K. P. Keywood (*B.B.*, 41:117) saw a winter flock of between 100 and 150, but this was exceptional.

Some of the pied wagtails bred in this country migrate to France or Spain, but the only London Area pied wagtail so far recovered abroad was found in the valley of the Garonne in western France in March, 1917, having been ringed at Limpsfield in May, 1916. By contrast, a pied wagtail ringed as a nestling at Harrow in June, 1934, was next heard of in mid-winter at Watford in January, 1940. Pied wagtails on passage in the London Area in autumn reveal their presence mainly by flocking, but have also been seen flying high above central London.

The white wagtail is recognised annually in spring, and with less regularity in autumn when it is harder to tell the two races apart. Almost all the records are from the reservoirs and sewage farms, but despite the intensity with which such places are watched only a dozen or so white wagtails are noticed each year and doubtless the numbers passing through the Area are small. It is unusual to see more than three or four together and mostly they occur singly.

GREY WAGTAIL, *Motacilla cinerea* Tunstall. Breeds annually in small numbers in widely separated localities; at other seasons is widespread though never numerous; commonest on autumn passage.

The nesting of the grey wagtail around London at the beginning of the century was unknown except for five nests in the Cray valley up to 1904 (Ticehurst 1909). By 1906 it was known to be breeding along the streams south of Godstone, beyond our southern boundary. The first record inside our boundary at Godstone was in 1912 and thereafter one or two pairs have bred almost every year by the waters of Ivy Mill and Leigh Mill. The waters at Godstone are part of the drainage system of streams which flow within sight of the escarpment of the North Downs through Tandridge, Oxted and Limpsfield and drain eventually into the Eden, and on almost any of these one would not be surprised to see a grey wagtail in summer.

The grey wagtail has bred from time to time in all the main river valleys in the south of the Area. The Darent probably has held more than the half dozen or so nests known since 1927. On the Mole one or two pairs have nested or attempted to nest almost every year since about 1930 at a favoured site near Leatherhead; and at several other places along this river and in the valley of the Wey a few miles further west there are records of nesting, or of birds being seen in summer, in the last 25 years.

In the much less pastoral valleys of the Hogsmill, the Wandle and the Beverley Brook, breeding has been known intermittently since 1933 in such places as Morden Hall on the Wandle, the Watermeads at Mitcham, or the artificially irrigated meadows of the sewage farms at Beddington and Epsom. The grey wagtail does not necessarily demand the freedom it enjoys in the deeper, wilder valleys of the north and west, as is shown by its successful breeding among the waterfalls and lakes of suburban parks around Beckenham in 1934 and 1935, and by attempts to do so in other years. Pairs have even bred within the last ten years as near to London as Greenwich Park or its environs, and in 1929 beside a stream flowing into the Brent Reservoir in industrial Hendon. In 1952 a pair successfully reared two broods in London itself, in the basement of a bombed site in Cripplegate.

Apart from isolated records of pairs nesting in Bushy Park and beside the river at Twickenham in 1909, there were no reports of breeding along the Thames until the forties—at Bushy Park (twice), at Hammersmith (on the *roof* of the Distillers' Company's building) and probably at or near Molesey Lock. Further west, on the numerous little rivers which run southwards to the Thames, the records of breeding start at Cuckoo Hall Farm, where grey wagtails were reputed to have bred on the banks of the Chess for some nine years up to 1912, followed by a period of nesting further upstream and beyond our boundary, at Chenies. In 1909 two clutches were laid near Gerrards Cross, in the valley of the Misbourne, and a pair bred at Hamper Mill on the Colne in 1922. But it was not until 1929 that a pair nested in a hole in the ivy-covered walls of an old mill on the River Gade, where for the next ten years or so breeding was regular. Since 1940 there have been occasional records of breeding in the drainage area between Watford and Staines, and in 1954 there were pairs at Hamper Mill, Harefield and Staines.

The only other valley of importance to the grey wagtail in the northern part of our Area is that of the Lea. For a time it nested regularly in a bridge at Hatfield Park until holes in the brickwork were filled up in 1930, after which a nest with eggs was discovered in 1934 in Brocket Park, a few miles upstream. In 1954, and possibly in 1953, a pair bred successfully at Fisher's Green, near Cheshunt.

Further east, on the rivers and streams of Essex within our boundary, such as the Roding and the Ingrebourne, the grey wagtail as a breeding species is unknown.

The breeding season over, grey wagtails, either singly or in small parties, may be seen from time to time wherever there is water. They have been seen in gardens in Kew and Kensington, beside park waterfalls and fountains, on the sprinklers of a sewage farm and even among the sea-lions at the Zoo. In the City they may be seen on the bombed sites or beside puddles in the almost empty emergency water-tanks. In places they seem addicted to perching on roof tops. In winters since 1946 one or two have stayed for several months from October onwards in Charlotte Street and Tottenham Court Road, where they kept to the roofs and gutters. One was seen in several consecutive years up to 1947 running about in search of insects amongst the puddles of a flat roof in Kensington, and others have frequented the roofs of the grandstand at Lords and the tube station at Edgware. Their presence in Inner London in autumn and winter was the subject of comment by Macpherson during the First World War, so that although we may have become more aware of them in recent years they are not such a new sight after all.

YELLOW WAGTAIL, *Motacilla flava flavissima* (Blyth)
BLUE-HEADED WAGTAIL, *Motacilla f. flava* L.

The British race, *flavissima*, breeds regularly along the main waterways and drainage areas and, more locally, on various types of agricultural land and beside comparatively isolated waters. More widespread on passage, when *flava* and variant forms occur in small numbers.

Yellow wagtails breed in the drainage area formed by the southerly course of the Colne and its associated streams, from Radlett in the north to the fertile plain of west Middlesex. In 1905 W. Bickerton (*Trans. Herts. N.H.S.*, 13(1):54) referred to their nesting in large numbers in the water meadows of the Colne, and they still breed, or have lately bred, at the gravel pits of Moor Mill and Hamper Mill, and at a number of localities around Watford, Croxley Green, Rickmansworth and Harefield. At Ruislip reservoir they appear on passage but seldom nest. E. C. Rowberry in 1931 reported 12–15 pairs nesting in the "lower Colne valley", which probably included the west Middlesex plain. Here in 1950 H. A. Bilby and others recorded breeding in nine separate localities, in some of which several pairs were present. Near Greenford up to ten pairs were breeding in derelict cornfields near the canal in 1951. On the gravel-worked ground south of the Molesey reservoirs, and in the Thames valley from Hampton to Chiswick, some have nested regularly since the war.

Along the Lea they nested in the earliest years of our period on Edmonton sewage farm and the grassy embankments of the Walthamstow reservoirs. From about 1920 they were increasing and were quick to exploit the formation of two major reservoirs—the King George V reservoir in 1920 and recently the William Girling, which held six pairs in 1950—and also the chain of gravel pits and sewage farms which extends for eight miles south of Stanstead Abbots. Between the Lea and the Thames yellow wagtails nest in small numbers in parts of the Roding valley, notably between Ilford and Romford on an overgrown dump, at Chigwell sewage farm and at Navestock. There are also a few pairs at Romford sewage farm, between Romford and Chadwell Heath and at South Ockendon.

On the Thames marshes there are nesting yellow wagtails as close to the East End of London as Beckton, where there were five pairs in 1945, and at Ripple Level and Mayesbrook Park gravel pit. The conversion of this pit to a boating lake in 1949, the transformation to football pitches in 1948 of part of Blackheath (where up to five pairs bred annually during the war) and building on a former breeding ground at Perry Street, near Dartford, in 1950, are but three examples of their being ousted by development—though one pair bred again on Blackheath in 1951. South of the river, A. P. Macklin said yellow wagtails nested plentifully near Woolwich (Turner, 1909), and according to J. F. Burton there were over 30 pairs between Greenwich and Broadness saltings in 1952, which was an exceptionally good year for them.

Nesting is regular beside the reservoirs at Brent (6 pairs in 1954) and Barn Elms (4 pairs), and on Beddington sewage farm (18 pairs). These sites were in existence by 1900 and doubtless yellow wagtails have bred annually, certainly since 1909. They have nested even in such totally enclosed areas as Wormwood Scrubs and Chiswick Park, and in Regent's Park during the war, while exceptionally a pair bred on Hampstead Heath in 1952. Yellow wagtails nested in bracken in Richmond Park up to 1912, and on Wimbledon Common, where J. Nichol (*Zool.*, 1902, p.313) found six pairs in 1902, one of the nests being among gorse. They have bred rarely in the valleys of the Mole, Hogsmill, Darent and Cray. Three or four pairs have been regular at Elmers End since 1935, and they currently breed in cornfields and on allotments and grassy areas around Mill Hill. There has been extensive ploughing of pasture and drainage of marginal land during and since the war, and some sewage farms have been closed; but these restrictive effects and the spread of London are offset by the new reservoirs and increasingly numerous gravel pits.

Exceptionally, passage starts in the last few days of March, but the main arrival is from the second or third week of April, and in 1951 there were about 400 yellow wagtails at the King George VI reservoir on April 29th. Noticeable movement continues until early May, with stragglers to June. Return passage begins in July, and from August to the first half of September flocks of twenty and upwards are not unusual and small parties may be seen flying south over the North Downs, while at some of the reservoirs numbers may for a few days exceed a hundred—there were 300–350 at the King George V reservoir on August 16th, 1951. In most years a very few are noticed in October, and there are three November records.

Blue-headed wagtails, *M.f. flava*, reported only three times in the first thirty years, have been recognised annually ever since, and in many recent years there have been reports of wagtails not typical of either *flava* or *flavissima*—in 1953 there were as many as 20. The true identity of these birds must remain in doubt, though the possibility of some being *Motacilla f. beema* cannot be excluded if we accept Williamson's recent hypothesis (*B.B.*, 48:382–403). Some have had paler heads than the typical *flava*, or have differed in having no white supercilium, or a whitish supercilium extending only behind the eye; while others have had grey upperparts and whitish (instead of yellow) underparts and resembled plate 6 in *The Yellow Wagtail* (Stuart Smith, 1950). Most have occurred between April and June, a few in autumn. Several have been watched on Staines Moor carrying food and defending territory (*vide L.B.R.* for 1947, 1948) and they occur there annually on migration. A pair considered to be *flava* nested near Sidcup in 1933 (D. H. Meares, *B.B.*, 27:133).

WAXWING, *Bombycilla garrulus* (L). An irregular winter visitor appearing not at all in some years, in small numbers in others and, very occasionally, in larger numbers with flocks sometimes up to or exceeding twenty.

As a migrant from the forests of northern Europe the waxwing from time to time visits Britain in large enough numbers to justify the use of the terms "invasions" or "irruptions". The winters of 1903–04, 1913–14, 1921–22, 1931–32, 1936–37, 1943–44, 1946–47, perhaps 1948–49 and certainly 1949–50 are in this category. In all of these, with the exception of 1931–32, the London Area saw something of the visitations of waxwings, although in some of the winters they were recorded only in one or two places.

The biggest invasion was that of 1946–47, when waxwings appeared throughout the London Area and Gibb (*B.B.*, 41:2–9 and 34–40) showed that over twelve thousand were recorded in Britain. Apart from this exceptional occurrence, the main irruptions affecting our own Area have been in the winters of 1913–14, 1943–44, 1948–49, and 1949–50. In each of these winters waxwings were noted in from six to eight localities, often singly or in small parties but occasionally up to twenty at a time. Since 1900 they have appeared around London in 19 years which have not been so-called "waxwing years", usually not more than five birds being seen together, but once as many as twelve; and for twenty-seven of the years there are no records at all.

Against this background of years of scarcity and years when irruptions were on a very moderate scale, the winter of 1946–47 stands out clearly and unforgettably. Five hundred waxwings, or thereabouts, were recorded in the London Area between December and April. This figure is only approximate but it does at least show that the numbers of waxwings were very much out of the ordinary. They came in small parties and even flocks of twenty or thirty, to open ground and to the suburbs all around London where quiet, residential roads or busy thoroughfares were equally acceptable providing they were relieved by trees and berried bushes.

Although not shy and apparently unheeding of traffic waxwings were not seen in central London or the closely adjoining ring of dense building where berries were lacking. But from the middle and outer suburbs, even as close as Herne Hill, where the berries of rowan, privet, cotoneaster, hawthorn and other fruiting shrubs could be obtained so freely, the records outnumbered those from the open spaces by four or five to one. In back gardens, road-side gardens and in the trees (often rowan) with which some of the streets are planted, a plentiful food supply remained open throughout this exceptionally cold winter. Gibb (*loc. cit.*) has shown that over the country as a whole the largest flocks appeared in December and early January, and that most had left before the weather hardened. In the south, by contrast, numbers remained high until February, and in the London Area right through the cold spell into the milder second half of March. With only the thrushes and blackbirds to offer serious competition for the available food, they probably found the shelter of the built-up areas, together with the varied supply of berries, much to their liking. Little bands of waxwings would stay several days, a week or longer in one area, and move on when the bushes were almost stripped of berries. Even as late as April 1st thirty or more remained about the north-east corner of Wimbledon Common and the adjacent residential area, the last, a party of six, being seen on April 8th.

There are three records for Inner London: five in Kensington Park Gardens on January 22nd, 1942; one in St. John's Wood on April 4th, 1947, and five in Hyde Park on January 30th, 1954.

GREAT GREY SHRIKE, *Lanius excubitor* L. Passage migrant and winter visitor.

The great grey shrike is an irregular visitor on migration and in winter to suitable habitats within the Area, the records showing a marked increase in frequency in the last twenty years. While it is difficult to say whether or not this is due to the increase in the number of observers, in several of these later years birds have been seen in three or four widely separated localities. For instance, in 1946 there are December records from Walton Heath, Burgh Heath, Stanmore and Loughton. Although there are reports for every year since 1936, birds were seen in only twelve of the previous thirty-five years, and from 1928 to 1935 inclusive there was no record at all.

There are round London many commons and parks with scattered hawthorns in an open setting, which appears to constitute a favourite winter habitat of this attractive bird. Notable among the places where it has been seen most are Banstead and Walton Heaths, the commons at Ashtead, Epsom, Ham, Mitcham, Ruislip, Stanmore and Wimbledon, Richmond Park and Epping Forest. In three recent winters one has been seen as near central London as the Brent reservoir.

The duration of the great grey shrike's winter visit covers the months of November to April inclusive; in three successive winters when they have either wintered on Mitcham Common or been recorded on passage the first record has been on the 21st, 2nd and 3rd November respectively. There is an early record, however, of a bird seen in Bushy Park on September 10th, 1938, and considered by J. E. Roberts to have been correctly identified (*Royal Parks Report*, 1938:23), and there are three reports for October. A bird was seen on Ham Common by Miss G. H. Towsey on May 15th and 20th, 1920, and again on June 13th (*B.B.*, 14:45). This is the latest spring record, but there are two other May occurrences. One bird visited, of all places, the yard of a firm of taxidermists in Camden Town on May 23rd, 1949. It was first seen by F. C. Gerrard at a leaking water pipe and then perched on a wall in full view at close range. After about two minutes it flew to a roof and then away, but remained long enough for the plumage to be compared on the spot with the description and illustration in the *Handbook*. No evidence could be found of any bird of this species having escaped from the London Zoo or elsewhere (*L.B.R.*, 14:16). Secondly, on May 30th, 1950, E. L. Crouch had a brief but adequate view of a great grey shrike in the grounds of Hampton Court Palace.

WOODCHAT SHRIKE, *Lanius senator* L.

On April 24th, 1934, a male woodchat shrike was seen by D. C. Keef at Longfield, and a dead bird, probably the same one, was found nearby in the following month (*Field*, 163: 1076 and 1190). In 1951 one was seen on Bookham Common on May 26th and 27th (*B.B.*, 45:258), and in 1953 there was an immature bird in Richmond Park from April 13th to May 5th (*B.B.*, 46: 305–6).

RED-BACKED SHRIKE, *Lanius collurio* L. A local breeding species, chiefly on common-land interspersed with tall bushes. Despite restriction of suitable haunts through building and ploughing it persists in favourite sites as long as possible.

In the first decade of this century the red-backed shrike's breeding range extended as far into London as Barnes Common, Dulwich, the Brent Valley, Hampstead Heath and Kingsbury. It bred freely around Epsom, Leatherhead and Reigate in Surrey (Bucknill), was not uncommon around Beddington and Croydon, and was common all round the north of London (Lodge), but was nowhere very plentiful on the south-east side. Further out it was still fairly common in the Dartford district (Davis, 1904).

There is one observation of decline before 1907, but it is impossible to say when this became general. Geoffrey Dent informs us that the species is now much scarcer in south-west Essex than before 1914, which he attributes to the more drastic trimming of overgrown lanes and railway embankments. In Middlesex shrikes no longer breed at Kingsbury or Hampstead Heath, and Professor Warmington noted a decrease in numbers about 1933 and again after 1939.

Despite this confirmation of the widespread opinion that red-backed shrikes have decreased they return with great regularity to favourite haunts so long as these are not altered too drastically, and in 1952 forty-three of an estimated 61 pairs were known to have nested. The outskirts of Epping Forest are one of the regular localities and eight nests were found in 1921 near Warren Hill, while about twenty years later ten separate families were seen in an area of about 12 square miles near Connaught Water. Twelve pairs were noted in 1945 with another five at Sewardstone, but in 1949, as a result of the cutting down of bushes, only one pair was seen where there had been six in 1947. Other recent breeding localities in Essex are Aveley, Brentwood, Hainault Forest, Harold Hill, Hornchurch, Nazeing, Thorndon Park, Upminster, Waltham Cross, Warley and Woodford Wells. At the present time a few pairs are still regular in Middlesex near Edgware and Mill Hill, while in one or more recent years pairs have bred as near to London as the Brent reservoir, at Finchley within fifty yards of the North Circular Road and at Southgate. A great stronghold of the species a little further out is in the Ruislip and Northwood district, where there were still 6–7 pairs located in 1954; elsewhere in the county and in the Hertfordshire sector of the Area distribution is patchy and recent breeding records concern only about twenty pairs at the most.

As might be expected, the Surrey heaths and commons have always been favourite areas, but very few pairs now remain in inner districts such as Beddington and Croydon even though single pairs bred as close to London as Dulwich in 1949 and Wandsworth in 1950, while there have been two pairs recently in Putney Vale. Building was already reducing the nesting area at Ashtead in 1936 and an even greater reduction was caused in 1944 by the ploughing-up of part of the common. Though eight pairs remained, by 1949 further agricultural activity had reduced these to two. Despite these setbacks there were in 1952 at least 27 pairs in the Surrey part of the Area. In the Kent sector a few pairs still breed in widely separated localities but it is doubtful if these exceed a dozen or so. Exceptionally, in 1944 one pair attempted to breed as close in to London as Greenwich Park.

This is, therefore, a species which has been driven out a little way from the centre, but has suffered more severely from the encroachment of building and agriculture on the commonland further out, that ideally provides rough ground dotted with tall bushes. Unquestionably the birds are very persistent in their return to traditional areas such as Epping Forest and the Ruislip and Epsom districts. In spite of the great public activity on Mitcham Common, for example, five pairs bred successfully as recently as 1936, and after a fall in numbers there were again four in 1954.

First arrival dates in 47 years have been five times in April (earliest 16.4.04), twenty-one times between May 1st and 7th, thirteen times between the 8th and 15th, and eight times in the second half of May. Some birds appear to leave in July, a few are seen in most years up to the end of August and in seven years they have been observed in September (latest 19.9.49).

STARLING, *Sturnus vulgaris* L. Abundant resident; numbers augmented in winter by Continental immigrants.

The starling is the most ubiquitous, and apart from the house sparrow, the best known of all London birds. It breeds in holes in trees and buildings throughout the Area, including the parks, squares and bombed sites of central London. In the outer suburbs and rural districts it shows a preference for nesting near human habitations, probably because of the abundance and variety of the food supply but, unlike the house sparrow, it also nests freely in the open country. The starling was generally spoken of as increasing in the London Area at the beginning of the century but from all the accounts it appears to have been just as widespread then as it is now and it seems doubtful whether there has been any large-scale increase in the breeding population. It may be that a substantial increase took place towards the end of the last century, as Bucknill (1900) commented that "not so many years ago it was by no means so common" and he instances as evidence the publication in *The Field* in 1875 of the fact that a pair had bred in Richmond Park. On the other hand, Glegg (1935) said: "increased and increasing as the starling may be, so far back as one can trace it was a common bird even to Inner London".

There is no doubt that the starling ranks as one of the most successful of birds, and in the London Area this must be largely due to its ability to live in close association with man. W. H. Hudson was one of the first to point out, in *Birds in London*, that the starling is not parasitic on man, in the same sense as the house sparrow. It thrives in the built-up areas because of the abundance of food and nesting sites (especially under the eaves of houses) but there is little evidence that it is becoming any less common in the rural areas. Hudson, rather fancifully, suggested that to a starling a building is equivalent to a sea-cliff and the roar of traffic to the roar of the sea.

The starling is also notoriously catholic in its feeding habits, as well as in its choice of nesting sites, and its liking for a great variety of animal and vegetable matter is another reason for its success in London by comparison with birds with more specialised diets. In the winter, starlings are among the most frequent visitors to suburban bird-tables; in the summer they search for insects on the smallest of lawns as well as in the fields. Rubbish dumps, allotments and sewage farms, where they travel around on the rotary filter arms, are favourite feeding grounds. In May, the oak woods, even as close to the centre as Highgate, are frequently invaded by hordes of young starlings in search of the caterpillar of the green oak-roller (*Tortrix viridana*).

The advantages to the starling of living in London are to some extent offset by the greater dangers. Chief among these is the domestic cat, which according to Fitter (1949) numbers over half a million in the County of London alone: this may mean at least five cats to every starling! The danger from cats is clearly shown by the following table of the cause of death of 234 starlings ringed in Trafalgar Square in 1949–52 and subsequently found in the suburbs:—

Killed by cat	55
Fell down chimney	8
Shot	7
Drowned	7
Killed by dog	1
Other causes	6
Causes not reported	150

Starlings are especially vulnerable to cats in the breeding season, when so much of their time is spent searching for food on the ground, and most of the above were killed in April, May or June.

Our knowledge of the movements of the starlings which inhabit London has been greatly aided by the fact that many thousands have been ringed, both in suburban gardens and at the roost in Trafalgar Square. Up to the end of 1953, nearly 550 recoveries had been reported. Unfortunately, very few of these relate to birds ringed as nestlings or as juveniles in brown plumage. Nevertheless, these few do show that while some London-born starlings are sedentary in their first winter (nine were found where ringed between August 1st and April 1st) others appear to wander and a few to migrate for considerable distances. Two juveniles moved distances of 14 and 25 miles respectively, both in an easterly direction, within two months of ringing. Four others were found outside the Area in their first winter; one ringed at Ongar in June was found dead at Llanelly, Carmarthen, 184 miles to the west, in February; the other three had migrated distances of up to 40 miles, two in a south-easterly direction and one south-west. Juveniles which move away probably return to the London Area but not necessarily to their exact birthplace; three birds were found 8 to 14 miles away in their second summer and one 10 miles away in its third summer. It should perhaps be mentioned that the direction of each of these recoveries indicates a genuine movement rather than a temporary displacement while travelling to a roost.

The recoveries from the starlings ringed as adults are even more difficult to interpret, partly because until recent years few ringers attempted to determine the sex or age of the birds they caught. It does seem certain, however, that the majority of the adult residents are sedentary, as ringing returns show them to be in other parts of Britain. Thus 92 out of 96 adults ringed in the London Area in the summer were recovered where ringed in subsequent winters or summers. The other four had moved as follows:—

Place and date of ringing			Place and date of recovery		
Finchley	June, 1949		Severn Stoke	April, 1953	95m. WNW
„	April, 1951		Tring	Dec., 1952	24m. NW
„	May, 1951		High Wycombe	Jan., 1952	24m. W
Totteridge	May, 1951		Leyton	Jan., 1953	8m. SE

The last was possibly a first summer bird which had not yet acquired a territory, but the others were carefully examined and were certainly adult. The first was a female which was nesting when first ringed and was re-caught where ringed in March, 1951. Of the many thousands of adult starlings ringed and recovered in Britain, less than a dozen have been found in a subsequent breeding season more than a few miles from the place of ringing—the bird found at Severn Stoke on April 30th had travelled further than any.

Further evidence of the non-migratory habits of adult London starlings is shown by the fact that 230 out of 239 ringed in winter and recovered in summer were found at or near the place of ringing. The nine exceptions had moved away up to 75 miles, all but two in an easterly direction. Not all of these birds were critically examined when ringed but five, caught in Trafalgar Square, were judged to be in first winter plumage and it seems likely that the others were also immature birds which later returned to their birthplaces. The same tendency is shown by the recovery at North Mimms in July of a bird ringed at Oxford in January.

To summarise: a proportion (perhaps a third) of the starlings born in London move away for their first winter but very few move any distance once they are fully adult; in winter a number of juveniles born elsewhere in southern England move into or migrate through the London Area.

The winter population is also greatly increased, of course, by hordes of starlings from the Continent. These birds begin to arrive in October and from then until mid-November flocks can frequently be seen flying over all parts of the Area, including the centre of London, in the early hours of the morning. The general direction of the flocks is westerly and there can be little doubt that they are part of the huge numbers which migrate up the Thames estuary. Eleven starlings ringed in winter in Outer London and three at the roost in Trafalgar Square have been recovered on the Continent—six in Holland (including the three from Trafalgar Square), three in Germany and one each in Poland, Lithuania, Latvia, Denmark and Russia (Moscow). Seventeen birds ringed abroad and recovered in London in winter came from similar sources.

The roosting habits of London's starlings are discussed in the chapter on roosts and flylines.

[ROSE-COLOURED STARLING, *Sturnus roseus* (L.)]
A bird which was considered by C. A. White and several other observers to have been an immature rose-coloured starling was seen at Perry Oaks sewage farm in July, 1952, but as the colour of the crown and mantle was not typical of this species the record was not considered conclusive (cf. *L.B.R.*, 17:34).

In the early part of the century Frank Finn liberated a dozen specimens of this species in St. James's Park. One was killed by a stone and another was seen about 12 miles from London a fortnight later (*Ornithological and other Oddities*, 1907).

HAWFINCH, *Coccothraustes coccothraustes* (L.). Resident throughout the Area in suitably wooded localities, but rather thinly distributed and nowhere really common.

The hawfinch presents exceptional difficulties in the estimation of its relative abundance. Its shy and retiring habits, coupled with its lack of an audibly conspicuous song, make it possible for many people, even if they are interested in birds, to live for years in a district without ever discovering that there are hawfinches there. Moreover, there is reason to suppose that advancing years render some observers unable to hear the flight-note which is one of the bird's most useful field characters. Bearing in mind both this and the fact that the number of people recording their observations has very greatly increased since the beginning of the century, it is probable that the hawfinch has in fact increased in the London Area in the same way as it has over the whole country, according to Lack and Alexander (1944). However, some excellent observers record decreases in certain areas, and it is not possible to be entirely sure that there has actually been a general increase. Indeed the number of times an increase or decrease of hawfinches has been recorded in some part of the London Area since 1900 suggests that hawfinch populations regularly fluctuate to a greater degree than those of most other birds.

The hawfinch prefers well-wooded country, whether actual woodland or parks, gardens or orchards. At the beginning of the century its preference for orchards, especially in parts of Kent and Middlesex, seems to have been more marked than during the 1940's. Alternatively, it is possible that few modern bird-watchers choose to visit orchards. As a result of its liking for well-timbered districts, the hawfinch is absent from relatively treeless areas, such as the immediate surroundings of the Thames below London. It is also, of course, absent from Inner London, though stragglers appear from time to time in the Central Parks, and a pair frequented the sheepfold in Kensington Gardens from April 23rd to May 2nd, 1947. There are many well-wooded parts of the inner suburbs, however, and the hawfinch breeds regularly, or at any rate is seen regularly throughout the breeding season, in places as near the centre as Dulwich Woods, Tooting Bec Common, Wimbledon Common, Putney Heath, Hampstead and Highgate. In 1951 a family party was seen in Regent's Park in July and in 1952 young were being fed in June. Breeding has also been suspected in St. John's Wood. Epping Forest, of course, has long been known as a favourite resort of the hawfinch; and indeed it was from here that it was first recorded as breeding in Britain, by Henry Doubleday in 1832.

The great attraction of Epping Forest to the hawfinch is its profusion of hornbeams. At times in the early months of the year the flocks under the hornbeams feeding on the seeds may run into hundreds, and this flocking has been noticed elsewhere in the Area. Indeed one observer has been misled into supposing that these flocks, attracted to one spot by an abundance of food, are composed of migratory birds. There is, however, no evidence of anything but local movements among hawfinches anywhere in the British Isles. Unfortunately, none of the flocks alleged to run into hundreds have been accurately counted, though Howard Bentham records a flock of 260 in a Surrey locality only just outside the 20-mile radius, in March, 1919. In the London Naturalist for 1937, P. W. E. Currie describes an interesting association between hawfinches and thrushes on the North Downs in Surrey. The thrush flocks were feeding on yew berries and discarding the seed after eating the soft, sticky flesh; the finches were following them and eating the rejected seeds. The same association has been noticed by J. S. Wightman, who also remarks on their fondness for beechmast and hawthorn berries, which may be one of the factors influencing their distribution.

GREENFINCH, *Chloris chloris* (L.). Present throughout the year, breeding commonly where there are gardens, parks, shrubberies, hedges or scattered bushes.

At the beginning of the century the greenfinch was less common than it is now, and was only a winter visitor to Inner London. An increase was already noticeable in the 1910–15 period, and in a few instances as early as 1905. As a breeding species to-day the greenfinch is pre-eminently a suburban bird, though fairly common also in the more rural parts of the Area. It does not occur, except as a straggler, in the innermost parts of the built-up area, but breeds as near the centre as Hyde and Regent's Parks. In autumn and winter the breeding haunts are largely forsaken for more open areas, such as stubbles, ploughland, waste ground with weeds and cornstacks, where the greenfinch occurs in mixed flocks of finches, sparrows and buntings. The bird is a not uncommon visitor to suburban bird-tables, and in autumn flocks will also visit hornbeam woods, such as Epping Forest, for the fallen seeds.

Little is on record about roosting habits, but the blackthorn thicket in Epping Forest where twenty-five were roosting in January, 1949, is probably fairly typical of the sites chosen, while the single bird seen with starlings on the Public Record Office in October, 1945, was behaving quite abnormally.

The greenfinches of the suburbs do not appear to be sedentary and after the breeding season some at any rate take part in a south-westerly movement. Three birds recovered in various Middlesex suburbs in April had been ringed in winter at Ewhurst, Reading and Weymouth respectively. Similarly, it seems that greenfinches from farther north may winter in or pass through the Area: e.g. one ringed at Southall in January was recorded at Offley (North Herts.) in June, and another moved from Great Munden (Herts.) in February to North Yorkshire in March. The significance of moves from Southall in August to Oxford in February and from Epsom in February to Blackheath in March is more doubtful. Diurnal migration of small parties of up to thirty green finches flying in directions varying from south-west to north-west has been observed in the early mornings in October and early November in various parts of the Area.

GOLDFINCH, *Carduelis carduelis* (L.). Present throughout the year, breeding especially in gardens, orchards, parks and similar places.

Few birds now breeding around London can show a more spectacular recovery in numbers than the goldfinch, from virtual extinction to relative abundance. In 1900 it was reaching the end of a thirty- or forty-year period during which it had dwindled from being a comparatively common resident to one of the rarest breeding birds in the Area. About 1907–08 it seems to have begun to recover, and by the middle of this century it had regained its apparent numerical strength of the middle of the previous century. It has always been customary to attribute the decline of the goldfinch to the activities of the bird-catcher and its recovery to the enforcement of the Wild Birds Protection Acts, but there is no concrete evidence of this and it is in fact a mere guess. What does seem to coincide with this decline is the collapse of British agriculture, but the goldfinch began to recover before the farmers, so that here too we can only speculate as to a possible connection.

As a breeding species to-day the goldfinch is, like the greenfinch, pre-eminently a suburban bird, and in Inner London within the last few years fledged young have been seen in Battersea Park, Brompton Cemetery, Chelsea Hospital grounds and Regent's Park where at least two pairs bred in 1953. It has also been recorded in the breeding season in St. John's Wood. At other times flocks of up to 30 have been seen in Battersea and on the bombed sites in Cripplegate. Orchards and gardens are especially favoured in the breeding season, when it may also be found among hedgerows, copses and open commons, but less commonly than in the neighbourhood of human habitations.

In autumn and winter the goldfinch frequents waste ground to feed on thistles, gardens to feed on the seed-heads of various cultivated composites and groups of birches and alders. At these times of year it often flocks with other cardueline finches, and its numbers sometimes run into fifties or even hundreds, a flock of 200 at Watford sewage farm in March, 1949, representing the maximum normally to be expected, although larger numbers have been seen there.

The only evidence of migration is circumstantial, for at the turn of the century the majority of the few goldfinches seen in the Area occurred in autumn and winter and must have come from outside it. The Continental race of the goldfinch (*C.c. carduelis*) has never been proved to occur in Britain, and the presumption is that the London Area birds to-day are relatively sedentary. Observations from the Thames estuary, however, suggest that some goldfinches do take part in the westerly movement of other finches, and it may well be that immigration from the Continent does occur.

SISKIN, *Carduelis spinus* (L.). Regular winter visitor and passage migrant in fluctuating numbers.

The siskin is one of those seed-eaters whose numbers in the British Isles vary according to the success or failure of some seed-crop in its northern breeding haunts (Tischler, *Die Vögel Ostpreussens*, 1941, 1:122). This accounts for the fact that it is notably commoner in some years, such as 1935 and 1937, than in others. These fluctuations make it more than usually difficult to determine whether it has changed its status in the Area since 1900 or not, but there is no actual evidence of any change. The siskin is much more local than most regular passerine winter-visitors, on account of its marked preference for feeding (often in company with redpolls and goldfinches) on alders which are themselves comparatively localised in the Area. It also feeds, but less commonly, on birches, which are more widespread. It is therefore seen most often by lakes or rivers fringed by alders, such as Highams Park at Chingford, the Pen Ponds in Richmond Park and the River Colne near Uxbridge, or on sandy heaths and commons with birchwoods, such as Hampstead Heath and Wimbledon Common. Flocks of up to a hundred or more have been seen. The scarcity of both alders and birches in Inner London probably accounts for its extreme rarity there, the only records being of a bird feeding on an alder in St. James's Park in December, 1908, and of isolated occurrences at Holland Park and Ladbroke Square.

The earliest and latest dates for the species in the Area accord well with those given in *The Handbook of British Birds* for migration on the east coast: arrival, third week September to first week November (extremes August 28th and November 26th); departure, April and early May. First arrival dates are available for 34 years: September and December three each, October fifteen and November thirteen. Birds have been first seen throughout October and November, with a slight peak in the last ten days of October. The three September records are worth detailing: September 24th 1939, a small flock of about eight at Hayes (Kent); September 4th 1940, several near the Leg of Mutton Pond on Hampstead Heath and September 11th, 1943, about a dozen with redpolls at South Croydon. The large number of records in March and April suggests the probability of a passage movement through the Area at that time. The latest departure dates (for 40 years) show a very marked peak in April, suggesting that in the fifteen years in which the bird was last seen in one of the three earlier months there has been insufficient observation. In twenty-one years the bird was last seen in April, the actual dates being evenly spread out over the month. There is a single record for May: a bird in breeding plumage on Wimbledon Common on May 1st, 1935.

There is no definite breeding record for the Area during the period under review, although Walpole-Bond (1901, see also Ticehurst 1909) watched a pair building a nest in Sundridge Park, near Bromley, in April 1901. On his next visit the nest had been destroyed, so it is not certain whether the birds ever laid. There are only two other records for the breeding season: Weybridge, one singing in May and on June 9th, 1924;

and Bushy Park, ten present from July 23rd to 29th 1941. It is idle to speculate on the origin of these birds.

LINNET, *Carduelis cannabina* (L.). Present throughout the year; widespread and fairly common in the breeding season and out of it.

Like other cardueline finches, the linnet appears to have increased in the Area for the first ten or twenty years of the century, and it is reasonable to suppose that the virtual cessation of bird-catching may have had something to do with this. In recent years there seem to have been only local fluctuations in numbers due to the ploughing-up of commons or rough ground and subsequent reversion of such land to a natural state. The linnet is intermediate between the greenfinch and the redpoll in both abundance and habitat. Commoner than the redpoll, it is less restricted to bushy places, for it nests in quite low vegetation, even in cabbages. Unlike the greenfinch it has never colonised the inner suburbs, and is much less partial to gardens. Its chief haunts are gorse-covered commons and patches of rough ground dotted with scrub or unkempt hedges. On the marshes along the Thames the linnet breeds freely in hedges, bushes and thick ground vegetation, even as far upstream as Greenwich.

In winter the linnet tends to flock and move away from its breeding territories to open ground, wastes and stubbles. Such a large proportion of British breeding linnets emigrate in autumn that the majority of those seen in winter are probably immigrants either from the Continent or from further north in Britain. Though there is no definite evidence of their origin, there is a marked westward movement of linnets in late autumn in the Thames estuary which must presumably come into our Area. The three relevant ringing returns from a distance all point to emigration of London-breeding linnets to the Continent. A nestling ringed at Orpington in July was recovered in the western Pyrenees in the following November; another ringed at Woldingham in June turned up in the Gironde, also in November; the third, ringed at Limpsfield in May, had gone no further than Eastbourne by the following October, but it is reasonable to suppose that it would shortly have crossed the Channel.

Among the seeds on which linnets have been recorded as feeding in the Area are those of *Onopordon* and other thistles, a dock (*Rumex palustris*), bur-marigold, goosefoot, persicaria, mugwort and water-cress.

In Inner London the linnet is normally distinctly uncommon, and the only record of its breeding in our period is for Hyde Park in 1918. Within the last few years, however, there has once been a party of 15–16 in Cripplegate at the end of March and in early April, and a flock of up to about 56 in Regent's Park from February to April.

TWITE, *Carduelis flavirostris* (L.). Very rare winter visitor.

The twite can easily be overlooked and may, therefore, be less uncommon than the five authentic records would suggest. E. M. Nicholson saw two in Kensington Gardens on November 21st, 1925 (*Field*, 146:978). H. Murray saw a pair in the Roding Valley, near Barking, somewhere about 1930. Two, which were probably both females, were identified by S. Cramp at Barn Elms Reservoir on October 28th, 1946, and R. H. Ryall saw two on Staines Moor on September 29th, 1948. Four were seen at Staines by H. P. Medhurst on February 2nd, 1953.

One other record, without any details of identification, is contained in Walter Johnson's "*Animal Life in London*", in which he refers to seeing a bird of this species on an allotment on Clapham Common on January 1st, 1918. When the twite was a commoner breeding species in the north of England it may well have been a more frequent visitor inland as it was in coastal districts.

REDPOLL, *Carduelis flammea* (L.). Present throughout the year; the small breeding population consists of lesser redpolls (*C.f. cabaret*), the distinctly larger winter and passage population probably consisting mainly of this race with an admixture of an unknown proportion of mealy redpolls (*C.f. flammea*) and possibly other forms.

In the first decade of the century the breeding population of the lesser redpoll appears to have been expanding; thus in Kent Walpole-Bond (*Field*, 5.10.07) considered it had "increased wonderfully during the last few years round Bromley". A smaller increase is recorded for the whole country by Alexander and Lack (1944), and attributed by them possibly to the decrease in bird-catching. Apart from this, there seems to be little recorded change in the status, breeding or otherwise, of the lesser redpoll in the London Area since 1900. It is a widespread, but sparse and rather local, nesting species, especially on heaths and commons, and in the outer suburbs where there are large gardens or orchards. Well-known and favourite localities include Hampstead Heath, Epping Forest, Wimbledon Common, Ashtead, Beckenham, Oxted, Banstead Heath and Tadworth. In the more built-up and the purely agricultural parts the lesser redpoll is distinctly uncommon in the breeding season.

There is evidence of a marked influx of redpolls in both spring and autumn, though nothing is yet known of the origin of these immigrants. At these times, and throughout the winter, parties of redpolls, often with siskins and goldfinches, are commonly seen wherever there are alders or birches; the banks of the River Colne near Uxbridge, the West Heath at Hampstead, Highams Park and Arbrook Common are among their favourite haunts. Although the winter population is larger than the summer one, the increase may be at least partly due to the summer breeding population gathering together in a relatively few places instead of being widely scattered. It is not known what proportion of British breeding birds emigrate in winter.

The identification of the mealy redpoll in the field is a highly skilled exercise, for it must be differentiated not only from the lesser redpoll, but also from the Greenland redpoll (*C.f. rostrata*), a regular immigrant into Britain, and from the two races of the arctic redpoll (*C. hornemanni*) which have occasionally been reported in the British Isles. Nevertheless, enough birds have been seen by reliable observers to make it very probable that mealy redpolls do visit or pass through the Area each year unrecorded. Bearing in mind that many mealies are indistinguishable from lessers in the field, it is probable that many winter flocks have in the past been uncritically assigned to the latter race, and the same applies to the records of immigrant lesser redpolls on the east coast of England. It has to be remembered that the lesser redpoll is a race of the mountain systems of south and central Europe, while the mealy occupies northern Europe, which is the source of the bulk of our wintering species. It follows that such lesser redpolls as do pass through the Area are most likely to originate from further north in Britain although it is possible that some arrive with the westerly movement of finches and other species that reaches south-east England in October and November.

In addition to the catkins of birch and alder, the recorded food of redpolls in the London Area includes the seeds or buds of pine, hazel, witch-hazel, hawthorn, rhododendron and laurel, and the seeds of stinging nettle, meadow-sweet, mugwort, reed-mace and hairy willow-herb.

Hardly any information is available as to roosting habits, but a flock of over a hundred roosted in some rhododendrons in Epping Forest in February and March, 1935. Roosting has also been recorded in hawthorns mixed with gorse.

In Inner London redpolls are occasional autumn visitors, and there are recent records for April, July and October.

BULLFINCH, *Pyrrhula pyrrhula* (L.). Resident, and fairly common in all suitable places.

The status of the bullfinch in the Area appears to have been stable throughout the first half of the century, except perhaps for a slight retreat towards the country as the larger gardens of the inner suburbs have been built over. The bullfinch can be found throughout the rural and outer suburban parts of the Area in woods, parks, and large gardens, and on heaths and commons; it is especially fond of great overgrown hedgerows such as those of the Essex green lanes north of Epping, and shuns Inner London more than most woodland birds. It seems never to have bred there, and is only a scarce wanderer. Since 1945 the bullfinch has continued to breed as near the centre as Shooters Hill, Dulwich, Ranelagh and Hampstead Heath. All the evidence points to it being purely sedentary in the London Area, though family parties tend to wander a little in winter and may turn up in places where they do not breed.

An unusually wide range of food-plants has been recorded for the bullfinch in the London Area. Contrary to the bird's usual reputation, there is hardly any mention of attacks on fruit buds. However, it has eaten the buds of cherry-plum, wild cherry, and Japanese quince, and the seeds or fruits of the birch, bramble, mulberry, laburnum, sycamore, loganberry, raspberry, delphinium, sunflower, dock, stinging-nettle, willow-herb and dandelion.

Although one or two observers have considered that birds seen have resembled the northern race of the bullfinch (*P.p. pyrrhula*), there have not been any undoubted records in our period.

CROSSBILL, *Loxia curvirostra* L. Irregular late-summer and early-autumn immigrant, often staying through the winter, and occasionally breeding.

The crossbill irrupts across the North Sea in years when the spruce-cone crop fails in northern Europe. In the period under review there have been two important "crossbill years" when the bird has invaded the Area on a large scale, viz. 1909–10 and 1935–36, several other years when minor irruptions have occurred, notably 1927–28, 1930–31 and 1953–54, and a good many others when odd birds or parties have been reported. In fact, the crossbill has occurred in the Area in twenty-nine years out of the fifty-five here reviewed, and there have been two periods of relative frequency, from 1907–14 and 1924–39. During the 1940's crossbills were strikingly scarce in the Area. Usually not more than ten or twenty birds are seen together, but flocks have sometimes reached up to fifty or so and once, near Woodmansterne in 1909, there was a party of 150.

Breeding has occurred on a number of occasions. Macklin wrote that young birds were often seen at Keston but the period covered is not clear (Turner, 1909). In 1910, after the biggest invasion of all, pairs bred at Gerrards Cross, Walton Heath (and again in 1914, possibly showing continuity), Keston, Croydon, Weybridge and Bostall Woods; at the last named place, actually within the County of London, no fewer than six pairs bred. Later invasions have produced far fewer records of breeding; Addington, 1926; Iver Heath, 1931; Kew Gardens, 1936. In 1943 a pair was seen carrying material to a nest-site on Reigate Heath, but breeding was never proved.

The occurrences of crossbills in any district are regulated by the distribution of conifers, and this is the case also in the London Area, where they have been recorded on larches, Scots pine and the Corsican pine. Only two records connect the bird with any other type of tree: in August, 1927, two were feeding on woolly aphis on an old apple tree at West Ealing, and in September, 1953, a party fed on white-beam berries at Shirley, Surrey.

In Inner London, where there are very few conifers, crossbills have been recorded once: a party flying over Kensington Gardens on November 21st, 1909.

CHAFFINCH, *Fringilla coelebs* L. Abundant and widespread resident; numbers augmented in autumn and winter by Continental immigrants.

The chaffinch is probably the most common and widespread of all the birds in the London Area, for while the house sparrow is more numerous in the heavily built-up districts, the chaffinch may well outnumber it in the outer suburbs, as it unquestionably does in the rural areas. This status does not seem to have altered appreciably in the present century; in 1900 the chaffinch had already disappeared from the Bloomsbury squares and it was by no means common in the central parks. The East-end bird fanciers were very numerous at this time and they prized chaffinches above all other species. Hudson (1898) describes how the fanciers used to go in large numbers to Victoria Park and slouch about in the shrubberies looking for wild birds for their caged birds to challenge and sing against. There is no doubt, as Hudson said, that these men frequently used bird-lime and other means to catch wild birds; the *Times* of January 1st, 1901, contains a report of a man found in Richmond Park with forty chaffinches and other birds on him. To-day, with a more enlightened attitude, the chaffinch is a little more common in central London and it breeds in small numbers in all the larger parks, as well as in the large gardens of St. John's Wood and Campden Hill, but it has not returned to nest in the central squares. In the suburbs and beyond the chaffinch breeds in abundance wherever there are trees, that is practically everywhere except on some of the marshes and levels bordering the lower reaches of the Thames.

The breeding population of chaffinches appears to be more or less resident. Some of the birds may join up with the winter flocks and move about within the Area but, to date, the only recovery away from the place of ringing of a chaffinch ringed in the breeding season is of a young bird ringed at Dartford, Kent, on May 20th, 1952, and recovered 13 miles N. at Brentwood, Essex, on January 3rd, 1953.

In the autumn and winter the resident population is greatly augmented by immigrants from the Continent. These birds begin to arrive towards the end of September and the immigration, with, presumably, some birds stopping in the Area and many others passing through, continues until early November. The visual observation of the vast movements which take place was first described by F. D. Power, who kept watch at Brixton from 1874 to 1909. To quote from him:—

"On a favourable occasion flock after flock, containing half a dozen to fifty or more birds, will pass in an almost continuous stream for hours i.e., from 8 a.m. to noon or thereabouts. One of the most remarkable of these passages occurred in 1902, when the first flock passed over on the 7th October, and others almost daily until the 5th of November; . . . during this time many thousands must have passed before my eyes. In that year the heaviest 'rushes' were between the 21st and 26th, and throughout this time the wind was chiefly W. by N."

Power referred to these immigrant chaffinches as "foreign visitors" and that he was right was shown by the famous observations of Eagle Clarke, in 1903, of vast westerly movements in the Thames estuary. There are no further records until the Octobers of 1925, 1927 and 1928, when Professor Warmington, A. Holte Macpherson and L. Parmenter recorded small isolated movements over Bloomsbury, Hyde Park and Kensington Gardens respectively. Thereafter, there are scarcely any published notes until 1948 when W. G. Teagle reported a pronounced north-westerly migration through the Green Park, St. James's Park and Kensington Gardens on five dates in October and early November. In the following years, systematic watching from the rooftops of Trafalgar Square and other vantage points in and around London has shown that movements similar to those observed by Power can still be seen. On October 14th, 1950, for example, 75 flocks of chaffinches, totalling 715 birds, were counted passing over Trafalgar Square between the hours of 7.30 a.m. and 10 a.m. There was a light W.S.W.

breeze and the direction of flight was always westerly and in all but one case between W.S.W. and W.N.W. Parallel observations in the suburbs have shown that these movements take place on a broad front, with no evidence that the Thames is closely followed, although nearer the estuary, on Swanscombe marshes, chaffinches have been seen coasting along the river wall.

Some of the migrating parties have been seen to alight in the Area but whether they go on again or stay the winter is uncertain. It is certain, however, that the winter population is much higher than in the summer and some, probably most, of the birds which flock with other finches and haunt stack yards, arable land and beechwoods are of Continental origin. From the observed direction of migration, these birds are most likely to be *F.c. hortensis*, the Central European form, and Dr. J. M. Harrison (1953) has shown that, in Kent, most of the winter visitors are of this race although the Scandinavian race, *F.c. coelebs*, also occurs in small numbers. An immature female chaffinch ringed at Cricklewood on December 31st, 1949, seems clearly to have been *coelebs* as it was recovered at Harads, North Sweden, on August 12th, 1950, while a male ringed in the Province of Aland in October, 1955, was caught in Weald Park, near Brentwood, a month later. There are four other recoveries showing movement from the Continent (France, Belgium and Holland), but as the dates of ringing and recovery are outside the breeding season the evidence of origin is inconclusive.

The winter flocks are frequently entirely, or mostly, of one sex; for example, a flock of 150 at High Beech on April 14th, 1941, was composed almost entirely of females while another at the same place on January 10th, 1942, was 70% male. When the weather is cold, chaffinches are frequent visitors to garden bird tables and they sometimes occur in quite busy streets.

There is very little evidence as yet of migration in the spring on a similar scale to the autumn movements. A. Holte Macpherson stated in the Park Sanctuaries reports that there was an annual spring movement through St. James's Park with the early arrivals all hens and the later birds all cocks. In 1932 this movement lasted from January 25th to March 22nd. It is referred to in subsequent reports, but seems to have ceased about 1936. There is also some evidence of an influx in late February; J. E. Roberts noticed large numbers in Bushy Park on February 27th, 1934, and a tremendous influx of many hundreds on February 18th, 1935. Other writers about this time referred to a similar "spring rush" but it does not appear to have been noticed in recent years.

BRAMBLING, *Fringilla montifringilla* L. Winter visitor and passage migrant, varying greatly in its relative abundance from year to year.

Like the siskin and the crossbill, the two other immigrant seed-eaters which in the south are winter visitors only, the brambling is highly variable in its appearances. In some years it is common in many places besides its favoured haunts in Epping Forest and on the North Downs; in others the united efforts of the bird-watchers of the district may fail to discover one even in Epping Forest. In every year since watching became regular, however, several have appeared in some part or other of the Area. Records in the 40's, especially during 1945–49, are so singularly few as to suggest that perhaps people did not bother to submit records of bramblings during that period.

Bramblings are essentially ground-feeders, and are well known to prefer feeding under beeches. Indeed, it may be supposed that their predilection for the North Downs is largely due to the number of beeches there, just as in Epping Forest they are also fond of feeding under hornbeams. However, when joining, as they often do, with other finches they will commonly feed in the wide variety of ground-sites favoured by seed-eaters in general, such as stack yards and arable fields. In West Middlesex about 1934 they were said to be especially fond of the ploughlands after hop-manure had been applied.

Brambling flocks do not normally total more than fifty birds, but in a few favoured localities, notably Beddington Farm, they regularly run into hundreds, and in early 1953 flocks of 100 or over were seen near the William Girling reservoir and at Harold Wood, Perry Oaks sewage farm, Stone marshes, Keston, Barnes and Epsom. In late February and early March, 1954, there were up to about 300 at Romford sewage farm, and 100–150 at the Watford farm. During the daytime the largest flock on record for the Area is of 500–600 at Osterley in December, 1931, and January, 1932 (E. C. Rowberry). In 1951, however, about 3,000 bramblings roosted in rhododendron bushes in two acres of woodland at Westerham (*B.B.*, 44:386).

Especially at migration times, the brambling is fairly well distributed over the rural and outer suburban parts of the Area, coming not infrequently to such peripheral open spaces as Hampstead Heath, Richmond Park and Kew Gardens. In the centre it is an occasional visitor on passage, especially to the parks.

Analysis of the dates of arrival and departure of the brambling in the Area for the period 1919–53 shows that in twenty-five of these years it has first been seen in October, and in fourteen of them in the middle third of that month, between the 11th and 20th. The earliest date on record is September 28th, 1930, when one was seen at Sutton, Surrey, by P. H. T. Hartley; H. Bentham has seen the bird as early as October 1st in the Tadworth district. It is probable that some at any rate of the October and November birds are passage migrants, though we cannot know whether they emigrate or merely pass on to another part of southern England. In some well watched years hardly any seem to appear before November or even December. At the other end of the season there is clear evidence of a return passage movement in March, but in only nine out of the thirty-two years after 1919 were no bramblings seen in the Area after March 31st. The middle third of April holds the largest number of last dates, but in no fewer than six years stragglers stayed into May, once as late as the 6th (Wimbledon Common, 1938). There is also a record for Dulwich Park on May 9th, 1910. The exact status of a little group of June and July records is difficult to determine, as they are separated by nearly five weeks from the latest spring record, and by more than eleven weeks from the first autumn one. Perhaps they represent birds which were in some way delayed until they lost the migratory urge. There are four of these summer occurrences; a male shot at Enfield on July 7th, 1923 (R. B. Lodge, *B.B.*, 17:83); a male on Hampstead Heath from June 28th to July 9th, 1926 (R. W. Pethen, *Ib.*, 20:149); a male in Epping Forest from June 12–25, 1932 (P. D. Hayward, E. Mann); and one on Wimbledon Common on June 12th, 1938 (R. E. Windsor).

YELLOWHAMMER, *Emberiza citrinella* L. Resident, and a passage migrant of indeterminate status; fairly common in the more rural parts of the Area, scarce vagrant in the inner built-up area.

The principal change in the distribution of the yellowhammer since 1900 has been its retreat from many suburban districts. During the 40's and early 50's there have been local increases in a number of areas, such as Beckenham and Mill Hill, where it is attributed to the wartime intensification of agriculture, but whether these increases are maintained will depend on political and economic rather than natural circumstances. The presence of yellowhammers in a district is a good test of the retention of its country status, so that a list of the inner ring of recent yellowhammer breeding-season records may be of some assistance to those seeking a rural nook "within 40 minutes of Piccadilly". It runs as follows:— Shooter's Hill, Eltham, Beckenham, West Wickham, Park Downs, Epsom Downs, Wimbledon Common, Richmond Park, Horsendon Hill, Roxeth, Hendon, Mill Hill, Totteridge, Enfield, Chingford and Upminster. Within this ring the yellowhammer now occurs only in winter or on passage, if at all; beyond it, the bird becomes increasingly common towards the perimeter, especially in districts where hedges have not yet been sacrificed to the Moloch of mechanised agriculture.

On Hampstead Heath, where the bird was not uncommon up to about 1915, it seems to have hung on until about 1928–31, on the evidence of Dr. C. H. Andrewes and P. Z. Mackenzie. Then there is a gap till 1948, when one appeared on some allotments on March 22nd, evidently on passage. For a time after this it was regular in winter in flocks of up to 22 birds, but decreased again with the rehabilitation of the allotments and gun-sites. In 1954, however, there were five singing males in summer and nesting may have been attempted. In South London the yellowhammer was still breeding on Wandsworth Common at the end of the last century (Hudson, 1898), and it was occasionally seen in winter on Tooting and Wandsworth Commons by H. G. Attlee in the first decade of this century; towards the end of our period it was regarded as an occasional autumn passage migrant in the Dulwich and Peckham area by L. R. Evans in 1940–41. In Central London there are only seven records from 1900 to 1954, four of them since 1950; two have been in December and one each in January, March, April, July and October. All this points to sporadic passage migration, and it might be supposed that it represented dispersal of local breeding birds to and from their breeding territories and such feeding grounds as Barnes Common, where a flock of over 40 was seen in December, 1947. However, there is one record of visible migration; on October 29th, 1941, a day when snow had fallen on the east coast, eight were seen flying over Thornton Heath by L. Parmenter. As in most parts of the country, the yellowhammer flocks in winter and parties of a hundred or more may be seen, especially in hard weather.

CORN BUNTING, *Emberiza calandra* (L.). Resident; localised in the breeding season, but increasing in Essex in recent years; disperses from some breeding areas in late summer.

The status of the corn bunting is particularly hard to assess, for two reasons. First, since its nest is commonly esteemed to be one of the half-dozen hardest to find among British passerines, actual breeding records are so few that one has to rely on records of singing males as evidence of breeding. This procedure is normally reprehensible, but inevitable with the corn bunting. Second, its distribution is everywhere patchy; as Gillham & Homes (1950) put it, "there is a strong tendency for birds to occur in small colonies and to be absent from similar areas of intervening country". Hence, when one is dealing with periods when observation was also patchy, such as the first half of our period, it is impossible to say whether the blanks on the distribution map are due to the vagaries of buntings or of bird-watchers. In consequence until the last few years no definite statement could be made as to the change or otherwise in status of the corn bunting in the outer parts of the Area. The exception to this was in Surrey, where the bird does seem to have suffered a catastrophic decline even in those districts of the North Downs that have not been built over. Thus the only report since 1945 of the small colony that existed during the 1930's on Ewell Downs is of two singing males in the spring of 1952, though the land is still agricultural. Nearer to London, the bird was apparently common prior to 1914 over a region, mainly in the Wandle valley, stretching from Chipstead, Coulsdon and Purley to Worcester Park and Lower Morden. Apart from a single bird at Beddington sewage farm on May 3rd, 1948, there are no records at all of the bird here since 1940, and Beddington is the only part of the region where any were even seen between the wars, most of the district being now too much built over to be congenial to them.

On parts of the West Middlesex plain corn buntings are still quite well established where their nesting ground has not been lost in the construction of houses or reservoirs, and in 1953 H. A. Bilby located 15 singing males in the Harlington, Harmondsworth, London Airport and Sipson districts. On the Thames-side marshes corn buntings are probably more numerous than anywhere else in the Area: in the north up to 20 singing males were found at Rainham in 1951 and two years later three pairs were present as near in to London as Romford sewage farm. They appear to be extending their range annually and have now reached as far from the Thames as Brentwood sewage farm. South of the river in 1953 pairs were reported from Abbey Wood marshes eastwards, and up the Darent valley as far as Eynsford. There are some also on the downs around Long-field and Green Street Green. Elsewhere corn buntings are reported most frequently from the Old Parkbury and Shenley districts of Hertfordshire, and especially from Hare-field, Hainault, Molesey and Itchingwood Common. Though there is virtually no proof of breeding, it is apparent from the evidence of recent years that the corn bunting is less scarce than had been thought.

Out of the breeding season the corn bunting is a little more scattered. Along the Thames small parties resort to stubble-fields and rickyards in late summer and by September have disappeared entirely from the marshes, to which they return in March. A flock of 30 was seen at Brentwood sewage farm on November 29th, 1952. Within the built-up area the corn bunting is exceptionally rare and there is no record for Inner London at all, the nearest reports to the centre being as follows:— H. G. Attlee heard one singing on Wandsworth Common on March 12th and 14th, 1904, and saw some there again in February, 1908; he also saw about 40 on waste ground at Earlsfield in early March, 1904, and a dozen at the same place in November, 1907. One singing on Wool-wich Common on May 10th, 1946, probably originated from the colony on the Abbey Wood marshes.

CIRL BUNTING, *Emberiza cirlus* L. Resident, but extremely local and sporadic in its occurrence.

There is no evidence that the cirl bunting has changed appreciably in status since 1900. It appears always to have been a very local breeder, largely confined to the North Downs in Kent and Surrey, and the belts of country flanking the downs for a mile or two north and south. Only sixteen nests have been reported in the Area during the period, and of these ten were on or very near the North Downs:— at Banstead in 1900, Shoreham c.1902, Epsom 1905, Tadworth 1922 (2 pairs), Biggin Hill 1935, Chipstead (Surrey) 1942–43, Betchworth 1947 and Chaldon in 1949. Only one breeding record south of the Thames (Weybridge 1905) comes from outside this region. The cirl bunting is easily overlooked when in small numbers, and the frequency of recent reports of singing males around Chipstead and Betchworth, for instance, suggests that a few pairs may at one time have bred regularly in these districts. Birds were also seen regularly, both in and out of the breeding season, at Sutton in 1930–35 and at Tadworth in 1922–25, while in four years since 1927 they have occurred in Richmond Park or on the adjacent Ham Common during the breeding season (though breeding has never been proved), and also on Wimbledon Common in 1950. There have been three recent occurrences near the Thames, at Crayford, Dartford and Stone respectively.

North of the Thames the only certain breeding records are from Harrow (four nests from 1919 to 1928), and a number of the few remaining reports come from the Colne valley or Northwood district:— West Hyde and Staines 1949, Watford sewage farm 1950, Bushey Heath 1952 and Northwood 1954, all except the Staines record being during the period April–June. It seems probable that a pair or two may still breed occasionally somewhere in West Middlesex. The only other cirl buntings recorded this century north of the Thames were on Hampstead Heath in the winter of 1901–02, at Elstree in 1923, New Edgware in 1930 and Colney Street in 1947.

ORTOLAN, *Emberiza hortulana* L. Very rare vagrant.

In the *Zoologist* for 1908 (p.269) J. A. Clark recorded that a male ortolan in fine plumage had been obtained by R. M. Presland at Plaistow, E., on May 6th, 1908. It was preserved by Mr. Houghton of Dalston, but its present whereabouts are not known. Though this date falls in the migration period, cage-birds were in those days more numerous and the ortolan was a popular species. More recently Pounds (*B.B.*, 41:20) observed an adult on the North Downs in Surrey on August 23rd, 1947.

REED BUNTING, *Emberiza schoeniclus* (L.). Resident, breeding not uncommonly throughout the more rural parts in suitably damp places; also passage migrant of unknown origin, and perhaps winter visitor.

There is no evidence of any general change in status in the reed bunting in the rural parts of the Area since 1900, though inevitably the vast surge of building has engulfed some former breeding sites in what are now inner but were then outer suburbs. There have, of course, been local fluctuations, such as an increase in western Essex and a decrease in Richmond Park. Now, as in 1900, the reed bunting breeds in marshy meadows, swamps, gravel-pits, riversides, overgrown ditches, and similar places, where it can be reasonably looked for beyond an inner ring running roughly as follows:— Greenwich Marshes, Foots Cray, Elmers End, Wimbledon Common, Richmond Park, Ham Common, Syon Marsh, Horsendon Hill, Brent Reservoir, Mill Hill, Chingford, Walthamstow, Mayesbrook Park, Hornchurch Marshes. In 1946 there was an isolated breeding record for Hampstead Heath, the first for 25 years, and in recent years one pair has bred at Barn Elms.

Outside the breeding-season the reed bunting flocks, and visits arable fields and similar feeding grounds in places such as the North Downs, where there may be no breeding-ground for miles. Howard Bentham, in observations extending over many years, has noted a sharp increase in the numbers of reed buntings in Surrey in October, and a similar increase has been noted in other parts of the Area in autumn, and to a less extent in spring. It is always hard to decide whether such increases represent a banding together of breeders from a few miles around or a genuine immigration, possibly from abroad. However, the passage of reed buntings on the east coast is so marked and well known that the temporary appearance of parties of up to thirty on the Thames Marshes in October may reasonably be presumed to be part of this movement. Whether, if there is an immigration, some of the birds taking part stay in the Area through the winter is more obscure. It is most surprising that none have ever been seen in the Inner London parks.

[LAPLAND BUNTING, *Calcarius lapponicus* (L.)]

A bird with the flight and shape of a Lapland bunting was flushed at Perry Oaks sewage farm by W. H. Dady and A. Gibbs on October 10th, 1953, and the characteristic call was heard clearly. Though both observers had had recent experience of the note it was felt, in view of the rarity of the species inland, that the record should be left in square brackets as no plumage details could be obtained.

SNOW BUNTING, *Plectrophenax nivalis* L. Rare passage migrant, mainly in November.

The snow bunting appears in our Area with some regularity, usually in the late autumn, at which time it is presumably on passage to coastal wintering areas. Nearly all the reports are of single birds, although parties of four and five have been seen on two occasions.

Only two records are known before 1925. Whiting (*Selborne Magazine*, 13:75) refers to some seen on Hampstead Heath during the winter of 1901–2, and one was seen at Brockley, S.E.4, in the winter of 1905 (Macklin in Turner, 1909).

During the latter half of our period snow buntings have been seen more frequently, especially at the reservoirs and other waters. The only spring record is of one at High Beech, Epping Forest, on March 13th, 1925. Twelve of the remaining fifteen records have been in November, and one each in September, October and December. The September record, an exceptionally early one, is of a single bird seen at Mill Hill by Professor E. H. Warmington on September 12th, 1929. All the records from 1925 onwards have been north of the Thames with the exception of single birds seen by H. E. Pounds on Dulwich Common in November, 1951 and 1952.

HOUSE SPARROW, *Passer domesticus* (L.). Common resident, occurring in all parts of the Area, although, except for foraging parties in the autumn and winter, it is rarely found far from buildings.

The house sparrow population is most dense in central London, where the greatest numbers are found in parks, gardens, bombed sites, docks and other open spaces rather than in the completely built-up zones with few trees. The density tends to decrease as we proceed outwards and on the fringe the population is much more scattered. For example, H. A. Bilby carried out a breeding census in 1948 over 618 acres at Harlington, Middlesex (consisting mainly of agricultural land and orchards, with only 80 acres of gardens and built-up land), and found approximately 65 pairs of house sparrows, or about 0.2 birds per acre. This may be compared with a density of 4.3 birds per acre found by S. Cramp in 43 acres of Bloomsbury (mainly built-up but including three squares and some gardens), and with 4.0 birds per acre counted by W. G. Teagle in Lambeth (again mainly built-up, but with bombed areas), both in the 1950 breeding season. There are few other estimates of population. Nicholson (*Birds and Men,* 1951) states that surveys in Battersea Park, which is, in his view, an exceptionally favoured area, indicated a density of some five sparrows per acre in the spring of 1945 and 1950. A series of winter counts made by E. M. and B. D. Nicholson in 1925–26 in Kensington Gardens gave an average density of about nine sparrows an acre (*Discovery,* August, 1926), but when similar counts were made in the winter of 1948–49 by Cramp and Teagle (1950) the average density was only about three birds per acre.

These last results lend some support to the view of several observers that the sparrow population of central London has declined during this century. The most common explanation is that this is largely due to the reduction in their food supplies following the almost complete replacement of horse-traffic by motors. A decrease has also been noted in parts of the United States, Canada and France, especially in towns, but it has occurred in some localities in the United States, such as poultry farms, where this factor would be of little importance (H. N. Southern (1945) *Annals App. Biol.,* 32(1):57–67). Similarly the sparrows of Kensington Gardens are likely to be only slightly affected by it, as bread forms a large part of their food. It is possible that the species is suffering a general decline in various parts of its range, due to causes largely unknown. As, however, house sparrows rapidly colonise newly built-up areas it is almost certain that the striking growth of London in the last fifty years has led to an increase in the total sparrow population of the area.

House sparrows now obtain relatively little of their food from the streets, except in certain areas, such as Covent Garden, where food is specially abundant. Their staple fare in most parts of London is now bread, provided by the public in parks, squares, gardens and backyards. For this reason there are noticeably fewer sparrows in those squares in central London not open to the public. They also feed on seeds of all kinds and in summer hawk crudely for insects and search the bark of trees like treecreepers. They have been seen investigating railway engines and car radiators for crushed insects. On the Thames they flock round grain barges as they are being unloaded, and they feed along the tide-line at certain seasons. Their degree of tameness varies considerably.

Thus, although in some parks and elsewhere they will take food from visitors, often perching on the hand, such behaviour is not universal, and in other places, including parts of Inner London, they will not allow close approach. They are quick to exploit new sources of food, and have been seen entering the wards of the Central Middlesex Hospital, perching on the beds and collecting scraps of food from the floors and even from plates. In one large London brewery they have found such a rich diet of fallen grain that they rarely leave the building, while in a dairy in St. Pancras they readily enter the bottle-cleaning room to feed on the scraps of fat left in the necks of the empty bottles.

The house sparrow will use any hole or cranny at a safe height for its nest. In the suburbs most nests are to be found under the eaves of houses, but in Inner London they commonly make use of the ventilation grids in modern office blocks, the crannies in statues and stone ornaments, or the holes made by bomb splinters. Where holes are lacking the sparrows will wedge their bulky nests behind drain-pipes or in rainwater heads. Sometimes they nest in trees, using natural holes or building large, untidy structures in the branches. In many parts of the Area they build in ivy and other creepers on the walls of houses, while lamp-posts are a favoured site in some districts, such as Regent's Park, where these contain a suitable cavity. Many sparrows use their nest holes for winter roosting, as has been described in the chapter on roosts and flylines.

In the late summer and autumn (and sometimes into the winter), large flocks of sparrows are found in cornfields, on sewage farms, the Thames marshes and other open spaces. Earlier naturalists believed that these flocks consisted of sparrows from Central London. This may have been so in the last century when London was much smaller but at the present time it is almost certain that they are made up of birds from adjacent areas. There is no noticeable diminution in numbers of sparrows in Inner London at this period, and an analysis of the ringing returns shows that British sparrows are extremely sedentary, very few having been recovered more than half a mile from the place of ringing.

TREE SPARROW, *Passer montanus* (L.). Resident, but distinctly local; probably also passage migrant.

There is no evidence of any general change in the breeding status of the tree sparrow in the Area since 1900, even to the extent of a retreat before the build r in the suburbs. Then, as now, it was a remarkably local bird, small colonies becoming attached to particular clumps or lines of trees, often in a park or along a river bank, but rarely straying far from their favoured spots during the breeding season. Whole tracts of the Area, notably the North Downs, may hold remarkably few tree sparrows in spring and summer, yet in others, like the Colne valley, especially in its Hertfordshire sector, Epping Forest and Beddington sewage farm, the bird is frequent, if not common. In Middlesex especially gravel pits are sometimes the site of thriving colonies, one of which at Feltham even uses the conveyor of a gravel storage tower for nesting. So localised is the tree sparrow at this time of year that only a very careful *ad hoc* survey of the whole Area would reveal its actual parochial distribution; it is unsafe to assume that an absence of reported occurrences means an absence of birds, particularly in such still relatively neglected districts as rural Hertfordshire and Essex and the Kentish North Downs. The Surrey North Downs, however, are annually watched and traversed by so many bird-watchers that it is reasonable to suppose that the relative scarcity there is a genuine one. Pounds (1952), for instance, who has watched the easternmost sector of the Surrey North Downs assiduously for twenty-eight years, knows of no breeding record for the district in that period.

The inner ring of recent breeding-season records runs as follows: Greenwich Park (till 1944 and possibly again in 1947), Chislehurst, Elmers End, Beddington, Mitcham, Richmond Park (a well-known haunt), Twickenham, Osterley Park, Horsendon Hill,

Barn Hill, Hendon, Mill Hill, Finchley, Enfield, Chingford, Walthamstow (where they have nested in drain-pipes), Woodford Bridge, Upminster. At Hampstead it does not seem to have been seen even in winter since 1933. The colony at Beddington is probably the largest, comprising some fifty pairs on the sewage farm and fifteen in the nearby park.

In autumn and winter the tree sparrow is rather more widespread, and visits sewage farms, arable fields, and other places where seeds are to be had, sometimes in exclusive flocks, but often with house sparrows, finches and buntings. Flocks of over 100 have been seen recently at the sewage farms at Beddington, Perry Oaks and Romford, and also on the Stone marshes. Until the 1890's it could be supposed that some of the winter flocks were composed of immigrants, as Power (1910) had regular records of migrating flocks of tree sparrows at Brixton. However, these ceased after 1898, nor had he any records of the bird at all after 1904. Although there is no subsequent direct evidence of migration, the tree sparrow is a well-known immigrant in the Thames Estuary, and J. F. Burton records that small flocks often occur in autumn and winter at Shooter's Hill, Southend and Eltham, where they do not breed. It is more than probable that the flocks which appear with house sparrows from October onwards on the marshes between Erith and Northfleet consist, at any rate partly, of Continental immigrants. The only tree sparrow reported from the central parks was in Regent's Park in October, 1952. Three were seen by Colonel Meinertzhagen in Kensington Park Gardens in May, 1928, and a small flock by L. R. Evans in the grounds of Cleeve Hall, Dulwich, in November, 1940.

APPENDIX

We have included here three species which have attempted to breed in a wild state, although introduced originally, and a few others the only records of which are thought to be of birds escaped from captivity.

BLACK STORK, *Ciconia nigra* (L.)
One was seen by R. Marlow with a party of herons in meadows at Hampton Mill on September 17th, 1946.

FLAMINGO, *Phoenicopterus ruber* L.
A flamingo was seen by W. A. Wright at King George V reservoir on July 14th and 15th, 1934 (*Essex Nat.*, 24:196).

RUDDY SHELDUCK, *Casarca* spp.
Four species of *Casarca* are kept in captivity in Britain, and as few observers who report "ruddy shelducks" are competent to distinguish between them, it seems better not to assign records to any one species. Apart from one old and now unprovable occurrence at Wallington, Surrey, from January 12th–19th, 1929 (*Country-Side*, summer 1929) practically all the records of ruddy shelducks in the Area appear to stem from the release of a number of South African shelducks (*C. cana*), together with possibly at least one hybrid of *C. cana* with *C. ferruginea*, from Kew Gardens at the outbreak of war in 1939. Some of these birds frequented the Thames at Chiswick, Kew and Richmond right up to 1950. One female took up residence on the small pond on Barnes Common and remained there on and off till it was found dead on May 24th, 1952, apparently killed by the cob of the resident pair of swans. In the winter of 1945–46 she was joined by a male and in the following summer they reared a brood on the river; since they left the pond in several subsequent breeding seasons they may well have reared other broods (H. A. Baylis).

Two were seen flying about and perching in trees in Richmond Park on March 11th, 1946, by Miss C. M. Acland. Several, possibly from Kew, frequented Ruislip Reservoir during 1940–42 (T. L. Bartlett) and on April 7th, 1940, one was prospecting burrows in Copse Wood.

A record of two seen flying over Brent Reservoir on May 9th, 1950, by A. Gibbs and T. Bispham, may refer to genuine wild *C. ferruginea* or to full-winged birds which are known to have been present at the time in St. James's Park and to have been in the habit of flying across to Regent's Park. Much the same applies to the bird seen at Brooklands Sewage Farm on April 22nd, 1939, by R. C. Homes.

EGYPTIAN GOOSE, *Alopochen aegyptiacus* (L.)

A pair of Egyptian geese made unsuccessful attempts to breed at Hamper Mill gravel pit in 1936 and 1937 and hatched off three young in 1938. It may have been this pair which was reported from Connaught Water, Epping Forest, about 1937. One frequented Ruislip reservoir from 1941 at least until the end of 1942. There have probably been many other cases of these geese straying from captivity.

BLACK SWAN, *Cygnus atratus* Latham

For at least the last twenty years black swans have been at large on the Thames and elsewhere in the Area, as a result either of deliberate introduction or accidental escape. Indeed so familiar have they become that at the annual swan-upping the black swans are always counted in with the Vintners' birds—in 1947 they had two (Fitter, 1949). During the middle 1930's a black swan frequently entered the West India Dock. More recently several were apparently released on the Thames, but only one survived the winter of 1946–47 and this could be seen regularly on the river between Teddington and Hampton Court (S. D. Stone, *Birds and Country Magazine*, June 1951, p.8; *Field*, 200:109). A single bird was present at Walthamstow reservoirs from June 28th to September 1st, 1936, and was possibly the same as turned up at the Sewardstone gravel pit on November 6th, 1937, and stayed until at least July 10th, 1938, when it deserted a clutch of infertile eggs it had laid in May. Meanwhile another bird, believed to have escaped from Chessington Zoo, was seen at Fetcham Pond, Surrey, from May 22nd to June 8th, 1937, and yet another at Elstree reservoir on December 26th, 1937.

BLACK KITE, *Milvus migrans* (Bodd.)

On May 18th, 1906, a black kite, which had escaped from the London Zoo, was seen perched on the Houses of Parliament by Sir Herbert Maxwell and others (Fitter, 1949). At the outbreak of war in 1939 several of these birds were released by the London Zoo, and one of them was seen by P. W. Horn flying over Stratford on two occasions on October 24th, 1939 (*B.B.*, 33:198).

BLACK GROUSE, *Lyrurus tetrix* (L.)

A black grouse was shot in Gullet Wood, Watford, on December 1st, 1906, possibly one of the many birds of this species which have been liberated at various times in the hope of establishing a breeding stock.

ROLLER, *Coracias garrulus* (L.)

On January 31st, 1945, a roller was seen at a range of fifty feet on a post on the banks of the River Ravensbourne by H. S. Kerley, who was able to give a detailed description, and in spite of the unusual nature of the record the editors of *British Birds* considered that the bird was probably a wild one (*B.B.*, 39:119). In view of the extraordinary date we feel that there is a strong possibility of the bird having escaped from captivity on one of the ships in the docks.

CHOUGH, *Pyrrhocorax pyrrhocorax* L.

The only record of the chough is of one shot near Hendon in the early part of 1900, and exhibited by J. E. Whiting at a meeting of the Hampstead Scientific Society on February 2nd, 1900.

SERIN, *Serinus canarius* (L.)

One was seen by Eric Simms at Dollis Hill on November 13th, 1951, but although its identity was not in question it was recorded in square brackets at the time in view of the possibility of its having been an escape (cf. *L.B.R.*, 16:8).

BIBLIOGRAPHY

So MUCH has been written on the birds of London and its surroundings in the present century that we have been obliged to restrict the bibliography to those books or papers which are quoted in the text or which have contributed materially to our work. The task of selection has at times been an invidious one, and many useful papers of local interest or whose scope is restricted to a single species have had to be omitted. In a few cases where a work has been quoted once only, it has been given in full in the text and not in the bibliography. A full list of all the papers which appeared in the *London Naturalist* or *London Bird Report* up to 1948 inclusive will be found in a summary by Ashby (1949).

We have included in full the list of periodicals and journals consulted, and most of the scientific societies whose transactions we have abstracted.

PERIODICALS AND JOURNALS

Avicultural Magazine
Bird Notes and News, continued as
    Bird Notes
British Birds
Country Life
Country-Side
Essex Naturalist
The Field
The Ibis
Journal of Animal Ecology
Journal of Ecology

London Bird Report
London Naturalist
Middle-Thames Naturalist
Naturalists Monthly Review
Naturalists Quarterly Review
Nature Notes, continued as
    Selborne Magazine
Oologists Record
South-Eastern Bird Report
South-Eastern Naturalist
The Times

The Zoologist

PROCEEDINGS, TRANSACTIONS, REPORTS OR RECORDS OF SOCIETIES

Barnet & District Natural History Society
British Empire Naturalists' Association
British Ornithologists' Club
Committee on Bird Sanctuaries in Royal Parks (England)
Croydon Natural History Society
Epsom College Natural History Society
Essex Bird-Watching and Preservation Society
Eton College Natural History Society
Hampstead Scientific Society
Hertfordshire Natural History Society
Holmesdale Natural History Club
London Natural History Society
North London Natural History Society
Oxford Ornithological Society
Plumstead & District Natural History Society
School Nature Study Union
South-Eastern Union of Scientific Societies
South London Entomological & Natural History Society
Wimbledon Natural History Society

SELECTED REFERENCES

For economy of space the following abbreviations are used:—

British Birds   *B.B.*
London Naturalist   *L.N.*
London Bird Report   *L.B.R.*
Natural History Society   *N.H.S.*
Zoologist   *Zool.*

ALEXANDER, W. B. & LACK, DAVID (1944). Changes in Status among British breeding Birds. *B.B.*, 38:42–5, 62–9, 82–8.

ASHBY, C. B. (1949). The status and distribution of birds in the London Area: an index to relevant notes and papers in the *London Naturalist* and *London Bird Report*, 1916–1948. *L.B.R.*, 13:56–9.

BALSTON, R. J., SHEPHERD, C. W. & BARTLETT, E. (1907). Notes on the Birds of Kent.

BARTLETT, T. L. (1948). The Story of Roxeth. East Molesey, Surrey. (Chapter 8 on Birds).

BEADELL, ARTHUR (1932). Nature Notes of Warlingham and Chelsham. Croydon, Surrey.

BEVEN, G. (1951). The Bird Population of an Oakwood in Surrey (Eastern Wood, Bookham Common). *L.N.*, 30:57–72.

BOND, J. A. WALPOLE (1901). The Birds of Bromley (Kent) and its neighbourhood. Bromley, Kent.

BUCKNILL, J. A. (1900). The Birds of Surrey.

—   (1901–02). Ornithological Notes from Surrey. *Zool.*, 1901: 247–54; 1902: 223–31, 305–12.

COLLENETTE, C. L. (1937). A History of Richmond Park.

CORNISH, C. J. (1902). The Naturalist on the Thames.

CRAMP, S. (1949). The birds of Kensington Gardens and Regent's Park. *L.B.R.*, 13:37–45.

—   (1950). The Census of Swifts, Swallows and House-Martins, 1949. *L.B.R.*, 14:49–57.

CRAMP, S. & TEAGLE, W. G. (1950). A repeat bird census of Kensington Gardens. *L.B.R.*, 14:41–8.

—   (1952). The Birds of Inner London, 1900–50. *B.B.*, 45:433–56.

—   (1952A). A Bird Census of St. James's Park and the Green Park, 1949–50. *L.B.R.*, 15:48–52.

—   (1955). A Comparative Study of the Birds of Two Stretches of the Thames in Inner London, 1951–53. *L.B.R.*, 18:42–57.

CURRIE, P. W. E. (1950). Some notes on the birds of the bombed sites. *L.N.*, 29:81–4.

DAVIS, W. J. (1904). The Birds of the Dartford District. Dartford, Kent.

—   (1907). The Birds of Kent. Dartford & London.

DIXON, CHARLES (1909). The Bird Life of London.

FITTER, R. S. R. (1943). The Starling Roosts of the London Area. *L.N.* for 1942:3–23.

—   (1945). London's Natural History.

—   (1949). London's Birds.

FITTER, R. S. R. & PARRINDER E. R. (1944). A Check-List of the birds of the London Area. *L.B.R.* for 1943:20–8.

GILLHAM, E. H. & HOMES, R. C. (1950). The Birds of the North Kent Marshes.

GLEGG, W. E. (1929). A History of the Birds of Essex.

—   (1929A). The Thames as a Bird-Migration Route. *L.N.* for 1928:3–15.

GLEGG, W. E. (1930). The Birds of Middlesex since 1866. *L.N.* for 1929:3–32.
    –   (1934). The birds of the Lea Valley Reservoirs. *Essex Nat.*, 24:179–209.
    –   (1935). A History of the Birds of Middlesex.
    –   (1937). Birds in Middlesex. *B.B.*, 30:249–50.
    –   (1938). Birds in Middlesex. *B.B.*, 31:297–301.
    –   (1939). Changes of Bird-Life in Relation to the Increase of London. *L.B.R.* for 1938:34–44.
GOODCHILD, HERBERT (1913). Chapter on birds in "Hampstead Heath, its geology and natural history" by members of the Hampstead Scientific Society.
HANSON, P. J. (1927). Notes on birds round Winchmore Hill 30 years ago and to-day. *L.N.* for 1926:41–5.
HARLEY, B. H. (1949). Birds of the Harrow District. Harrow, Middx.
HARRISON, JAMES M. (1942). A Handlist of the Birds of Sevenoaks or Western District of Kent.
    –   (1953). The Birds of Kent.
HARRISSON, T. H. (1931). Birds of the Harrow District. *L.N.* for 1930: 82–120.
HARTERT, Ernst & JOURDAIN, F.C.R. (1920). Birds of Buckinghamshire and the Tring Reservoirs. *Nov. Zool.*, 27:171–259.
HAYWARD, H. H. S. (1947). A list of the vertebrates of Hertfordshire: 3. Birds. *Trans.* Herts. N.H.S., 22:173–226.
HOMES, R. C. (1942). Sex Ratios in Winter Duck Flocks. *B.B.*, 36:42–50.
    –   (1949). Winter Duck Population of the London Area. *L.B.R.*, 13:46–56.
    –   (1953). The Duck Census in the London Area 1951–1953. *L.B.R.*, 17:38–41.
    –   (1955). Gull Roosts of the London Area. *L.B.R.*, 18:37–9.
HORN, P. W. (1921). The birds of West Thurrock Marsh. *Essex Nat.*, 19:262–66.
HUDSON, W. H. (1898). Birds in London.
    –   (1906). Aves (of Kew Gardens). *Kew Bulletin*, ser. 5:2–10. (Supplements in *K.B.* for 1911, 1934 & 1936).
KENDALL, W. B. (1907). The Birds of Willesden. Unpublished manuscript deposited in Willesden Public Library.
KERR, GRAHAM W. (1906, 1908). Birds of the district of Staines. *Zool.*, 64:179–84, 230–4, 307–10, 386–9; 66:137–43.
KEYWOOD, K. P. & MELLUISH, W. D. (1953). A Report on the Bird Population of Four Gravel Pits in the London Area, 1948 to 1951. *L.B.R.*, 17:43–72.
LOCKLEY, R. M. (1936). Birds of the Green Belt.
LODGE, R. B. (1901). Pictures of Bird Life in Woodland, Meadow, Mountain and Marsh. 2nd ed. (Chapter on bird life at Enfield).
MACPHERSON, A. HOLTE (1928). London Reservoirs and their influence on bird life. *L.N.* for 1927:5–11.
    –   (1929). A list of the birds of Inner London. *B.B.*, 22:222–44.
MANN, E. (1935). Notes on the birds of Edmonton sewage farm. *L.N.* for 1934:76–83.
MANSER, G. E. (1945). Bird notes of the Elmers End sewage farm, 1935–38. *L.B.R.* 9:23–8.
MAY, E. S. (1949). Recent changes in status of some Hertfordshire birds. *Trans.* Herts N.H.S., 23:45–53.
McCULLOCH, GEOFFREY (1939). Some notes on gulls and terns in the Colne valley. *Trans.* Herts. N.H.S., 21:90–105.
NICHOLSON, E. M. (1925). Birds of Kensington Gardens. *Nineteenth Century*, Dec. 1925: 922–32.
    –   (1926). A bird census of Kensington Gardens. *Discovery*, Aug. 1926:281–5.
PETERKEN, J. H. G. (1953). Habitats of the London Area. *L.N.*, 32:2–12.

PETHEN R. W. (1925). The Birds of Walthamstow Reservoirs. *L.N.* for 1924: 22–7.

POUNDS, HUBERT E. (1952). Notes on the Birds of Farleigh and District and the North Downs, Surrey. Dulwich, London.

POWER, F. D. (1910). Ornithological Notes from a South London Suburb.

PRICE, K. (1947). The birds of Buckinghamshire. *Records of Bucks.*, 15:20–31.

PRICE, M. P. (1903). Notes on the Vertebrate Fauna of Harrow, 1899–1903. Mem. Harrow Sci. Soc.

ROBBINS, R. W. & DEAR, H. R. (1932). Chapters on birds in "Oxted, Limpsfield and neighbourhood", edited by Lewis G. Fry.

ROWBERRY, E. C. (1934). Gulls in the London Area. *L.N.* for 1933:48–58.

SWAYNE, F. G. (1934). Birds of the Norwood district, *L.N.* for 1933:90–7.

TICEHURST, N. F. (1909). A History of the Birds of Kent.

TURNER, H. J. (1909). Aves in "A Survey and Record of Woolwich and West Kent", edited by C. H. Grinling *et al.*

WAINWRIGHT, E. D. (1926). The Fauna and Flora of Haileybury. 3rd ed. Hertford.

WEBB, WILFRED MARK (1907). The Brent Valley Bird Sanctuary.

WEBSTER, A. D. (1902). Greenwich Park: its history and associations. (Section on birds).

  –   (1911). The Regent's Park and Primrose Hill.

WHITING, J. E. (1900). Some notes on the birds of Hampstead. *Hampstead Annual,* 1900:37–45.

  –   (1912). Bird-Life of Hampstead, in "Annals of Hampstead", by T. J. Barrett, vol. 3.

INDEX

Where the numbers of two pages are linked by a hyphen it does not necessarily imply that the reference is continuous, but that the species or subject is referred to on each of the pages and on those intervening. There may also be more than one separate reference on each page. The section in the systematic list is indicated in heavy type.

THE NEW NATURALIST

"A new standard in natural history books"

TIMES LITERARY SUPPLEMENT

Published in the Main Series

SPECIAL VOLUMES
in the New Naturalist Library

THE HERON

FRANK A. LOWE

" Those who know Mr. Frank Lowe's long and enthusiastic work as an ornithologist will welcome the *New Naturalist* monograph on the heron by him. Few birds have played a more interesting part in the folklore and sport of Britain; and few offer a wider range of problems to the student. From their powder-down patches to their 'blushes', and from their varied nesting-sites and material to their distribution and fluctuations of numbers, there are a number of questions presented by them to the student. Mr. Lowe's book is a record of patient observation, of real research, and of a fascinating subject, and it is beautifully illustrated."

CANON C. E. RAVEN

"A fascinating book of value to the serious ornithologist and one which should also have a wide appeal to the general reader."

BRITISH BIRDS

" The latest addition to *The New Naturalist* Series is a handsomely illustrated book by the well-known North Country naturalist who has made a life study of this water-bird. He covers the whole ground; the history, ecology, dispersal, folklore. A book to enjoy at leisure, for it is also well written.

COUNTRY LIFE

THE RABBIT

HARRY V. THOMPSON and ALASTAIR N. WORDEN

" This important monograph could not have been published at a more opportune time. It deals with the familiar rabbit in a remarkably thorough way: its history and distribution, its structure, reproduction, behaviour, and manner of life, the diseases and parasites that play their part in its life-history; and then discusses at some length myxomatosis and its effects. It should be studied by every county council and indeed by every farmer."

MANCHESTER GUARDIAN

" Of all the writing that has been done on the rabbit, this is the culmination and, beyond any possible doubt, it will be the guide book and the reference book for your lifetime and mine. This is a real piece of modern research, using the most modern techniques of investigation. One thing has to be stressed: it is that this book can be read with pleasure and profit by anyone able to read and understand the King's English. Here, for the first time in any detail, the rabbit's breeding biology is fully investigated, including the phenomenon of pre-natal mortality. No person who ever thought he had a right to an opinion on the rabbit in any context can any longer claim that right if he does not digest the contents of this book."

SCOTSMAN

THE REDSTART

JOHN BUXTON

" Mr. Buxton writes as an ornithologist and as a poet; his is a rare and happy combination of talents."

SPHERE

"An ideal choice of author is Mr. John Buxton, who bears a name famous in the annals of bird-watching . . . the distinction of the monograph is the infectious delight of the observer in the ways of his red-tails."

SIR WILLIAM BEACH THOMAS *in the* OBSERVER

" It deals in easy language, but in admirable detail, with one of the most charming of the migrant birds."

TIME AND TIDE

" The great charm and value of the *New Naturalist* monographs published to date is that the bulk of their contents is a record of pure observation and that theory is subsidiary to it."

ILLUSTRATED LONDON NEWS

LONDON'S NATURAL HISTORY

R. S. R. FITTER

" Shows a quite extraordinary comprehensive acquaintance with London's plants and animals and their vicissitudes through the nineteen hundred years that have elapsed since London was founded by the Roman invaders. The book is packed with information from the most varied sources as well as from Mr. Fitter's own observations."

SUNDAY TIMES

"A fascinating narrative of the processes at work in the evolution of wild animal and plant life in an area that contains the largest aggregation of human beings ever recorded in the history of the world as living in a single community."

IRISH TIMES

" This is a very good book indeed: one that will not be superseded in our lifetime nor the lifetime of our children."

FIELD

" Mr. Fitter has written a delightful book, full of out-of-the-way information. Altogether this is a very readable and useful book, in which Mr. Fitter, who is primarily an ornithologist, shows an admirable grasp of natural history in general."

ENDEAVOUR

" He has brought together almost every imaginable scrap of information connected with London's natural history. The book is full of what our ancestors called 'curious information'. The book is likely to be the standard work on London's natural history for a great many years."

BIRMINGHAM POST

" Exceedingly interesting and stimulating."

FRANCES PITT *in* COUNTRY LIFE